PRAISE FOR TH
CODE TO

"This fast-moving book will fill your mind with great ideas to instantly help you become more successful than you could have ever imagined."

— Brian Tracy – Speaker/Author –
"Success Secrets of Self-Made Millionaires"

"Edward Munoz has combined great advice with fabulous storytelling to do what he always does—help people. This book will surely become one of my favorite gifts for people who want to understand success and how to achieve it."

— Bryant K. Smith, Author, Speaker
& "Human Potential Specialist"

"This touching, authentic tale of a young man's climb out of poverty and into wealth will inspire readers to make the most of their potential—regardless of the circumstances they were born into. Munoz's hard-earned wisdom delivers timeless, pragmatic advice for developing a wealth mindset."

— Jason Rockwood, CIO, Oasis and former Vice
President Mobile Innovation at the Miami HEAT

"Edward Muñoz has written a story filled with inspiration, motivation and guidance, designed to share lessons learned mostly the hard way. Edward has taken years to research, craft and polish this work into a tale designed to empower and enable readers to make choices that benefit themselves and the world."

—Carmen Reynal, CEO of Creating Greatness LLC

"An inspiring peek into the possibilities of personal growth. In it lays wisdom and advice that can enrich every human on this planet."

— D. Hutchins Jr., Championship Basketball
Coach, Double Black Diamond, Zija International

"Edward's principles may be simple, but don't take them for granted for it has the secret to achieving success, personal effectiveness, and individual happiness all in one book."

— Chris Rosario - United MC2 Inc.
Chief Marketing Officer

"This book will impact your life in a very positive way."

— Chris Estes - 7 Figure Network Marketing Mentor
Speaker/Author – "The A.P.P.L.E. Principle"

"Every youth in the world needs to read this book. Doing so will guarantee a bright future."

— Ruben Gonzalez - The Olympian Speaker/Author -
"The Courage To Succeed"

"The Underdog's Code to Riches is the buzzword in business these days and Edward R. Munoz throws light on how to approach life powerfully and make the most out of it."

— Rafael Alvarez - CEO of ATAX
Accounting & Financial Services

"So many people fail to develop a millionaire mindset. Reading the tips in this book will help anyone overcome that obstacle and succeed."

— William Schutte - Executive Vice President
Better Homes & Gardens Real Estate Wilkins & Associates

"A heartfelt, wise, honest, and inspiring book. Enormously helpful both to those facing failure and major challenges in their life."

— Tyrone Jackson - Managing Partner at
Centerstone Wealth Management

"The one book on succeeding in the face of obstacles I'd have if I could have just one."

—Vanessa Cabrera
Qualified Field Director - Premier Financial Alliance

"This is a remarkable book, not only written skillfully but with a rare mix of courage, redemption, practical wisdom, and a deep sense that two people are taking the journey in opposite directions and the outcomes of their choices."

— Kimsan Ting - CEO and Founder
of KIMSAN Technologies, LLC

"The Underdog's Code to Riches' does a brilliant job of making self-empowerment and personal success accessible to a demographic that is often forgotten. It's vivid narrative tells a tale of hope that will inspire one to action!"

— Alexis Aquino, Motivational
Speaker & Social Entrepreneur

"I've known Edward for many years and have always admired his relentless commitment to success. More importantly, he's committed to other people's success and happiness just as much. His book will entertain you, inspire you, and give you solid real world time-tested strategies to move beyond any current set of circumstances to a better life."

— Sean Smith, President, Elite Coaching University,
"North America's Next Greatest Speaker"

"Edward R. Munoz uses a novel like approach to offer motivation through life lessons. In addition to personal growth and self improvement by the choices we make. It is a real page-turner indeed."

— Nancy Scovotti, Senior Vice President, The
Great American Title Agency Inc. & Emeritus Director
of the National Association of Hispanic Real Estate
Professionals (NAHREP Westchester/Bronx Chapter)

"I believe everybody deserves a second chance in life and I believe that second chance is many times initiated by a catalyst. Edward has written a book that will inspire, educate, and enlighten you to the power of a mentor in your life who can kick start that second chance. I highly recommend this to you if you're serious about building your bigger future."

— Coach Micheal Burt - Best Selling Author
"Everybody Needs a Coach in Life"
Founder of Monster Producer Coaching Program

"Edward Munoz has the ability to provide top notch success coaching while drawing you in through his captivating and relatable storytelling. This book will surely leave you inspired and it also makes a great gift!"

— Sarita Covington - Social Entrepreneur
Co-founder of Upper Manhattan Forest Kids

"This book is a must read for anyone seeking to learn how to overcome obstacles and turn them into opportunities. Boom!!!"

— Rahz Slaughter - Motivational Coach - Personal Trainer
Owner at Meta-Burn Studios and Fitness Business Mastery

"Edward Munoz has created a captivating tale that condenses complex philosophies of personal development and personal fulfillment into a simple way of living. It is nothing less than sensational."

— Lucas Baez - Territory Master Director
Royal Prestige

"The Underdog's Code to Riches is part true, part fiction, educational and inspirational. Edward Munoz delivers a fun yet powerful message of hope, personal development, business and financial empowerment, all through good old story telling."

—Juan Guillen – Entrepreneur
Founder of LatinTRENDS

"The Underdog's Code to Riches is an inspirational story about the temptations that teenagers have to overcome. The story of these young men represent the challenges that individuals go through. As you go through obstacles in life, you can refer to this story to gain advice, motivation, and guidance."

—Kenny Colon
East Stroudsburg University Student
Aspiring Entrepreneur

"In reading this book I feel like it's an amazing asset to the male community. Very often it's said that people are a product of their environment. This book proves that you don't have to be. It proves that you can go through everything and still have everything."

—KS Oliver
Author of "Flatlined -Almost Doesn't Count"

"This book's simple and school-of-hard-knocks approach is one that easily resonates with the everyday living of life. Its relatable approaches are easily integrated into anyone's life because it is so practical. It will make the thing you already know, become 3D. Get ready for an "oh this makes sense," and don't be shocked if you start doing the same things differently and start automatically producing the desired results you been wanting- BRILLIANT!"

—Craig Duncan
High Performance Coach

"I've known Edward Munoz a long time and have been watching his journey into becoming the leader he is today. In his new novel, Edward uses an innovative approach to motivate the masses. It's an important read for anyone who's interested in self-improvement."

—Iman Khan
CEO of Red Elephant

"At last, an easy read that packs a punch. Friends, after reading The Underdog's Code to Riches there are no more excuses!"

—Milton Olave, Author & Speaker

"I've read hundreds of books, but the first 2 chapters of "The Underdog's Code to Riches" were eye-popping! I actually went in and highlighted several areas of the book because it was filled with life-transforming tips. Way to go Edward!"

—Cj Areté
Success Coach at Coach CJ Arete-Success

"The Underdog's Code to Riches, offers basic and advanced strategies that will help you become successful at whatever you do."

—Pablo Zabala, Diamond, Amway

"If you're truly ready to break out of the ordinary into your extraordinary life, change your schedule today and dive into *The Underdog's Code to Riches*! You will be inspired and invigorated to escape mediocrity and achieve personal mastery. Edward R. Munoz is the undisputed champion of personal motivation for 7-figure success!"

— The Power Coach™ Madeline Alexander, Speaker/Author
Your 90-Day Financial Breakthrough, How to Break Through Barriers & Achieve Power Results, and POWER MINDSET II; Choose To Be A Champion

vi

THE UNDERDOG'S
C.O.D.E. TO RICHE$

EDWARD R. MUÑOZ

Disclaimer: The advice and strategies contained herein may not be suitable for every situation. This work is sold with the understanding that the Author and Publisher are not engaged in rendering legal, accounting, or other professional services. Neither the Author nor the Publisher shall be liable for damages arising herefrom. The fact that an organization or website is referred to in this work as a citation or a potential source of further information does not mean that the Author or the Publisher endorses the information that the organization or website may provide or recommendation it may make. Further, readers should be aware that internet websites listed in this work may have changed or disappeared between when this work was written and when it is read.

Champion Development Enterprises
info@edwardmunoz.com
877-440-5299
www.EdwardMunoz.com

Ordering Information:

Quantity sales. Special discounts are available on quantity purchases by corporations, associations, and others. For details, contact the publisher at the email address above.

Paperback ISBN: 978-0-692-05036-1

Cover Design: Makhdoom Riaz
Cover Image: Fotolia_161314452_M
Book Editors: Mona Lisa Safai, Alexis Aquino, Aaron Cohen & Laurel Wright

Interior Layout: Naveen Bisht

DEDICATION

This book is dedicated to the most important people in my life-my family. My father-Virgilio R. Muñoz; my mother-Luz Maria Muñoz; my wife-Yaniris Avila Muñoz and my three children- Arlene, Ariann and Edward Elias.

Thank you for your unconditional love.

Join my Weekly Motivational E-Newsletter and Receive the Exclusive Interview I did with a Self-Made Billionaire

Text keyword: freeaudio to 66866

(Write it as one word)

In my weekly e-newsletter, I cover topics such as entrepreneurship, personal growth, wealth creation, and many more. More importantly, you will gain access to a wide variety of strategies to empower and inspire you to design your destiny, based on what you want and what matters most to you.

THE UNDERDOG'S CODE TO RICHES MISSION

—Changing One Million Lives, One Conversation At A Time—

As part of our commitment to make a difference on the planet, we will donate a percentage of the royalties from each copy of *The Underdog's Code to Riches* to nonprofit charities, including The Dream Project and the Robin Hood Foundation.

This is not including the thousands of copies that will be donated each year to organizations that are in desperate need of inspiration and transformation. Our mission is to get *The Underdog's Code to Riches* in the hands of millions of people so that we can do our part in inspiring this generation and generations to come to spread positivity, love, and hope.

Thank you for your support.

DREAM project

DOMINICAN REPUBLIC EDUCATION AND MENTORING

ROBIN HOOD

"The fact of being an underdog changes people in ways that we often fail to appreciate. It opens doors and creates opportunities and enlightens and permits things that might otherwise have seemed unthinkable."

– Malcolm Gladwell

If you are tired, keep going. If you are scared, keep going. If you are hungry, keep going. If you want to taste freedom, keep going.

– Harriet Tubman

CONTENTS

MY MESSAGE TO THE READER

Have you ever been considered an underdog? Do you ever find yourself chasing after the code to riches? If you answered yes to both of these questions then you will benefit tremendously from this book. No matter where you are in your life right now, this book will inspire you to get to the next level. For in the book lies the C.O.D.E. to unlock your full potential, regardless of your past or present circumstances.

One thing people have in common is that we all want a better life. Whether you are at the top of your game or are searching to make meaning of your life and discover your true purpose, this book will inspire you to see past what you already know. It will challenge you in unique ways to break through into your next level of growth and wealth. And that really excites me. I say this because unless challenged or stretched, life will just continue on the same path.

It is my intention that this book serves as an interruption -- A good interruption, if you know what I mean. Physicist and mathematician Isaac Newton once said that "An object in motion tends to remain in motion along a straight line unless acted upon by an outside force". That is exactly what this book will be for you: an impact that will vault you in a completely new direction.

In this book, Richie and Diego, the two main characters, are teenage sons of a drug-dealing father. After their father is arrested and sentenced to 25 years to life in prison, Diego follows in his father's footsteps and joins a drug dealing circle in NYC.

Richie, however, is determined to follow his own path, and he must overcome great adversity to achieve his goals. As fate would have it, he is introduced to a highly successful entrepreneur, Mr. Rodriguez. He becomes a mentor for Richie and a journey of transformation begins to discover the code to riches that lies in every person whether rich or poor.

As an author, keynote speaker and life/business success coach, my work is focused on helping people uncover their blind spots and creating new beliefs and possibilities to empower others to move forward with velocity. But instead of sharing my success principles in a "how to book", I decided to share it through a powerful story. Although the story is fictitious, it is told in a captivating way that draws you in, chapter by chapter. Warning: many people have said that once you make it to chapter 2, the books is hard to put down.

This particular modern day tale will take you on a journey of self discovery, and each chapter will reveal gems of information that will cause new breakthroughs in how you think and look at life. By the end of the book, you will be left with a new outlook on life, one that will leave you feeling joyful, clear on what next steps to take and most important of all, inspired and empowered to tackle life's challenges with confidence, intentionality and power.

To write this book, I conducted hundreds of hours of interviews with drug dealers, NYC police officers, informants, prison inmates, single mothers living in public housing, public school teachers, millionaire entrepreneurs, successful real estate investors, and countless life/success coaches. Many of the people I interviewed were *underdogs* in their own right and nature or spent their entire lives around other underdogs. People who were committed to greatness.

During these long interviews, they shared their stories of struggle, their current pain, their past mistakes and their many successes. Most important of all, I got to understand each person I interviewed at a deeper level. I was able to relate why they did what they did, how they viewed life and what led to their choices.

Each character in this book was written from the point of view from the people who I interviewed. In reality, it's their story, told through a tale. I decided to make it a tale because the majority of these people never wanted their names mentioned. They wanted to remain anonymous. This is why the book has a sense of realness to it. Be prepared to be inspired, laugh and be moved to tears as you read this story of trials, tribulations, and triumph.

Now for people who feel stuck, depressed or are going through a tough and challenging time, *The Underdog's Code to Riches* can be a godsend. You know you are stuck or depressed if:

1. Being frustrated is the norm.
2. Confusion is your middle name.
3. You are constantly unmotivated.
4. You are constantly tired and depressed.
5. You feel lost in your life or business.

6. You are constantly worried about even the smallest things.
7. You think you will never amount to anything or accumulate riches

If this list describes you, you should know that this book will make an enormous difference in your life. This book will take you on a journey of self discovery and you will become one with the main character. You will relate to his struggles and see how he is coached by his millionaire mentor in the book. You will feel like his mentor, "Mr. Rodriguez", is giving you the coaching personally. I only say this because this is what other readers have told me they have experienced. This powerful coaching will empower you to go from "Stuck to Unstoppable" in all areas of your life once you discover the code. As a result of this effective style of coaching, you will find yourself making bold decisions and experiencing new breakthroughs way before you finish the book.

Now for achievers and top performers, *The Underdog's Code to Riches* can be revolutionary and transformative. You know you are an achiever or top performer if:

1. You are empowered.
2. You consider yourself a leader.
3. You achieve almost everything you set your mind to.
4. Advancing and moving forward are your top priorities.
5. You are very driven to succeed.
6. You are an accomplished person who knows how to take action.
7. You relate to yourself as a fearless leader.
8. You know yourself to be a courageous person.

If this list describes you, you know that the best way to stay at the top of your game is by always seeking new ways to increase your personal growth. When you're at the top of your game, you keep increasing sales, income, leadership skills, fulfillment and happiness. Getting outside of your comfort zone is what will keep you expanding, and this is exactly what this book will do for you.

I know I have made some pretty huge promises, and soon you will see that I was not wrong for a single second. In closing, I want to say that the best is yet to come and I am excited for your next-level breakthroughs. I am excited in sharing *The Underdog's*

Code to Riches with you. I consider it an honor to share this journey with you. You should know that I did everything on my end to ensure this book makes an everlasting difference in your life. Hopefully it will live up to your expectations. Now let the journey begin!

(Join Our Pvt Facebook Support Group)
www.TheUnderdogCommunity.com

With love and gratitude,
- Edward R. Muñoz

BOOKS WRITTEN BY
EDWARD R. MUNOZ

1. The U-Effect
2. Happiness Is a Habit
3. The Underdog's Code to Riches
4. Overcoming the Frustration Barrier
5. How to Create Miraculous Breakthroughs Today
6. Success Through Persistence in Hopeless Situations
7. Como Transformarte En Un Líder Imparable
8. (Spanish Motivational Book)

Chapter One

A DAY IN THE LIFE OF A
YOUNG MILLIONAIRE

"You can make a million dollars or you can make one million excuses of why it can't be done."
— Edward R. Muñoz – Speaker/Author –
"The Underdog's Code to Riches"

"The single biggest financial mistake I've made was not thinking big enough. I encourage you to go for more than a million. There is no shortage of money on this planet, only a shortage of people thinking big enough."
— Grant Cardone – Speaker/Author/Serial Entrepreneur –
"Be Obsessed or Be Average

Life is good. I'm sitting on the balcony of my penthouse condo enjoying the view of the sunset in Punta Cana, Dominican Republic, while sipping on my favorite island drink—Mama Juana. As I gaze into the beautiful skies, I can't help but get sentimental. I begin to think of Mr. Rodriguez and everything he's done for me. If it weren't for him, I would have probably ended up in prison or the Ortiz Funeral Home, just like many of my friends. I certainly would not have accomplished everything I have up to this point in my life.

While enjoying this breathtaking view of the dancing palm trees that swing to the ocean breeze, I struggle to not think about my work back home. Then, I remember I promised my wife, Yani, that while on vacation with the family, I would not talk or even think about business. Of course, there are times that I cannot help myself, with so much activity happening with my business. But you just learn to deal with it. You learn to be present, which is something that is very hard for most folks. One thing I've learned is that wherever you are—is exactly where you need to be, otherwise you'd be somewhere else. The goal is to be present energetically in mind, body and spirit. When you are not fully present, you won't truly enjoy the moment. However, when you are fully present, you are honoring yourself and the time others are choosing to give you. When you are fully present, the joy that you bring is made available to everyone around you. That is why it's so important to be present, especially while away on vacation.

We usually come out here for a week every few months just to unwind. Vacationing here gives me the opportunity to enjoy some quality time with my wife, kids, and occasionally some friends. I usually invite the friends who believed in me when nobody else would. These are friends who I've come to love and respect.

But I digress. Back to Mr. Rodriguez and why he's been on my mind. When I was sixteen years old, I set a goal for myself to have this condo. I can remember the day it all happened. I was working at a grocery store for Mr. Rodriguez during evenings and weekends. One evening, I was mopping the floors. While they were still wet and soapy, I figured I'd sneak into the back and flip through one of my favorite magazines. What harm could it do? I was just killing a little time, that's all. Well, Mr. Rodriguez didn't see it that way when he caught me lazily flipping through my magazine.

"Richie, what are you doing? Put that down and finish what you started." And then, the ever familiar line, "You know, successful people—"

"I know, I know, successful people start what they finish and they finish what they start." I finished his old line for him. "Don't you get tired of saying the same thing over and over?"

"No, I don't. So just put the magazine down and get back to work," His voice was deep and serious.

"Really, though, take a look at this incredible apartment on the beach here." I showed him the impressive double-page spread I'd been looking at. "Wow! I would love to have an apartment on the beach like this one."

Then, he said something that would impact the rest of my life.

"Do you know why most people never achieve the goals they want in life?"

The tone of his voice told me I had better pay attention. "No. Why?"

"There are two main reasons why people fail to achieve their dreams. First, most people are never fully clear on what they want. It's like they're in limbo. With every passing day, they want something new and different. Secondly, most people are not willing to pay the price to get it. They are not willing to put in the sacrifice–you know, good old blood, sweat, and tears. One thing is for sure; if they do not pay the price now when they are young, they will most certainly regret it when they get older." He paused to make sure I was listening. "So, Richie, the secret is to first figure out what you want in life. Then, you'll be one step ahead of the majority. Once you know that, be willing to pay the price so you can reap the rewards you so dearly desire."[1] That was how Mr. Rodriguez spoke: forcefully, persuasively, and so vividly that it allowed me to visualize all the success he saw in me.

His words hit me like a ton of bricks. On that day, I decided I wanted to be a successful businessman like Mr. Rodriguez. I was willing to pay whatever price necessary to achieve my dreams.

As I sit here now, watching the sunset and thinking about that day, I take a deep breath and exhale with a smile as I realize I have succeeded on so many levels. Anthony Robbins once said, "Success without fulfillment is failure." If this is the case, I know I'm highly successful because I feel so fulfilled. Glancing at my watch, I realize it's time to get ready to go. I still need to call the taxi service that is taking us to the airport. Ten days of bliss have passed and now it's time to get back to the Big Apple. Time to get back to work.

*****

In New York, it was back to business as usual. Every morning I jump out of bed around 5:30 a.m. Being an early riser is important to me–I'm one of those guys who hates to get a late start on my day. I mean, if you start your day anytime after 10:00 a.m., before you know it, it's noon and half your day has gone down the drain. Usually my day starts out with going to the gym around 6:15 a.m. You would probably think the gym is empty at that time. But, you're wrong, it's packed! In my neighborhood, most of the people are businessmen, stockbrokers and high-paid executives. Waking up early and working out at the gym energizes me to start strong everyday.

Today, I was going to do a workout with my good friend, Anthony. We agreed to meet at the gym parking lot at 6:15 a.m.

He was extremely anxious to meet me today. He needed to ask for some advice on a business deal he was working on. It's amazing to me that I've spent the last twenty years asking for advice from my mentors and now, I am a mentor to many.

Anthony and I met each other when we both were PhD graduates. It's not what you're thinking! I am not referring to the degree Ph.D. (Lord knows we don't have one of those). To us, 'PhD' means 'Poor', 'Hungry' and 'Determined'. We were certainly graduate students of that class.

We were two young boys trying to survive in the streets of Brooklyn, New York. And survive it we did. No, let me correct myself, we did more than just survive. We came out on top. Especially considering that everything was against us from succeeding the honest way. We grew up in drug infested neighborhoods where most boys were trying to outrun the fates of death or jail. Their inevitable future was drugs, stabbings, shootings, early pregnancies, prison, or permanent vacations in the local cemetery. We were one of the few to escape.

*****

After our workout, we decided we would go to the local diner for breakfast and discuss the possibility of opening a nightclub in an up-and-coming sector of Brooklyn called Bushwick.

Coincidentally, Bushwick is the same neighborhood where my dad, Papito, once sold drugs over twenty years ago.

Anthony was on time as usual. He approached me like a caged tiger, let loose for the first time. His energy was contagious. Anthony was a true champion—always in a good mood no matter what was happening in his life. Anthony had a light brown complexion. He was tall and handsome. His physique was athletic in nature. His clean-shaven face and almond-shaped eyes glittered when he saw me get out of my car. What proceeded next was his famous love hug.

"So, Richie, Julio told me that you were training to do a marathon. Is that right?" Anthony said as we entered the gym.

"Yes, sir!" I replied.

"Man, you never cease to amaze me, Champ!" He hit me lightly on my shoulder. "You are one of the most committed people I know."

"Thanks, bro. That means a lot to me coming from you."

As we signed in and headed towards the workout room, a serious expression crossed Anthony's face. "Hey, why is commitment so difficult for people?"

"Great question! Let's talk about it while we handle this workout—I'll start by asking you to answer a couple questions." We reached the free weights and started setting up.

"Okay, go for it."

"Make a mental list of all of the areas of your life where you have pretty decent results. Let me know when you're done."

After just a few seconds, Anthony said, "Okay, got it."

"Now, make a list of all of the areas where you are not thrilled with your results." We started our physical workout, while discussing the mental exercise.

Anthony nodded, "Okay. Got that too."

"Awesome. Now, here's what I want you to see from this exercise. The areas where you got the positive results are where you are the most committed right now. But, your unsatisfactory results reveal areas in your life where you are the least committed right now. In these areas, you are more committed to making excuses than taking action. You are more committed to wasting time than doing what needs to be done. You are more committed to mediocrity than success.

"Sean Smith, a motivational coach, says, mediocrity is nothing more than a commitment to a comfortable sense of safety. Whenever we fall into our comfort zone and we're doing nothing but familiar things, we start to form the mediocre state of mind. I know it sounds yucky, but it's the truth. Success, on the other hand, is the commitment to uncomfortable growth. It requires you to do things that at first seem super uncomfortable, stretching you faster than the elastic man from the *Fantastic Four*. But the good news is that if you allow yourself to keep stretching and embrace being uncomfortable, this will create the momentum necessary for you to obtain the results you want."

"Richie, you hit the nail on the head. You are so right, it disgusts me." He set the weights down and looked at me, shaking his head.

I laughed, then said, "Since we are on the topic, do you know what the definition of commitment is?"

"Yeah, who doesn't?" He started his lifting again, sounding confident.

"Alright, what is it?" I challenged.

"You know, it's like doing what you said you were going to do, something like that, right?" Anthony said, the confidence he started with wavering by the end.

"Well, you're close. The real definition of commitment is this: giving yourself to a new possibility, then following through on your word. Now, here's the kicker. If you are truly committed, you will do what you say you were going to do, even if you're not in the mood. The key is to keep your word and take the actions you originally declared without hesitation."

Definition of Commitment

G.Y. → N.P. → F. T. → WORD

Giving Yourself To A New Possibilty Then Following Through On Your WORD!

Anthony looked stunned. It took him some time to digest, but the more he thought about it, the more he realized it made sense "That is so true," he finally said.

I nodded and continued, "When people make goals or decisions, they're usually very enthusiastic at the moment they declare their new commitment. But, as time passes they forget to follow through. Resistance sets in. They run into obstacles and start to get lazy. All of a sudden, three weeks go by and they forget the promise they made."

"How do you stay committed when the mood has left you?"

"What people say they are going to do and how they live their lives are two different things. If you want to live a life that is consistent with your commitments, you have to learn to honor your commitments over your feelings."

"That just sounds too easy, Richie."

"I know it does. But it is as true as the sky is blue. For example, say you plan on going to the gym four days a week and lose fifteen pounds in that time. On day four, you wake up feeling lazy and you think '...ummm...I don't really feel like going today, I'm just not in the mood'. Now guess what will happen if you keep on saying that? Chances are you will never get out of bed. That's gonna happen, but if you catch yourself and say, 'No, I'm not going to honor my feelings, I am going to honor my commitment!' just imagine how much more you could accomplish in your life by honoring your commitments."

Anthony took a deep breath. I felt the message was driving home.

"So, if you seriously think about it, you never feel like doing anything. You're never in the mood. You will always have reasons and excuses not to do something you intended to do. This is a very normal state of behavior for human beings. But, when you start to honor your word again and again regardless of your feelings, reasons, and excuses, you start to build a new muscle, called the 'Commitment Muscle.' At first, it's tough and it may even hurt. But as time passes, commitment becomes a part of you. Does that make sense, Anthony?"

"It sure does! You know, that reminds me of something Scott Hamilton said once, in reference to commitment. Remember him? He won a gold medal in the 1984 Olympics. He said, 'You have to be willing to commit at a level your competitors won't', and, if I might add, that will only happen when it becomes a part of you."

I was impressed, and my voice showed it, "That's really good, bro. Here's another mistake most people make when they set new commitments. They try to fit their commitments into their personal life. And the sad fact is that this simply doesn't work."

"It doesn't?" Anthony replied.

"No, it doesn't work. Your commitments should not revolve around your life; rather your life should revolve around your commitments. This leaves no room for excuses. Are things becoming clearer, Anthony?"

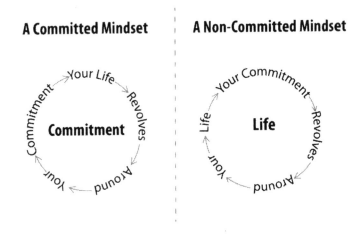

"No, not really. Exactly how does that work?"

I was glad he asked. "Let's say you want to go back to college to finish your degree, but you use the 'I do not have time' excuse to not follow through. Then, one day you are inspired to go back, but don't know how to make it happen. Days and weeks pass by, and the more you try to fit it into your life, the more impossible it seems to complete your degree. The truth is that you cannot see the solution because you are trying to fit your new commitment into your life. This way of thinking does not work. It is not until you decide to fit your life into your commitment that solutions appear on the surface. In the moment you take this daring leap and make this new commitment a must, then—and only then—will you find ways to make it happen.

"After you make the commitment and take the leap, you'll probably develop the courage to ask a family member for some support to help out with the children while you go to school, or your wife might decide to work a few extra hours per week so you could work less and study more. All these solutions will lead to more opportunities to achieve your goals. With this new way of thinking, you will find yourself asking people for support, providing new openings for actions that were unseen to the uncommitted eye."

"Richie, that's good stuff. I'll remember your example the next time I don't feel like doing what I said I was going to do. From now on, I'll look at the word 'commitment' in an entirely new way. This is one of the reasons why I love spending time with you!"

"I am only as good as the friends I surround myself with," I chuckled.

To download a pdf and infographic of the commitment conversation you just read, check out
http://www.theunderdogcode.com/bookresources

*****

After the workout, we went to a local diner for a quick breakfast so we could catch up on our business projects. Anthony had his usual—an omelet consisting of five egg whites, and green peppers with onions and mushrooms. A small cup of orange juice and two plain slices of wheat toast, without butter on the side. I joined him and ordered the same.

"So, Richie," he began, after the waitress took our orders. "I have this new deal that was just proposed to me last week. But, I was waiting for you to come back from your trip so you could give me your input."

"Okay, shoot. I'm all ears."

"Well, as you know I've wanted to open my own night club for the longest time now. But, I just haven't found the right spot. And, of course, the funds haven't been there to make it happen. Last week, a real estate agent approached me with a pretty good deal. But, I could use some help in structuring the terms and price so they are in my best interest."

"What are they offering you?"

"They have this corner property building for sale that has a commercial space with 3,000 square feet. Additionally, in the back of the lot there is a two-family property with a rental income of $2,400 per month."

"How much is the asking price?"

"They are asking $1,150,000. Now, the best part of the deal is that it comes with a liquor license worth $80,000. That is huge.

If you're lucky it takes about eight months to get a liquor license here in New York."

I nodded. "What kind of business did they have there before?"

"They had a huge seafood restaurant. Don Pepe's Seafood House. What happened to them is a long story, but there are a few people looking at it as we speak. I'm trying my best. No. I am committed to finding a way."

"Okay, now you're speaking my language! So how much money do you have?" I smiled.

"I have $180,000 and some extra funds I will borrow for the repairs of the business. The realtor gave me the inside scoop. He told me I could probably get it for $980,000. If that's the case, I will still need $120,000 to qualify for the loan."

"Now, let me think." I began calculating the numbers and scribbling the different possible scenarios on a napkin.

With a broad Brooklyn smile, I said, "I have a proposal. I'll be willing to loan you the $120,000 to help you finance the purchase of the property, if you agree to these four conditions."

"I'm listening."

"First, I want a 35% monthly return on my investment, which would be $3,500 per month. Secondly, I am not your partner in the business. So, I will collect my money whether you do well or poorly that month. I also want you to buy me out in exactly five years. I will expect a payment in the amount of $120,000. Lastly, I want all of this language to be part of the contract. Why don't you think about it? If you agree, get back to me." I watched him as he worked out the conditions in his head.

"Hey, hold on a second!" Anthony had quickly done the calculations and then said, "Richie, you once told me that people lie, but numbers never do. After punching the numbers, I feel I deserve a better deal considering we are friends. I mean it's okay and doable, but could you do better? That interest rate sounds kinda high."

"Let me share something I first learned about in a book by negotiation expert Chester L. Karrass. He said that in life, you don't get what you deserve; you get what you negotiate. Deserving has nothing to do with it. Truthfully, you are my friend, but this is business. Those terms are non-negotiable, so I stand firm on my proposal."

"Okay, okay. I agree. You sure are tough when it comes to putting deals together."

"Awesome! After this meeting, I'm going to call my assistant so we can get the ball rolling. Well, enough about business. I'm hungry. Let's eat!"

*****

After breakfast, I said goodbye, went home for a quick shower and changed into some comfortable clothes. I kissed and hugged my wife, Yani. Then I was ready to drive my two girls to school. I really get a lot of joy and fulfillment from this daily routine. It's a quick ten-minute ride. Too quick for me. But I use it as my opportunity to have great conversations with them. If you were to ask my energetic nine-year-old daughter what her name was, she would reply with a lot of enthusiasm, 'My name is Arlene The Champion.' Then, my little five-year-old would follow by saying 'My name is Ariann The Champion.'

I feel it is necessary at a young age that they think of themselves as champions. They love it and always share their confidence with their friends at school. Every once in awhile when they misbehave, all I have to say is 'Now, girls, you aren't behaving like champions.' They always reply with, 'Okay, you're right, Dad', and fix their behavior.

After I dropped them off, I rushed to my supermarket on New Lots Avenue to meet with my manager. We were going to discuss the possibility of doing business with a new vendor. The vendor's company really wanted us to promote their products. Honestly, I also wanted their product line, though they were unaware of this. I've learned over the years when it comes to negotiations you should never show your weaknesses.

First, I met with my manager to go over the game plan. I always want my business managers to feel like they have a say in the matter, that their input is greatly appreciated. I learned this from Mr. Rodriguez. He always said that everything is possible through communication. But the opposite is also true. Missing communication leads to conflict. This is why communicating often is key, especially when you run several businesses. I believe being able to communicate powerfully leads to success in building leaders. I always strive to make my communication clear, concise and to the point. The ability to empower and be empowered by others only happens through effective communication.

I was able to speak to the store manager for about three uninterrupted hours. We spoke about our financial goals, our current monthly expenses and how to implement the marketing budget to reach those goals. Once we were clear, we could make decisions on opening new vendor accounts. I have a rule: unless I have in writing my company's projected financial goals, expenses and marketing budgets from my business managers, I will not make any decisions that are relevant to the company's finances. This is always the starting point.

Then we spoke about the pros and cons of the products in our store. I asked that he request specials from the vendor for the first 30 days and we would buy it on a trial basis so we can measure the result 90 days from now. After three hours I left so he could meet with the vendor. I felt great. It was a productive meeting. I used to meet with these vendors but I know that's not the best use of my time. Now, I have business managers who I empower through communication.

By now, I was hungry again. I walked down the aisle to the deli section, craving my favorite sandwich.

"Good morning, Josh." I greeted the young man in charge of the deli.

"It's not morning sir. It's already the afternoon," Josh replied.

"Oh, yeah. As the saying goes, 'Time truly flies when you're having fun.' Good afternoon, could you give me the regular?"

"Sure thing, boss. Coming right up."

I took my sandwich and walked around the store to see if I saw anything out of place.

Everything looked fabulous and soon I was off to inspect the construction site where I was developing six new duplexes. I spent the rest of the afternoon with my architect and site manager. I had to be firm in my demands. We were running behind on our deadline. A huge part of building properties is keeping within budget and meeting project deadlines. If you spend one dollar more than your budget, then you pay that dollar out of your pocket. If you are not meeting deadlines then that is more money out of your pocket, too. Every day counts on a construction site. Sometimes, I can come across as cheap, but it's only because I learned from Mr. Rodriguez that meeting budgets could make or break a business.

The architect and site manager both tried to convince me we would need three additional weeks to complete the project. I stood firm and told them if they need to work extra hours to meet the deadline, that is what needs to happen, end of question. I was very clear from day one what I expected and explained that if we go over our budget and deadline, it's coming from their pocket, not mine. They gave me a puzzled look as I left the site.

*****

My last stop for the day was to pass by my commercial building on Knickerbocker Ave. and pick up the rent from my tenant, Tyrone. Normally, he would deposit it into my bank account, but he wanted me to stop by this time. He said he wanted to discuss something with me. Tyrone owns a diner called Brooklyn's Best Pancake House. The funny part was Tyrone started there as a dishwasher. Over time, he became a waiter. I saw him work long hours and save most of his earnings. When the owner decided to sell, they worked out a deal and he bought him out.

As I walked in, Tyrone greeted me with a pleasant smile, "Richie, it is always a pleasure to see you."

"Hey, same here Tyrone. Wow! Love what you've done to the place. It looks great. It kind of makes you feel like you're in a '50s diner. Who did the decorating?"

"That was my wife's idea. Come to think of it, she did an admirable job." Tyrone looked around the diner, like he was really seeing it for the first time.

"She sure did. What is it that you wanted to talk to me about?"

Tyrone put his arm around my shoulder and took me to a quiet corner. "Richie, as you know I have the utmost respect for you," he said, his voice beginning to waver.

"Well, thank you." I smiled in appreciation.

"No, really, you always have my admiration. You know, I knew your father back in the day. I know where you came from and what obstacles you had to overcome to make it this far. I mean, you had to deal with your crazy brother and all his drama, your dad going to jail when you were a teenager, and your best friend getting shot by being mixed up with the wrong people. You even went to jail for a short time for being at the wrong place at the wrong time with the wrong people." His voice grew louder as he listed off the things I've been through.

"I hope you're going somewhere with this." I said dryly.

"I most certainly am!" He smiled and cleared his throat. "Considering your success story, I was wondering if you could take my son, Darnell, under your wing. You know, knock some sense into him. Ever since he turned seventeen a few months ago, all he wants to do is hang out with his friends, come home late, and he's been just outright rebellious lately. I can't figure out why he's behaving this way. He doesn't want to help out here at the restaurant, and when he does, he has a nasty attitude. Last night, I tried to have a heart-to-heart with him, you know, a good old father-son conversation, but we ended up arguing. He's terribly upset with me and says that I am too strict and am always embarrassing him in front of other people." As he spoke, he paced around the corner we were in. He came back to a stop in front of me and sighed, exasperated. "I just don't know what to do."

"Okay, I got it. Well, consider this, the real reason he is rebellious may not be the reason you think."

"What?" He furrowed his brow. "What does that mean?"

"If he's acting this way, there must be an underlying issue. Don't worry, I'll give it my best shot. So, where is he now?" Just as Tyrone was going to answer, Darnell walked through the front door.

"Darnell, can you come here for a moment?" Tyrone called. "I want to introduce you to someone." Darnell was a tall and handsome teenager with an angular face, a black velvet complexion, and a cool, watchful gaze, occasionally undone by an irrepressible wide smile.[2]

In a rapid-fire New York accent, Darnell nodded his head in acknowledgement of me and said, "Hey, Richie what's up?"

"You know me?" I couldn't keep the surprise out of my voice.

"Yeah." He shrugged. "My dad is always talking about how famous you are."

"How did you attach my face to my name?" I asked, genuinely curious.

"Just a hunch, I guess. And your car." He tilted his head in the general direction of where I had parked.

"My car?"

"Yeah. I love to check it out whenever you're around. It's one of my favorites. Well, nice meeting you. Gotta go." He smiled that wide smile of his, and started to walk away.

"Now, wait a second, young man."

Darnell stopped and turned back toward me.

"I want to talk to you. Your dad tells me you've been acting out lately."

"Oh, God! Not that again!" He groaned and rolled his eyes. "Look, I really gotta go. I don't have time for this." He started to walk away again.

I held up my hands to pacify him, "Just give me five minutes. Do you think you can do that?"

"Fine. Five minutes, not a minute over. Start talking. The clock is ticking," he said, rolling his eyes again as he leaned against the red-and-black-checked counter.

"I just have one question for you." I made sure to keep my tone calm and friendly.

"What do you want?"

"If you could have anything you want in your life right now, what would it be?" A commonly asked question, but the answer could tell me a lot.

Young Darnell was puzzled for a moment. Then, all of a sudden, he lit up like a Christmas tree, his eyes wide and his smile bright. "Okay. I'll tell you. But you have to promise that you are not going to laugh."

"I promise." I held my hand up as a swear.

"What I want most in this world is to have a cool car, like yours, and learn how I can become super successful without having to work hard." He looked at me as he spoke and I could see the conviction in his eyes.

"Okay. I got it. Here's the deal. I have to go to Boston tomorrow to meet with some people for business. Meet me at my house and I'll show you my car collection. I can't wait for you to see my babies, then we'll drive to Boston in my brand spanking new Porsche 911 Turbo. I'll show you not only how you can get a car like those, but how you can get as many as you want, whenever you want them."

"You've got a Porsche 911 Turbo? How much did that cost you?" His brown eyes got even wider.

"We can talk about that later," I grinned at the boy. "Are you coming or not?"

"Yeah, that sounds awesome. What time should I be there?"

I wrote my home address on the back of my business card. "Look, here's my address. Meet me there, at 6:00 a.m. sharp."

"6:00 a.m.?" He took the card and looked at it, eyebrows furrowed and a small frown on his face.

"Yes. You heard that right. I want to get a head start on traffic so we can get there in time for my business meeting. I'll see you then." I pointed a stern finger at him, "Remember, don't be late."

"I won't." He was all smiles again.

Despite his assurance, something told me he was going to be late.

Chapter Two

DARNELL'S FIRST LESSON

"Some people come in your life as blessings. Some come in your life as lessons."

— Mother Teresa

The next day, I woke up at 5:30 a.m. as usual. I got dressed, drank my orange juice and headed out to the garage to warm up my two babies: my Porsche 911 Turbo, and my 1965 Porsche 356 SC. Seeing my 1965 Porsche sit in the corner of my garage reminded me of the day it arrived at my home. I could hardly sleep the night before. I was like a child, waiting for Christmas day to open his gifts under the tree. I bought the Porsche at a car auction in Fresno, California and they shipped it out the following day. The crackling popping noise she makes as I rev her up always makes me grin from ear to ear. She sounds just as good today as she did the day I first brought her home. I especially loved this model because Porsche attached a smooth, quiet, and comfortable package to a powerful engine with agile steering. The 356 had a wind-cheating body with a compact interior layout. It's bad to the bone—simply badass!

People like me who own these cars get so much out of just turning the engines on. It may be because we remember the sacrifices we made earlier in our lives that allow us to afford these luxuries now. Either way, I always enjoy revving her up or taking her out for a spin whenever I get a chance.

Today, my main goal was to impress Darnell, not with my cars, but impress upon him that if he is open and willing to be coached, he, too, can have all the cars he wants in his life. The truth is, I was not going to focus my entire conversation on how he could get all the cars he wants in his life. That was just a starting point. At the age of seventeen, those are some of the fantasies a teenager dreams about. The real focus of today was to help him become aware that he is the source of his results. I want him to get that if he wants things to change, the change must come from within him first. When you truly get that you are the source of your own transformation, then you can have access to real power. Tapping into this power makes anything possible. This personal transformation leaves you empowered to accomplish and operate at your best. That is what I want him to see for himself.

When I came out of the garage, I saw Darnell walking up my driveway with a look of disbelief and awe. "Hey, Richie, is this your house? Wow! Dude! I did not know you lived like this."

"What do you mean by that?" I asked, grinning at the amazed expression on his face.

"You are filthy rich! I've never seen so many mansions in my life, only on TV. So, how many rooms are there in your house?" Darnell asked, holding up his fingers, like he was going to start counting on them.

"So many I lost count. Look, don't worry about that. Why are you so late?" I looked sternly at him after glancing at my watch.

"Late? Only by ten minutes!"

"Okay," I said as I took a deep, silent breath because I did not want him to know that I do not put up with lateness very well.

Darnell turned his attention back to my garage. "Look at your car collection...Oh my GOD! I think I've died and gone to heaven! Today is, unquestionably, the best day of my life!" Darnell paused in his admiration of my cars and turned toward me, "Hey, how did you get so rich?"

"Darnell, the short answer to your question is that rich people think very differently than poor people. But we'll get more into detail on how to develop a rich mindset when we get on the road. Fair enough?"

"Yeah, sounds good! I must admit, I'm very excited about our trip," Darnell replied with a dimpled smile.

At that point, I just let him soak it all in. I could tell Darnell was very impressed with my lifestyle, so I left him there for a quick moment while I went inside to get my briefcase. I purposely let him enjoy the moment because I knew that pretty soon I was going to start pounding on him for being late.

"Alright, are you ready to go?" I asked.

"Yep, let's go." He grinned at me, excited at the prospect of a ride in such a fancy car.

I revved up the engine of my black-on-black Porsche 911 Turbo one last time. Then, I rolled my baby out of the garage and headed towards interstate 95 north. Once on the highway, I looked over to Darnell. By now, he was quiet and just sitting back and enjoying the whole experience. I knew I was about to ruin it for him though. "Why were you late?"

"C'mon Richie, what's the big deal? I was only 10 minutes late. Don't you think you're blowing this out of proportion? C'mon, don't destroy this beautiful moment," Darnell replied with his arms across his chest.

"My young champion, just relax for a moment, take a deep breath and answer the following question. Are you ready?"

"Okay. Let's see where this is going." His arms uncrossed a little bit as he tried to relax.

"Trust me, something amazing is going to come out of it."

"Okay," he whispered.

"So, here goes: What do you think is one of the most important qualities all powerful people possess?"

"I don't know," he said.

"Well, just think for a moment. There is no right or wrong answer," I encouraged.

"I'm still thinking."

"While you're thinking, I want you to know that most people are lazy when it comes to thinking. Don't analyze too much. They say too much analysis leads to paralysis. Just say the first thing that comes to your mind when I asked the question."

"Well, my first thought was focus. All powerful and successful people need to be extremely focused to achieve what they really want to accomplish. Focus is a very important quality." He sat up a bit straighter as he spoke.

"I certainly agree with you on that. What else?"

"The next thought that popped into my mind was a positive attitude. Without a positive attitude you won't get very far in life."

"You're right. The late motivational speaker Zig Ziglar once said that your attitude will always determine your altitude. All of those are good answers. Now, for those qualities to work, there is one that is the most important of all. It is like the foundation of the house. Without a solid foundation, the house will not stand a chance, especially when the storms and hurricanes arrive."

"Okay. So, what is it?" Darnell asked impatiently.

"I'm glad you asked. The single most important quality to have is *integrity*."

"Integrity." Darnell's tone was skeptical.

"Yes. You heard me right. I know, this probably sounds like a church sermon." Darnell already looked uninterested in anything more I had to say at this point. He rolled his eyes and looked out the window.

"Darnell, why did you decide to accompany me to Boston?" I glanced at him out of the corner of my eye, waiting for his answer.

He shrugged, still staring outside. "You are really successful and have everything I want, so I thought I could learn a thing or two from you."

"So, let me see if I understand you. You see me as a coach, right?"

He turned his head to look at me for a moment. "I guess you could say that."

"You guess?" I prodded him for a real answer.

"Okay," He rolled his eyes again as he faced me, sounding exasperated, "Yes, I see you as a coach."

"What is a coach then?"

"A coach is, like, someone who inspires you and brings out your best. Right?"

"Yes, that's pretty good but I would add that a coach makes you do what you don't want to do, then holds you accountable for what you said you were going to do. Now, are you still up for my coaching?"

"Yes, I am," Darnell replied with a nervous but serious smile.

"Okay, so here's my coaching. Darnell, I need you to pay close attention and put everything you know aside so you can listen in a new way. Listen to me as if you are eager to learn what I am about to say. This will help you really get the message so you can own it and apply it."

"Apply it to what?"

"To whatever it is you'll need to do so you can accomplish all your dreams." As I said this, Darnell took a deep breath.

"Alright. You got my full attention, sir."

"Great, but there's no need to call me 'sir'. Richie will suffice."

"Yes, sir— I mean, Richie."

I could tell Darnell was nervous, but I had him exactly where I wanted him. I had his full attention and it was time to have a conversation about the importance of integrity and the difference it could make in his life.

"Darnell, what comes to mind when you hear the word integrity?"

"Well, um, I think it's… nah, I know it, I just can't explain it." He crossed his arms again.

"Okay. Good try. Here's my definition: The inner compass that guides the heart to justice is called Integrity. Without it, we would all be lost. When it is missing, nothing works."

"That sounds confusing; I still don't get it," Darnell admitted.

"Okay, thank you for being honest. Let me break it down in plain English. The definition of integrity is two things. First, it is saying what you are going to do, and second, doing what you said. When you follow this simple formula, life simply works, and when you don't, nothing works."

"That makes a little more sense, but can you give me an example?"

"Sure. Let's pretend you have an eight-year-old daughter named Lyanka and one cold winter day she asked you if you could take her to Disney World in the summer. Let's say you said, 'Yes, sweetheart, I'll take you, this summer, to Disney World.' Summer comes around and for whatever reason you don't take her. How do you think she will feel? Upset, right?"

Darnell just shrugged his shoulders and said, "Yeah, sure."

"Now, you are going to have to confront her and say, 'I'm sorry, sweetheart, things are kind of rough for daddy now, but I promise you I will take you next summer.' Let's assume that next summer comes around and for whatever reason you do not take her again. Then another summer passes by, and you still don't keep your promise. Chances are, she will grow up and always see you as a person with no integrity. It is no wonder why many children do not respect their parents today."

"Okay. So, what should a parent do in that particular case?"

"The right thing to do is say, 'Look, sweetie I cannot promise you right now that we can go, but as soon as I know we can go, I will let you know.' If you do tell her that you are taking her in the summer, you'd better keep your word so she will always see you as a person of integrity. If you have to cancel at the last minute, just have an honest conversation about what happened, then create a new promise. That, Darnell, is having integrity; it is called being your *word*! It is just as simple as clearing things up when you need to, then creating a new promise."

27

"Okay. I kinda see where you are coming from," Darnell said sheepishly.

"Did you know planes fly in and out of integrity all the time?"

"Now that's a first," Darnell replied skeptically.

"Let's say a plane takes off from New York to Los Angeles. The plane is actually 90% off course during the whole flight. Put another way, the plane is 90% out of integrity during the flight. First, the plane is on course, then it is off course, then it is on course, then it is off course. The winds and weather do their job very well and the plane has to constantly keep renewing its 'integrity' to get back on the right course. If it does not do so, the plane could end up landing in some other state, in a totally different destination.

"What I want you to get is this; many times we will have the best intentions to do something with integrity. Unfortunately, much like the winds to the plane, obstacles have a way of catching you off guard. As strange as it may sound, life is designed to interrupt your ambitions, goals and dreams. Much like the plane, we are constantly thrown off course as well. There are times when we are being our word, then we are not, then we are being our word, then we are not. It is the constant back and forth that can be frustrating. Just know that this is normal in the beginning, while you're developing your new integrity muscle. So, here's the basic rule I abide by. When you're on–you're on, and when you're not– you're not. When you're in integrity then, hooray! When you're not, just restore your integrity, like the plane, so you can arrive at the destination you so desire."

"If it's that simple why do so many people hesitate clearing up or confessing when they know deep down inside they messed up?" Darnell asked.

"Hey, now you're thinking! Keep asking those questions whenever they pop up. That's the only way to get it down. The main reason why most people avoid having these conversations is because deep down inside, they know open-hearted conversations about this topic will force them to make a new commitment in the end. This is one thing most people do not want to do. However, these conversations are the only way to restore their integrity.

"Resistance also has a lot to do with it. We are naturally resistant and, as human beings, this becomes our default in most situations. It's how we are wired. As a matter of fact, something tells me you're resisting what I'm telling you right now. Am I right?"

"You know what—you're right! Ha! I can't even lie about it."

"Don't worry, it has nothing to do with you. It's just second nature, Darnell. When you can distinguish your limitations, it frees you to be in touch with the real you—your inner champion. I once heard that what you resist, persists, but when you just let it be, it sets your inner champion free. You see, your inner champion is not afraid to confront, clear up and have empowering integrity conversations."

"Wow, I got it! That makes me feel a lot better actually, like, I don't have to feel bad for not having integrity all the time." He sat up straighter and looked at me, a smile on his face.

"That's right. And, taking action to maintain or restore integrity when the opportunity lends itself will make a huge difference in your life. It's the greatest hidden secret that all champions know. Does that make sense, Darnell?"

"It sure does, Richie, it sure does!"

"If it's one thing I learned from Mr. Rodriguez–"

"Who is Mr. Rodriguez?" Darnell interrupted.

"He was the first and only person I ever worked for in my life. I started working for him when I was a teenager at the local grocery. He became my mentor—more like the father I never had. Mr. Rodriguez taught me that powerful people only exist as their word.

"Their word becomes the floor on which they stand. For example, Barack Obama said he was going to become President of the United States, and he did. When you are your word, this reflects in how you are listened to in the world and your communities. All of a sudden, people don't listen to you as they did before, when you were not a person of your word; they only listen to you as who you are today in regard to your word. It's as if you created a new listening for yourself." I paused and glanced over at Darnell, to see how well he was taking this in. "Darnell, have you ever heard of the 'integrity thermometer'?"

"The 'integrity thermometer'? What's that?"

"It is a thermometer that measures your level of integrity at any moment in your life. For example, if your integrity is very low, you will find yourself at the bottom of the thermometer. Just like any thermometer, the bottom is always the coldest. In this case, it reflects a very poor quality of life. As the temperature increases on the integrity thermometer, so do your results and quality of life."

"Now that is interesting. What are the levels?" Darnell inquired. "I'm glad you asked."

THE INTEGRITY THERMOMETER

100	I am living a life of 100% integrity
90	I am Integrity even when it is inconvenient
80	I am developing the habit of being my word
70	I pretend to be at 100% Integrity, when deep down inside I know it is only 70% Integrity
60	I am Integrity when it is convenient
50	Being Integrity scares me
40	Integrity is not necessary
30	Avoid and resist Integrity at all cost
20	Living a Life of no Integrity
10	Integrity.What's that?
0	I hate Integrity

To download this infographic with full color, check out:
http://www.theunderdogcode.com/bookresources

Level 10% – Integrity, What's That?

Level 10% belongs to two groups of people. Those in the first group do not understand the definition of integrity, nor are they interested in learning what it means. It's no wonder why they live in constant turmoil. The second group knows what it means, but are in constant denial about integrity. They go about their lives, just pretending they don't know what it means. They think not knowing will make their lives easier, but if they only knew that the opposite is true. As I said before, what you resist, persist. It's only when you let it be, that it will set you free. For people in this group, I always recommend to just be aware of the impact that not having integrity has had on your life. This is definitely a good place to start.

Level 20% – I am Living a Life of No Integrity

These are the people who acknowledge the impact of integrity, but struggle to keep their word. They are frequently late, and typically don't call to communicate they will be late. They are likely to not return you the money they borrowed on time. They are constantly getting tickets and summons. They rarely work out payment plans with their creditors. They don't usually last long at their jobs. They almost never get promotions where they work. They are never in long-lasting relationships. Their health is always at stake because of poor eating habits. Their lives are unstable and they feel stuck as a result of it. For these people, doing more of the same will not bring a different result in their life. Albert Einstein once said, "You cannot solve problems by using the same kind of thinking you used when you created them." If what you know got you where you are today, and you would like to end up somewhere different tomorrow, change the way you think! It's time to start thinking about living in integrity so that you can create a complete turnaround in your life. It's time to start practicing being your word.

Level 30% – I Avoid and Resist Integrity At All Costs

This group of people know the definition of integrity. However, they avoid and resist integrity at all costs because it is just too uncomfortable. To them, integrity means going outside of their comfort zone and into the unfamiliar. Once in the unfamiliar, they know they will have to be vulnerable and held accountable for their actions. This is a frightening concept for many people— something many do not want to do. While resisting may seem more comfortable, it also leaves you living an unbalanced and frustrated life. Remember, it takes more courage to surrender than to put up a wall. I challenge you to surrender your limiting beliefs about integrity so you can start living a life of total abundance and prosperity.

Level 40% – Integrity is Not Necessary

This group knows what integrity means and certainly want to be their word. Unfortunately, they are at a constant battle within. Sometimes, we think our worst enemies lives across town or maybe even down the street. In reality, they live inside you.

They hang out in your head and appear as your negative voice. One side of you wants to honor your word, while the other side feels it is a total waste of time. Your 'complainer', as I often refer to him, starts to justify all the reasons why you should not honor your word. These reasons may sound justifiable, but they should not stop you from being your word. I often remind this group that there is an enormous difference between doing things right and doing the right thing. Furthermore, I highly suggest developing the muscle of honoring your word, even when you think it is not necessary. Doing so begins to create the balance and success you so much desire.

Level 50% – Having Integrity Scares Me

This group of people want to honor their word, but the thought of doing it terrifies them. They are the drama queens and kings of their own Halloween parties. They think that when they honor their word they will get hurt in the process. They actually link pain to integrity. In their minds, honoring their word will be more painful than not. This way of thinking has them stuck in the world of 'no integrity'.

To free them of this misleading concept, I often remind them of the need to associate massive pain with the actions they avoid taking now. When they see the pain they will receive in the future, due to lack of action in the present, it will serve as a wake-up call.

Now, at first this may sound a bit off the cuff, but trust me, this a powerful concept. The key here is to understand that taking no action will actually be more painful than taking action. Let me repeat that once more:

The key here is to understand that taking no action
will actually be more painful than taking action.

Most people focus on the pain they will get on the road to achieving a goal, instead of putting all that energy, work and discipline into seeing their goals achieved and thus avoiding the most frustrating pain of all: the pain of not finishing anything. For this group, I recommend thinking of the pain you will receive if you don't do what you need to do. Focusing on avoiding that negative energy will inspire you to radiate positive energy in finally moving forward. Inside of this positive space, you'll find yourself taking on new actions. It'll literally take you from 'stuck' to 'unstoppable.'

<u>Level 60%</u> – I Have Integrity When it is Convenient

Here is a group that is beginning the process of honoring their word, but only when convenient. They fool themselves into thinking they are living at 100% integrity. After all, 100% is the ultimate goal. The good news is, they are their word. The bad news is, they can only keep small commitments. When they experience a huge breakdown or are confronted with a tough decision, they revert back to old patterns of no integrity.

They justify their behavior by saying, 'well, at least I did my best.' What they fail to realize is that the only thing holding them back from living a life of 100% integrity are the stories they keep telling themselves of why they cannot be their word. My encouragement to this group is simply this: if you are already halfway on this journey to live a life of extraordinary peace, power, and fulfillment, do not let the stories you tell yourself of why you cannot do it hold you back. Doing the very thing you fear will give you power to experience new levels of joy and fulfillment.

<u>Level 70%</u> – I Pretend to Be At 100% Integrity, When Deep Down Inside I know it is Only 70% Integrity

This group is known as the pretenders. In front of their friends, family members, and colleagues they appear to be living at 100% integrity. They do such a convincing job that they sometimes even fool themselves into believing they are playing full out with the game of 100% integrity. They tend to be excited with all the results integrity is bringing into their lives, and the momentum can be deceiving at times. Then, there is that one day they did not keep their word with a small commitment and justification kicks in by saying, "It's Okay, 5 minutes late is no big deal, or I'll go to the gym tomorrow." Now their integrity is lost again. This back and forth is what I call the "I think I am in 100% integrity syndrome."

"Richie, can you explain what you mean exactly?" Darnell interrupted with a confused look.

"For example, if you set a room thermometer at 70 degrees Fahrenheit, the air conditioning will keep the room at 70 degrees and every time the room temperature drops below 70 degrees, the air conditioner will automatically kick in. This is exactly what the pretenders tend to do. They start out at 100 degrees on the integrity thermometer but then, the inevitable happens.

"It looks something like this: they will keep their word in certain areas of their life but lose it quickly in the weaker areas. They start to justify in order to make themselves feel good about not keeping their word, then they further justify by saying 'well, at least I kept it in this area'. Thinking this way becomes a death trap to living a life of 100% integrity. This specific action brings the integrity degrees on the thermometer down to 90, 85, 80, 75 then finally 70 degrees. It's not until they start to experience breakdowns that they realize that what was missing the whole time was their word.

"But the good news is that this group usually catches themselves early in the game. At the 70-degree mark on the integrity thermometer, their internal system kicks in, then they restore their word and that brings them back up 100 degrees. This back and forth prevents them from living an extraordinary life. My recommendation for this group of champions is to honor your word, especially when you don't feel like it. Whenever you catch yourself justifying, just repeat out loud 'No, I will do it, and I will do it now.' Justification is the enemy of integrity. Learn to honor your word, above your opinions and justifications."

Level 80%– I am Developing the Habit of Keeping My Word

This group is on their way to living an extraordinary life of peace, power and fulfillment. They are aware of the impact of their word on their lives, and others as well. This group tends to have a higher quality of life compared to the previous levels. Their only challenge is that sometimes they feel down when they do not keep their word. They constantly beat themselves up for not honoring their commitments. They put too much weight on integrity and can come across as too serious. They are still developing this new muscle and when they overwork it, growth stops. To the contrary, they end up hurting this new muscle. This form of pain becomes unbearable, so much so that they feel like quitting the Integrity Gym all together. My encouragement to this group is simply this: remember that a beautifully sculpted muscle is not built in one day. It is created over time, with consistency, persistence and above all, patience. Be patient along your journey to live a life of 100% integrity and do not beat yourself up whenever you do not keep your word. Allow some space for errors and do not attack yourself when you are out of integrity. Just be in communication about the reason for not keeping your word, and then create a new promise either to yourself or the person you were out of integrity with. It's that simple. If anything, feel proud because you are definitely very high on the integrity thermometer.

Level 90% – I Have Integrity Even When it is Inconvenient

You'll find the leaders of society in this group. Please remember a leader is not a person who has a specific position or role in a company. Examples could be a doctor, principal, a reverend, or even a CEO of a large corporation. Those are just examples of positions. When I refer to leaders, I am referring to people who have followers. A leader is a person who has people following their cause out of passionate desire. Leaders at this level of the integrity thermometer honor their word, even if it may represent losing a good business deal. They might have to fire their best friend at work because this person is not holding up their side of their job responsibilities. It may mean sharing an infidelity with a friend or a spouse. At this level of integrity, they may have to do things that are uncomfortable, but they also know that not doing what they know they should do would be worse. At this stage of the game, they have certainly developed what I call 'integrity maturity'. That simply means doing what you have to do even if you're scared. Even though this group is almost at the top of the integrity thermometer, the only thing that holds them back from being at 100% is that they tend to postpone the Big Fat Confrontations of Life. You know, the big messes that life throws at us on a pretty silver platter. Now I'm not saying this group does not confront these areas. They do! They just take longer than they should. I would like to remind this group that too much analysis leads to paralysis. Do not make the mistake of going into your head to analyze and process. I want you to consider that over-analyzing is simply a form of resistance. You may ask, 'okay, what am I resisting?' You are resisting a certain pain. You are either avoiding a feeling of pain or causing pain. Whenever you do that, you are not creating a space for miracles to happen. What you should do is just speak from the heart. Have a heart-to-heart conversation with whoever you need to clear up. Be as sincere as you can be, but do it. We have all heard that the truth shall set you free, but in order to be set free, you must actually follow through with it. Do not wait any longer. Do it today. Do it *right now*.

Level 100% – I am Living a Life of 100% Integrity

At the highest level of integrity, nothing is hidden and everything is transparent. It's as if you have integrity on auto-pilot. It is just who they are. For example, parents do not have to be reminded that they are parents. They are who they are. A singer does not have to be reminded he or she is a singer. They are just who they are. These are the people who return all their phone calls, are always on time, and have developed the muscle of integrity in just about every area of their life. They have already reaped great rewards out of keeping their word and they also know how dramatic life can be when they are out of integrity. They have mastered the art of taking care of all the small integrity issues so they never become big issues. People at this level tend to get quick promotions, be in better shape, have less stress, have better health, make more money, and have less drama in their lives. They usually live in better neighborhoods, have more friends, save more money, and have longer lasting relationships. The best part is they are well aware they got these results by living at 100% integrity. They also know that if, at any time they stop being their word, it will be like going back to the past, where everything was frustrating and chaotic. It's almost like sentencing themselves to prison. But, truth be told, they are not perfect. They still make mistakes, and occasionally break their word. The only difference is that they keep restoring it every time they break it, again and again. Now that is real power!

"So there you have it, Darnell. I just gave you the whole shebang. Before I get your feedback on everything we just discussed, I also want to let you know that some people will be on level 8 on the integrity thermometer when it comes to their wealth, and level 2 in their health. Others will be at level 7 in their career but level 2 when it comes to parenting their kids. In other words, they got a good grasp and are on top of things with their job responsibilities but are struggling with parenthood. It's not that they're bad parents, they just need to up their level of integrity in that area. Trust me, once they increase their integrity in the area where they are low, then in a very short time they will see drastic improvements."

*****

"So, when I say the word integrity now, what comes to your mind?"

"I guess, I'm looking at all areas of my life where I am out of integrity," Darnell responded.

"Good! That is impressive that you see that. This is very normal."

"It is?" Darnell asked.

"Yes, it is, because this conversation becomes a mirror for you to see your 'non-integrity' ways. It makes you realize the impact you have on others and yourself when you are not being your word, and also what you could have if you choose to be a person of 100% integrity."

"Damn diggity dog, that is some deep shit! Excuse me, sir. I'm just really excited. I tend to curse when I'm excited. I have to stop doing that. No, I am committed to not doing that ever again. What I mean to say is, now I understand this integrity concept."

"No problem, buddy. So, what do you understand?"

"I can actually see the impact of keeping your word and how keeping and honoring your word really simplifies your life. It is like a gateway for amazing, lightning-quick results."

"Yes, that is certainly true. Please, keep going." I nodded in encouragement.

"Well, Richie, if you keep your word with your daughter, then you will always have a great relationship with her. If you keep your word with colleagues at work, your friends, your significant other, and everyone you surround yourself with, it just allows for things to work smoother and almost effortlessly. If you keep your word at work, I can clearly see how you can get promoted quicker. And again, like you said, if you cannot keep your promise, just have a conversation, clear it up, then make a new promise. Yep, I really got it."

"You sure do, Darnell. The best part is now that you got it, you own it forever."

"That's really cool! I'm enjoying this talk, Richie. It's cool to see how much you know and how much you have accomplished already in life. Were you always this energetic and successful?"

"Do you mean to tell me that you don't know my story and where I came from?"

"No, I don't."

"Since we still have a lot of road to cover and some time to spare, let me share it with you."

Darnell settled back in his seat and turned towards me, eager to hear my story.

Chapter Three

HOW TO TURN A POOR MINDSET INTO A RICH MINDSET

"Fears are educated into us, and can, if we wish, be educated out."
     — Dr. Karl A. Menninger — American Psychiatrist

Growing up in the Langston Hughes projects was no picnic. I would not wish it on my worst enemy. The neighborhood was filled with rap star wannabes. Cars propped up in the air was a norm, with someones 'cuz under them, either trying to save a few bucks or pimping them so the honeys on the block would give them attention. Rhythmic beats of rap, merengue, and salsa songs blared on loudspeakers and came from different directions. Empty beer bottles and Colt 45's hung around, waiting for homeless people to pick them out of the trash and recycle them later for loose change. Young kids cut school to look cool or do stupid things. With no income coming in and a lot of girls to impress, selling drugs became a lucrative cop out.

Whenever everyone saw me they would secretly say, "Oh, that's Papito's son." That was my father's nickname. His real name was Juan Hernandez. But only his close family knew his real name. The reason why they referred to me as Papito's son was because they thought I was going to grow up to be just like him. To them, my father was a loser, but to me, he was Dad. Basically, he'd been on the streets all his life and they were afraid I'd follow his path.

By the time Papito was twenty-one, over seventeen of his friends had been killed and the rest were in jail. Yeah, he had gone to jail several times and had many close encounters with death, but, by the grace of God, he was still alive. He was a first generation Dominican who mostly worked in the basements of abandoned buildings selling drugs in Brownsville, Brooklyn. He would bounce back and forth from his other drug spot in Bushwick, about 15 to 20 minutes from Brownsville. He liked

Bushwick because it was the neighborhood where he was born and raised. But he decided to call Brownsville home.

Papito and his homies had many close encounters in the past with cops or other upcoming wannabe drug dealers who wanted to take over his territory. Whenever they were in trouble they would run on the rooftops of abandoned buildings in hopes of losing their chasers. This worked like a charm because very few people were crazy enough to jump across buildings that were six feet apart. If you fell, well… that was the end of you.

There was one time when the cops were chasing my dad and his friend, Mikey. They ran for their dear lives down Putnam Avenue. Then, they saw their rescue, a fire escape ladder low enough for them to grab. They climbed up and made it to the roof. Pretty soon, the cops caught up with them. When they saw how close the cops were to catching them, their ghetto kangaroo legs loped over the rooftops with drugs and hearts in hand. Going back to prison meant losing Dad's spot. This was every drug dealer's worst nightmare.

Back on the street, they ran into a building they knew well. There were some mattresses hidden under piles of garbage. As swiftly as they could, they slipped under the mattresses. They lay there, as silent as they could, waiting for the cops to either find and arrest them, or give up. Dread penetrated their bones and pierced their hearts. The thought of going back to prison terrified them. The cops searched everywhere, but had no luck. Eventually, they left because they knew they were in a dangerous neighborhood and didn't have sufficient backup. My dad and Mikey realized they had just missed prison by the skin of their teeth. They were trying to outrun their destinies. This time they won.

*****

The morning of October 4th, 1987, was a day I will never forget. It started off wrong from the moment I woke up.

Mom was screaming at Diego to get his lazy butt out of bed as usual so he wouldn't have to repeat 9th grade again. Being the first boy in the family, he was not only lazy but also the most spoiled of all of us. Mom had made enough breakfast for Diego, my little sis' Jennifer, and me and put it on the small kitchen table as she did every morning. Her usual shout rang through the house, "Por amor a cristo, salga de tu cama, Diego!" *For the love of God, please get out of bed, Diego!*

Mom came to the U.S. when she was fourteen years old. She was born in Valverde de Mao in the Dominican Republic, where she was taught at an early age to attend to the men in the family, even if they were your siblings. She was a traditional Dominican mom who would wake up early every morning to make sure we ate before leaving for school.

Before Diego was even in his seat long enough to get his orange juice down, harsh words would begin to fly across the table. She had just about had it with Diego. These arguments with Diego became the norm.

My younger sister, Jennifer, hated to hear Mom yell so much. She was always the more conservative and quiet type. She did not like loud music, bright lights and she especially did not like to see or hear Mom and Diego fighting.

Nearly every morning Jennifer would quietly ask, "Mami, can you lower your voice and stop fighting with Diego, *por favor*?" She always looked so desperate for a truce while Mom only replied with a rude face.

As for Dad, he just so happened to be sleeping over that night. You see, my dad would come over and sleep from time to time whenever he felt like it. This was his way of being a macho man. Mom and Dad fought all the time and they were always at war. If, at any point, he felt Mom was talking to other men, he would come over just to show he was still her man; the man around the house, if you know what I mean. It was just something we all got used to over the years.

Papito was her first and only love. And for the record, Mom had never been with another man. However, Dad had three children from his previous marriage, and being the player that he was, he figured that Mom was the same way. That's why she always called him *tramposo*. He despised being called a cheater.

Dad was rarely an early riser, because he always went to bed late. But, on that particular morning, I remember him waking up early.

"Richie, go on to school now and don't be late. If you wait for your brother you will become just like him– *un fracaso total*." A total failure. Dad joined us around the breakfast table.

I heard Diego in the background saying, "Dad, that's no fair!

C'mon, *dejame tranquilo.*" Cut me some slack. "Anyways, look at you. You just pretend to be a good man—a gentleman—when we all know how you make your dough," Diego blurted out, crossing his arms and glaring at Dad.

As I saw Dad reach for his belt, I sped off. I guess you could say their relationship was not the best. Diego had a lot of resentment toward him because he was hardly ever around.

*****

When the bell sounded at 2:15 p.m., my friends Anthony, Johnny, Jorky, and I would all go to *La Bodega* (the grocery store) on Mother Gaston Boulevard and Sutter Avenue to play video games at the arcade in the back of the grocery store. Nobody could beat me at Pac-Man. It was all about patience, skill, and strategy.

"Hey! You're not that good. My cousin beat your high score. He's coming down here today to beat your score again!" Jorky laughed.

"Just let him try!" I grinned at the challenge.

When the showdown occurred, I reigned victor once more.

At an early age, I noticed that I really enjoyed winning. But it was more than winning that I loved. It was actually a deep sense of accomplishment and fulfillment that juiced me.

As I was paying for some candy, chips, and a quarter juice, we all heard police sirens. About ten police cars flashed by us just like in the movies, except this time it was for real. We started running toward the flashing police lights to see what was going on. When we arrived, I experienced a rude awakening. Before my very eyes, I saw my father in handcuffs. He was sitting in an ambulance and bleeding profusely from his shoulder. I ran toward him in desperation, but the cops wouldn't let me get close to him.

I had all these questions running through my mind and I just wanted to know what happened. Why, of all people, was my dad in handcuffs? When he saw me there at the scene he started to cry. That was the first time in my life that I actually saw him cry. We were interrupted by a stretcher that passed between us. Later, I would find out the person on the stretcher was a cop my dad had shot. He was set up.

This is how it all went down. My dad was working at the spot on Putnam Ave. as usual, in the basement. The undercover cop went to buy some drugs from Papito. Buyers would normally go down the stairs to the basement and purchase their drugs through a hole that was in the door.

Today was no different. Upon arriving, he spoke in Dominican street language, good enough to confuse my father and told Papito's worker. *"Dejame hablar con tu jefe."* Let me talk to your boss, B.

Papito said, "What the fuck do you want?"

This undercover cop, going by the name Joselito, said, "Look yo, I don't need nickel bags, I'm looking to do some real business with you. *Mi pana, necesito hablar contigo en persona.* But I need to talk with you in person yo." He was actually a white Irish cop whose real name was Josh Spotski. Since he grew up in Brooklyn, he knew the Dominican swag well. Joselito was about 5'5", slim and not very intimidating in appearance, but he had balls made out of steel.

Waiting at the top of the stairs was a police team in case something went wrong. They told him if he doesn't come out in exactly five minutes they were coming in after him. If he needed help he was supposed to use some variation of the phrase 'that ain't cool' in any sentence, so they could come in and bust the operation.

Papito got up from the ragged, dirty sofa grumbling quietly to himself and peered through a peephole so small only a person with good eyesight could see. After he eyed-balled him he said, "Let the *maricon* in."

Papito's boys searched him and decided he was clean as a whistle.

After he came in Papito said, "So, what you want?"

"Look, I'm gonna need some cocaine—half a kilo for now. I'll probably buy it three or four times a month if business is good."

"What you need so much cocaine for?"

"I got some college kids in the city that I just started selling to, I actually met them through my cousin."

"Who told you about my spot?"

"What kinda question is that?" Joselito sounded offended. "Everybody around here knows this is where the good stuff is. You got the best coke and weed in the neighborhood, not that fake shit the other dudes sell around the corner. I've been here a few times already; your boys can testify to that. Look, we gonna do business or what?" He tapped his fingers nervously against his leg, well aware of the time limit he was under.

Little did Joselito know that Papito was pulling the ten-minute time test on him. This is the way it goes in these neighborhoods. Whenever a drug dealer was in doubt he would put his new buyer through this ten-minute time test. He would ask several questions and just watch their reactions to see if they were in a hurry or got nervous. If they were undercover cops or informants, they would eventually crack under pressure. Papito knew that cops or informants were given time limits and they would have to leave before the time was up. If, at any point, Joselito said 'look, let's just do this some other day' Papito would have to take him out. It was all a mind game, and the hourglass was quickly running out of sand.

When Papito didn't respond, Joselito repeated his question, "Are we gonna do business or not?" Papito noticed the quiet edge in Joselito's voice and decided to keep stalling. Something wasn't right.

"What neighborhood or street are you from?" Papito's tone was accusatory, almost angry. Joselito was getting visibly nervous, because it was going to go down any minute now.

"I'm from Euclid and Stanley Ave." He tried to keep his voice level.

Papito quickly got up and slammed his chair and yelled, "So you must be down with the Crips!"

"No, that gang ain't cool, I don't roll like that."

Joselito stood up in position and ready for his backup, when suddenly the doors flew wide open. His backup stormed in. Papito reached for his gun and Joselito jumped on him. They crashed to the floor and wrestled for the gun. With bullets flying everywhere; Papito got the upper hand, took control of the gun and pumped two bullets into Joselito's chest. When a fellow cop saw this, he fired a few shots toward Papito, who immediately threw the weapon to his side, balled up like a snail and screamed, "Alright, alright, yo, you got me!" Papito was lucky to survive, though he was badly injured. One bullet penetrated his right leg and the other his right shoulder. But, boy, was he in pain. And that's how it all went down.

*****

I could see that Darnell had a bunch of questions on his mind, but I wanted to wrap up this part of the story first. It was great to see this young man so engaged and captivated, and I knew he was beginning to understand just how much of a struggle I had been through.

"Dad was sent to Rikers Island. He would stay there until he was sentenced. It was so hard for all of us to adjust at home. It was especially hard for Diego because, growing up, Mami always spoiled him. And now with my dad gone, Diego being the man of the house was something new to him. It meant taking on responsibility and assuming a father-figure role for my ten-year-old sister Jennifer, and me."

Darnell finally interrupted with a question, "How did your mother take it?"

"Mom was always depressed, and to make ends meet she had to work two jobs so we rarely saw her much except on Sundays. Being a single mother on welfare was not going to cut it with three children to raise."

"Then, who took care of you guys?" Darnell's brows furrowed.

"We pretty much took care of ourselves. It wasn't easy, but that's what happens in the hood," I shrugged. "When dads are no longer around, moms find themselves working two, sometimes three jobs, and all of a sudden the TV, friends and other gangs end up raising and influencing these young kids."

"Since you're on the topic, did you ever experience any close encounters with a gang?" Darnell asked.

"Yep, one day I was walking with Big Homie Pops to the basketball court."

"Big Homie Pops!" Darnell repeated with excitement and anticipation.

"You heard right, Darnell. But Big Homie Pops was simply his nickname. His real name was Alfonso; people in the neighborhood called him Big Homie Pops."

"Why did they call him that?"

"They called him that because he was pretty big for his age—"

"You mean fat, right?" he interrupted.

"I guess you could say big boned, but not fat." I said, almost defensively.

"It's the same thing, Richie," Darnell rolled his eyes.

"C'mon. Let me finish my story."

45

"Ok, go ahead."

"Big Homie Pops was also taller than most kids. The chubbiness, as you like to call it, and his tallness made him appear five years older than he actually was. As I was saying, Big Homie Pops and I were on our way to the basketball courts across the street from my building, when out of nowhere, three older guys were coming toward us. It was obvious they were Bloods by the clothing they wore and their red bandanas. They were a really bad local gang. They confused Big Homie Pops with another gang member."

As we got close, they intentionally bumped him. Although Big Homie Pops was a lot younger, he was extremely fierce and crazy. Big Homie Pops immediately pushed the guy to the ground and before he hit the ground, we took off running. When we were about fifty yards ahead, Big Homie Pops turned toward them and said, "Hey bitches, come get some of this" as he squeezed his crotch[3]. I yanked him away by the shoulder and we started running again. Don't ask me how– but somehow we lost them. You tend to run faster when you are being chased.

When we arrived home, Wonderbread was sitting on the bench in front of our building trying to fix his broken CD player."

"Wonderbread?" Darnell interrupted, with a disbelieving look on his face.

"His real name was Steven, a white-as-powder Puerto Rican who lived on the same floor as me."

"Richie, where do people get all these crazy names from?" Darnell asked.

"In the ghetto, everyone either has a nickname or is given one," I explained.

"So what was yours?"

"Everyone called me 'The Champ'."

"Why?" Darnell wondered.

When I was a kid, I would tell people that, someday, I was going to be a boxer. Not just any boxer, but a champion boxer. The champion of all champions. Every time I would see a boxing match, or the movie *Rocky* with Sylvester Stallone, I would dance around the house as if I was fighting in a boxing match. I threw jabs, ducked, hopped, dodged and pranced around my imaginary contender. My family would say, 'There goes the champ again, watch out! Don't let him hit you.' I would often play-fight with my dad and, obviously, he would let me win. So, that's how I got my nickname.

"So, Champ, did you become a boxer?" Darnell asked.

"Can't say I ever did, just one of those things you dream up as a kid. However, the nickname stuck with me. Ever since then, I've always related to myself as a champion. It became who I am today.

"Anyways, back to Wonderbread, Big Homie Pops, and me. When we arrived at the building Wonderbread noticed how much we were sweating, so he asked, 'What happened?' As I proceeded to tell him, Big Homie Pops started laughing really hard. He had this unique laugh that resembled a donkey with hiccups, and each breath he took sounded like he was gasping for air. You couldn't help but laugh. Somehow, he found this whole thing hilarious. But then, the unimaginable happened."

"What?" Darnell asked impatiently.

"Out of nowhere, the gang showed up and one of them had a gun in hand. He scowled, 'What you gonna do now, huh, huh? Who's the bitch now, you punk ass?' Before any of us could say anything, the guy pointed the gun at Wonderbread's head and pulled the trigger. As I stood there watching this all go down, everything felt like it was happening in slow motion."

"Oh, my God!" Darnell shouted. "Did they kill him?"

"No. Wonderbread got lucky, because the gun jammed. The gang member tried pulling the trigger several more times and finally when he saw that it would not shoot, he just hit Wonderbread over the head with the gun. It all happened so fast; next thing you know we were all fighting. They finally took off when they heard someone nearby scream out, 'he has a gun!'

"On that day, I made a firm decision that I had to leave this neighborhood before someone made me leave. I'm referring to an early departure; first class–coffin style–if you know what I mean. You see, back in the days you were either college bound, Rikers Island Penitentiary bound or Funeral Ortiz bound. I chose to be college-bound."

"So what happened to Big Homie Pops and Wonderbread?" Darnell asked.

"Big Homie Pops later joined a gang for protection because he thought it was cool. Unfortunately, that did not last too long. He got caught stealing some rims from a beamer in Massapequa, Long

Island. That little stunt bought him a first class ticket to Rikers. To make matters worse, in prison he killed a rival gang member in a fight for which he got a ten-year extended stay. Talk about stupid." I shook my head at my old friend's senseless actions. "As for Wonderbread, he died two years later, in a gang initiation that went wrong."

"My God! What happened?" Darnell demanded.

"Word on the street has it that he had to rob an innocent bystander to be accepted into the gang. Unfortunately, to his bad luck, he chose the wrong guy to rob. When he approached the guy, somehow the guy grabbed his hand with the gun and, while they wrestled, a bullet went off and Wonderbread caught it in the chest. He died before the ambulance arrived."

As I talked about Wonderbread's death, I sensed it was time to impart some wisdom. I looked Darnell straight in the eye, and said, "Darnell, the old saying still holds true, 'if you live by the streets, you die by the streets'."

"Man, oh man! All this drama has me sick to my stomach. So, if you had it so rough, who was your positive influence?" Darnell asked.

"Darnell, everything started to change for me when I first met Mr. Rodriguez. Let me tell you how I ran into him. As a young boy, I visited the bodega across the street from our building almost every day. We never had much food at home and Mami had an account there so we were able to get food on credit. Mami would later take care of the bill. It wasn't your average bodega or grocery store as we know it today. It was more like a mini supermarket. They had everything you could think of there. This was the place to go for–"

"I know—for the best stuff," Darnell interrupted.

"Nope. Can I continue with my story?"

"Yeah, yeah." Darnell smiled as he leaned back in his seat again.

"For the cheapest stuff. In my old neighborhood, all that mattered was getting everything cheap, so you could stretch your hard earned dollars. My knucklehead brother was not allowed in the store anymore because Mr. Rodriguez had suspected him of stealing beer. One day, we all went in together as a group after school and he didn't notice Diego was with us. He happened to be wearing a baggy sweater and hoodie that covered half of his face. This time it worked."

I was headed for aisle three to hunt down some Lucky Charms cereal, and macaroni and cheese when I heard a scream that pierced my ears coming from the cash register. Mr. Rodriguez yelled, "Hey what are you doing!" in his heavy Dominican accent. Before I knew it, my homies were running out the door. The guys ran out of the store lickety-split. As for me, I took off like a madman too! My heart was pounding so loud I thought I would go deaf. Unfortunately for me, Mr. Rodriguez caught me at the front door and yanked me in like a criminal. I was so embarrassed that I lowered my chin and covered my eyes. He demanded that I pay for what the others had stolen.

He threatened to tell my mom that I was stealing if I didn't cough up the dough. Just the thought of this made me feel like crap because Mr. Rodriguez was the only help my mother received on the block, and without his help we would starve on those nights when the refrigerator was empty. Especially considering that Mom worked late most nights.

I begged Mr. Rodriguez not to tell on me. I also told him I would do whatever he wanted me to do so I wouldn't get a whoopin' from Mom. Boy, those thick leather belts sure sting when lashed with anger and, truth be told, I wasn't in the mood for one of those whoopins' anytime soon. He was a kind man and I knew I could win him over if I just kept quiet and listened to him. Sure enough, Mr. Rodriguez came up with an idea that would keep my brother and me from getting *una buena pela*—beaten by my mom.

He told me that if I helped him out everyday after school, for at least the rest of the year, he would not tell my mom.

This seemed like an okay idea, since I thought I would spend most of my time in the bodega playing Pac Man. Boy, was I in for a surprise. The 'deal' that Mr. Rodriguez made me sign excluded me from playing the game while I was in the store during what he called 'his time.' I remember this was the first deal I ever made, and it seemed to me like I was already making bad deals. I gave him my time and received no payment in return. Later on, I realized what I received was priceless.

Turns out, Mr. Rodriguez became the father I never had. To answer your question, Darnell, he was the first positive influence I ever had and if it were not for him, who knows what would have become of my life. He was strict, but fair. Remember that talk we had this morning about integrity? Well, I first heard that from Mr. Rodriguez. In the beginning, I would just nod my head in agreement and stay on his good side so he wouldn't tell Mom a single word of what had happened. Though, as time passed, the more he spoke, the more he made sense."

"So, how old was he?" Darnell interrupted again.

"Mr. Rodriguez was probably in his early to mid-forties. He was darkly handsome. He always had a clean-shaven face and a shiny bald head. He was slim, and a pretty fit man for his age. He never smoked and was an avid runner for most of his adult life. He was a pretty impressive person, I must say. I guess you could say he was a ball of surprises because he always had something up his sleeve. He came to the U.S. when he turned twenty-one, from San Pedro de Macoris in D.R., but you'd never think he was Dominican because his English was rock solid. Many times, people would confuse him with being black.

Everyday, I would go straight to Mr. Rodriguez's store and do my homework in his back office before starting my work activities. Those were his rules. One afternoon, Diego came by and asked me, "Hey, bro, can I put this meat I bought for Mom in your office fridge? I promise to pick it up before you leave tonight."

"Sure thing, just put it in there and don't forget to come back for it later," I said.

"Okay, gotta run, see you later."

Roughly four hours later, Diego returned with Paul and Steve. They would often tease me whenever they saw me sweeping, saying, "Look at Richie sweeping his life away" or point out wherever I missed a spot.

On this particular day, Steve purposely spilled some juice on the floor so I would have to wipe it up. When Diego saw what Steve did, he slapped him on the back of the head. He whacked him so hard that he took a nosedive into the *Goya* cans and spilled them all over the floor.

"Yo, just leave Richie alone! C'mon, man," This last part was said as he turned his attention away from Steve and back to me, "You're embarrassing the family by working here. Just come work for me so that you can make some real dough."

"Now, you know that's never going to happen, Diego, so just leave with your pathetic friends."

"Your loss." He shrugged, like he didn't really care what I had just said. "Just get me the meat in the freezer so I can leave and let you get back to your sweeping, Mr. Janitor."

To get rid of him, I ran to the office and got his package of meat. But when I handed the package to him, he handed the package right back to me.

"Richie, do me a favor and look at the meat in the bag to make sure you got me the right bag." When I looked inside, I could not believe what I saw. It was full of cash and rubber bands.

"Diego, are you crazy!" I thrust the bag into his hands "What's all this drug money in this bag? I should tell Mom what you are doing so she can knock some sense into your brainless head."

Diego handed over an envelope with cash to pay for the bribe he was going to attempt with me and said, "There's a gratitude bump in the envelope for you as long as you keep this thing our secret."

"Yo bro, just get outta here before Mr. Rodriguez catches us. Do you want to get me fired for storing drug money in his store?" I held the broom tightly in front of me, in case I had to whack him, and I would if he continued to press forward with his idiotic ways.

"Alright, I won't do it again." He tucked the envelope into his jacket, along with the bag of drug money, "I just wanted you to see how much money is available for the taking. The truth is, you're working for pennies when you could be rolling in the big bucks."

"Diego, I'm not getting into this conversation here; besides, you already know my answer, so just leave right now before Mr. Rodriguez catches us. You've already caused a lot of trouble. As a matter of fact, you're the reason why I'm working here. Please leave now."

"Alright, but from now on when the guys call you Mr. Janitor I ain't sayin' nuttin' to defend your sorry ass. You deserve it, bro."

"Whatever," I shouted, "Whatever!"

I was so hurt by his words that I ran to the back office and broke down in tears. I just couldn't take the pressure anymore. Mr. Rodriguez saw what happened and followed me.

"Richie, *que paso?*"

"Look, I don't want to talk about it right now!" I turned my back to him, wanting him to just leave me alone.

"Richie, just calm down and, please, remember what I once told you: anything is possible through communication."

*****

I turned to look at Darnell, making sure he was paying close attention to what I was saying. He stared at me, spellbound. "Darnell, Mr. Rodriguez went on to explain something that would have a long lasting impact on my life."

"What did he say?" He asked eagerly.

"I'm getting there!" I laughed and went back to my story.

"Richie," Mr. Rodriguez said, after thinking to himself for a few seconds. "I think I know why you are upset. Your brother is trying to get you to do something you don't want to do. Is that correct?"

"Yep," I said, still wiping off my tears. The silence stretched uncomfortably between us.

"Unfortunately, your brother thinks that the only way to succeed under his current condition is by selling drugs and, by the looks of it, you feel quite the opposite. Am I right?"

"Yes sir." I said halfheartedly.

Mr. Rodriguez continued, "Whether he realizes it or not, he sees you as the underdog,"

"What is an underdog?" I asked.

"An underdog is a competitor thought to have little chance of winning a fight or contest.[3] If you paid close attention, I said the word "competitor," not loser or lazy bum. Underdogs are competitors. They are in major action and usually go above and beyond what's necessary to come out ahead. They are competing in a fight to win. In your case, you are competing against poverty, and coincidentally, you are also competing against your brother. Instead of supporting you for wanting to do things the right way, he constantly ridicules you. This is usually how underdogs are treated by their peers and colleagues.

"Your brother senses you are weak at this stage of your life, and he is trying to bring you into his crew to make instant cash and make you stronger in his mind. But what he fails to realize is that underdogs have enormous heart and drive and are always striving to prove that they have what it takes to succeed on their own. Underdogs are committed to win, and will often do whatever it takes to come out victorious. Unfortunately, nobody bets on underdogs. But that's okay, because they bet on themselves and truthfully that's all that is needed to win," Mr. Rodriguez said enthusiastically."

"That description fits me well sir. I do have an immense desire to prove to the world that I got what it takes to win and become a millionaire. I just never knew there was a word for it," I said, speaking a bit more energetically."

"I know that to be true. I saw that fierce tiger in you when I first met you. Something tells me you want a better life, but you don't want to do it by compromising your integrity. Am I right?" Mr. Rodriguez asked.

"That's right sir. I want to succeed, but the honest way." I said once more.

"Something also tells me you think it will either never happen or it will take an entire life to accomplish it. Am I right?" Mr. Rodriguez asked.

How did he know I had those thoughts? Was he a mind reader? "Yes," I replied weakly.

"Richie, I am going to share something with you that I have shared with very few people, so pay close attention if you want lots of riches in your life. Do I have your full attention?" Mr. Rodriguez asked, watching to see my response.

I sat up in my chair, looked him in the eyes and nodded, "You sure do sir."

"Good!" Mr. Rodriguez grinned and clapped his hands together. "Richie, believe it or not, just because you are not so well off right now does not mean you can not be rich someday. As a matter of fact, within every person lies the code to create all the riches they desire. We were all coded with it when we were born. Once you know the code I am referring to, it will unlock your greatness and all the riches you have ever desired. Richie—"

"What code are you referring to?" I interrupted impatiently.

"Let me explain it this way—a code is secretive information and when used properly it can unlock something of immense value. And so it is with us. All people are born with their own unique code to create all the riches they desire. This code is the ultimate weapon against mediocrity and poverty. It is the key to success for any underdog who wants to succeed on high levels."

By now I was sitting at the edge of my seat with so much anticipation that if he waited a second more to tell me the code to unlock all the riches I so desperately wanted, I was going to demand it aggressively. "So what is the code, sir?" I asked as politely as I could.

Mr. Rodriguez shook his head. "Richie, I'm sorry, but I can not tell you what the code is. As I said before, we are all born with this code, and it's just a matter of unlocking it. You see, this code is already within you, and it's your job to discover it.

I stood up so fast that the chair fell behind me. "Why won't you tell me?" I demanded. "I really need to know this so called code so I can start moving toward my dreams of becoming a successful business person just like you, sir. I can't take it no more." My voice was loud and tense, desperate for the apparent key to change my life.

"Calm down, young man. Take a deep breathe and gather yourself. Go ahead and sit back down so I can tell you how I plan to help you discover it." Mr. Rodriguez said calmly.

After gathering my composure, I looked him straight into his eyes and saw his genuine desire to help me. I decided to take another deep breath, sat back down, and then quietly asked, "How do you plan to help me if you are not willing to reveal the code?"

"What I am willing to do is help you discover it through a proven process I have learned over the years and if you follow my every step, the words of the code will enter your mind and come out of your mouth when you least expect it. But you have to follow my lead and do as I say.

"The reason I am doing this is because if I share the code with you, it will have very little effect on how you view being rich or poor. I say this because your current mental programming will not allow you to appreciate and understand the importance of the code if I reveal it to you now. First, you must transform your beliefs, habits, and mindset so you can have a different mindset once you discover it. Without this mental shift, the actual code will be useless.

"It's kind of like forcing a woman to give birth to a baby when she is just three months pregnant--it simply won't work because she first needs to go through the process before delivering her baby. And the same goes with the code; you have to first go through the process. You can't rush it if you want the true power of the code to be unlocked. But don't worry, in due time, you will come to discover it for yourself as I help you through the transformative process. It will take some time to accomplish this, but the process will be worth it. You are going to have to trust me on this," Mr. Rodriguez said calmly, but forcefully.

"One more thing, young man—do not even think about asking me what the code is in the future, because I will never tell you what it is. What I will do, however, is share with you my success principles, and in the process of applying these principles, you will discover the code for yourself." He looked me dead in the eye. "Are you game?" He asked.

I guess I do not have a choice in the matter was the first thought that came to mind, but I would not dare say it out loud. The last thing I wanted to do was discourage him from helping me discover the code to riches that I so desperately wanted to know. But truth be told, my mind was set, and so was my heart, to start this transformative process.

After a few more seconds passed by, I tried to shake off my frustration and despair. I mustered as much courage as I could, and asked, "So you are saying that if I learn your success principles, I will eventually discover the code on my own?"

"Yes, that is correct. It will come to you in the constant application of my success principles. But the key here is to take them on like your life depended on it, because it really does. Now, if you decide to live by and constantly apply the success principles with the heart of a hungry underdog and the consistency of a professional athlete, over time you will start to notice how they will become a part of you. Doing so will be the entry point to discovering the code.

"Now that you have me intrigued sir, can I ask you what the concept of success principles means?"

"That is a great question Richie. Let me break down the two words so you can understand what it means fully. Success is a person that achieves desired aims.[3a] A principle is a universally accepted law that will bring about when applied a predictable result. In essence, I am going to share universal truths that have helped everyday people create massive successes for themselves. Keep in mind that I studied the greatest philosophers, psychologists, motivational speakers, and hundreds of multi-millionaires to distill the precise principles that have taken me over 30 years to master.

"Awesome, I am looking forward to learning your success principles." I said enthusiastically.

"I am glad you see it that way since these are the same principles I have used to create the life of my dreams and also generate massive wealth for myself. But you have to promise me that you will apply them on blind faith--otherwise, I will be wasting my time and time is something I truly cherish. This is why I need a commitment from you before I share these valuable pearls of wisdom. Can you promise me you will put into practice everything I share with you, young man?

"This is starting to sound like a school test." I said.

"Let me clarify, this information is not what they will teach you in school, yet when applied it will impact all the areas of your life, including school." Mr. Rodriguez siad.

"Will you also teach me business strategies so I can become a millionaire?" I asked.

Mr. Rodriguez smiled a little. "Yes, I will in due time if I see you are a good pupil. You should also know that you need to learn my success principles before learning business strategies. Learning these success principles will create the foundation for a successful life. The reason why I say this is because money has no principles--money is just a tool for trading and investing purposes. However, if you live a principle-based life, you will learn how to get it, get more of it, keep it, and ultimately invest it all while staying grounded in your principles. It may sound exciting, but it is going to require a lifelong commitment to living from these principles. Let me know if I can count on you to apply them on a consistent basis and if you agree then I will share with you the first of many success principles." Mr. Rodriguez stated.

I thought for a long second then nodded my head, accepting the agreement.

"I want to hear you say it. I want to hear 'yes I promise to apply the principles on a consistent basis'." Mr. Rodriguez demanded.

All I thought to myself was why this man was so willing to help. It didn't make sense, but what did I have to lose? Mr. Rodriguez watched me impatiently with his arms crossed, so I mustered up the courage and said, "Okay, I promise to apply the principles on a consistent basis."

"That is great news, my young champ. So, tell me, why were you so upset when your brother left the store?" Mr. Rodriguez asked.

After taking a few deep breaths and thinking over the situation,

I decided to tell him what happened and why I was so afraid. I mentioned that I was afraid I would never amount to anything, just like my dad and Diego.

"Do you mean to tell me that you see yourself as a failure, or that you are afraid you will become a failure just like your brother and your dad?" Mr. Rodriguez asked.

"Both," I replied.

"It's pretty apparent that you have an extremely poor mindset, and what is driving your negative outlook about yourself are your limiting beliefs."

"What do you mean by 'limiting beliefs'?" I asked him, genuinely curious as to what he had to tell me.

"Let me first explain what a belief is. The dictionary explains that a belief is usually defined as a conviction of the truth of a proposition without its verification; therefore, a belief is a subjective mental interpretation derived from perceptions."[4]

"Come again?" I replied.

"What I am trying to say is that what we believe in is who we perceive we are. It drives just about everything we do. Richie, there are two types of beliefs. There are limiting beliefs and empowering beliefs. A limiting belief is a belief that disempowers you to the point where it actually cripples you. Your limiting beliefs puts the brakes on your goals and aspirations, and holds you back from becoming the champion you were born to be. It's all occurring in the background of your life, and you don't even know it's happening."

"Can you give me a few examples, Mr. Rodriguez?"

He nodded. "Sure, some of the most common limiting beliefs are:

1. I'm too young.
2. Nobody is going to believe me.
3. I can't do that.
4. That is too hard.
5. I don't have enough money to start that business.
6. I'm not smart enough.
7. I'm too old.
8. It won't work.
9. I've never done that before.
10. I'm not good enough.

11. I'm not attractive enough.
12. I'm not brave enough.
13. I don't have anything to say.
14. Who would want to hear what I have to say?

The opposite of a limiting belief is an empowering belief. Empowering beliefs create abundance in all areas of your life. These beliefs empower you to take immediate action; they are the fuel in your Ferrari. They allow you to experience quantum leaps in whatever you decide to do. A few examples of empowering beliefs are:

1. I know I can.
2. I am the one.
3. If you can, I can.
4. Who says I can't?
5. If it's got to be, it's up to me.
6. Curiosity is the mother of all invention.
7. If I don't know, I'll just ask someone to teach me.
8. I was created to spread the abundance God created.
9. I speak up for what I believe in, and for myself.
10. I look forward to embracing the unknown.
11. If I fail, I will learn what not to do next time.
12. I am abundance; therefore, I attract abundance.
13. I give myself the green light to go ahead into a world of uncertainty.
14. My mind is my employee. He works for me, even when I sleep.
15. Success is a commitment to completion; therefore, I will always finish what I start.
16. My success is guaranteed as long as I am coachable, committed, and consistent.
17. It is impossible for me to fail because I always learn from my mistakes and will never quit.

I pondered what he said for a moment. "That is so interesting, Mr. Rodriguez! So why do we have so many *limiting beliefs*?"

"The real challenge is that they are the outcome of thousands of 'No's' we got as children. How many times have you heard as a child 'don't do that, no you can't, I told you no, how many times do I have to say no, look I already said no, no, no, no, and no.

The 'no' is just a simple word, but the real impact comes from the meaning we give to that no."

"Mr. Rodriguez, I understood everything fine up until now, but when you talked about the 'meaning we give to that no', you threw me off." My eyebrows scrunched up in confusion as I looked up at him.

"Richie, the negative meanings we give to those no's create a huge impact. Much bigger than you can imagine. It is crucial to address the meaning we give those no's, because whatever you don't change, you pass on to your children and they will pass it on to their children and so on. Here's how it works: we first form our own meaning, understanding, and interpretation when an event takes place. This event could be something you witness, or as simple as someone telling you something you don't necessarily agree with. When you witness something or disagree with someone, in that moment you form your own interpretation or story of what just occurred.

"My first experience of this was when I was a young boy," continued Mr. Rodriguez. "There I was, eight years old and eating my favorite vanilla ice cream on the front stoop of my house when I saw this man with long hair running down the street, screaming, 'Freedom, freedom, freedom, where are you!' This was a new neighbor on the block and my first reaction was, 'Wow, what mental institution did he run away from?' Well, a few weeks passed and I saw him again, but this time he was walking his dog. As he passed by me, the dog started licking my leg. He apologized after he introduced himself and said, 'I'm so sorry. Freedom likes to play with little boys; he does not have many friends.' His name was Freedom, Richie. Can you believe that? All along, I was thinking this man was crazy, when I was really the crazy one for making an assumption about what I didn't know. He was actually looking for his doggie and I immediately assumed the worse when I heard him screaming 'Freedom'.

"You see Richie, that's what we do as humans—we form our own interpretations, according to the way things occur to us."

"Okay, it's starting to make a little sense now."

"Please let me continue young man, I am not done," demanded Mr. Rodriguez.

"Okay, sorry for interrupting," I quickly said.

"Richie, have you ever noticed that when there is a car accident, we always hear different versions of what happened. Have you ever stopped to ask why that happens?"

"No, not really."

"The reason we get different versions is because we see life through different lenses, according to how the world occurs to us. We create different versions and realities based on our experiences in our world as we see it through our glasses. After we witness an event or hear a comment from someone, we immediately start to form our own interpretation or story of how it occurred. It doesn't matter if what just happened was good or bad, right or wrong, just or unjust; all that matters to you is how you interpreted the event that just occurred. Your interpretation, and how you saw it in your mind's eye will always be your truth; it actually becomes your reality. This is how interpretations are born. Now, let's observe the impact these interpretations have on our lives and how they create our limiting and empowering beliefs.

"Let's say you created an interpretation that you were stupid because one day your best friend jokingly said, 'Hey, shut up *stupid*!' God forbid that person invites you somewhere or needs a favor. Your answer would likely be, 'Nah, can't help you.' Richie, what I want you to understand is that this is a limiting belief you adopted, mainly because of how you chose to interpret that comment. Now, if this was your interpretation of the story, what do you think would be your end result? Well, you probably wouldn't even want to be around that person. If you did happen to be around that person, you would subconsciously or, maybe even consciously, try to prove that you are not stupid by doing things or making comments to prove you are smart. All along, the other person might be wondering why you are acting this way. It all started because in your mind—and only in your mind—you created an interpretation that led to a limiting belief that you were stupid. Now your friend probably didn't mean it, but that's how you decided to interpret it. To you, that became your reality. That became your new belief. Worst of all, it became a limiting belief. Tony Robbins once said, 'What we need to remember is that most of our interpretations are based on misinterpretations of what we think happened and once we adopt them as the truth—our truth—we forget it's merely an interpretation.'[5]

"The actions you take will always be in direct proportion to how you interpret life's events."

— Edward R. Muñoz

"The big problem with all these limiting beliefs is that they become limitations for what we truly are capable of. They become a crutch or anchor that hold us back from achieving our goals. For as long as we continue to regard ourselves as these limiting beliefs, we will always remain deaf to life's opportunities, blind to what's possible in the world and numb to unleashing our personal greatness.

"Now, here's the great news, Richie; you are not your limiting beliefs and they are not who you are!"

"I'm not? That's really hard to grasp."

"Look, just because you *act* stupid sometimes, does not mean you *are* stupid. Just because you say idiotic things occasionally does not mean you are an idiot. Here's a good question, Richie. Do you have a brain?"

"Yes, I do." I nodded my head slowly, wondering what he meant.

"Do you have a hand?" Mr. Rodriguez raised his eyebrows in expectation of my answer.

"Yes, I do." I glanced at it, as if making sure it was still there.

"Now are you your brain?"

"No, I am not."

"Are you your hand?"

"No, I am not." A small grin crept onto my face at the thought.

"Exactly! That's my point." He leaned back and looked satisfied. So, for the record, let me repeat it again: 'You are not your limiting beliefs and they are not who you are!' Who you are is a champion with unlimited potential. When I look at you, all I see is a Ghandi, a Martin Luther King Jr., Mr. Possibility, a World Class Leader, a Real Champion at Heart. That's who you are, Richie."

"Wow, thank you!" I looked into the distance and really thought about what my future might hold.

"Of the ones I just mentioned Richie, which one really lights you up?" asked Mr. Rodriguez.

"The one that really jumps out is Mr. Possibility." I smiled as I said it.

"Okay, what about that really lights you up?"

"I like it because it could mean anything I want it to mean, and I could change it at any moment and still be Mr. Possibility'."

"Now you got me lit up, Richie!" He leaned toward me and put his hand on my shoulder, looking me steadily in the eyes. "Richie this is the way we experience life:

Something happens, we make it mean something, then it becomes our belief...

Then something else happens, we make it mean something, then it becomes our belief...

Then another thing happens, we make it mean something, and it also becomes our belief...

"What you need to realize is that whatever happened is all that happened. Nothing more, nothing less. Everything else is just a story, or an illusion of your story. Whatever you do, just make sure you don't add anything on top of what actually happened because when you do, this is where the limiting belief is created. Now, at every given moment you have the power to choose how you are going to interpret any event, no matter what life throws at you. Human beings have the awesome ability to take any experience of their lives and create a meaning that either disempowers them or uplifts them to greatness."

"Real power is the ability to accept things that happened just as they are without adding a negative meaning to it. If you are going to add a meaning to it, make sure it is one that inspires you. This process will give birth to an empowering belief!"

"Mr. Rodriguez, this is so amazing, but I have a question that really concerns me."

"Okay, what is it young man?" He leaned back again, anticipating my question.

"So, all of this sounds really good, but what happens in the heat of the moment if something really bad happens? I guess what I mean is, in the heat of the moment how can I maintain my cool so that I don't go into reaction mode and make it mean something that is not the case?"

"Yes, you are right. We mainly form negative interpretations:

1. When something bad happens.
2. When someone screams at us.
3. When someone lies to us.
4. When someone rejects us.
5. When we get fired.
6. When someone steals from us.
7. When our spouse leaves us.
8. When we lose money on a bad business deal.
9. When we lose a loved one.
10. When we lose a good customer or account.
11. When we wake up in a wheelchair after a car accident.
12. When we fall behind on our mortgage payments and our home goes into foreclosure.
13. When our property taxes go up unexpectedly.
14. When the doctor breaks bad news.
15. When your tenant says he can't continue paying you the rent.

When, when, when, when, when, when, when, when, when...

"So this is the golden rule you should apply, especially when you catch yourself getting upset or annoyed. I call it 'The D.E.F.Y. Method'. I want you to follow this method to the letter exactly as I explain it. This method was designed to challenge your negative thoughts and limiting beliefs. Richie, in the dictionary, the word 'defy' is defined as 'to challenge'. The only way to defy the odds is by challenging yourself to think and act in a different way. Here is my ridiculously powerful and proven method for doing so:

The D.E.F.Y. Method

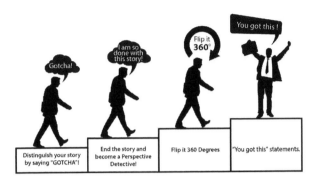

A Proven Method For Turning A Limiting Belief Into An Empowering Belief.

1. Distinguish your story by saying "gotcha!"
2. End the story and become a Perspective Detective!
3. Flip it 360 Degrees
4. "You Got This" statements + 1 action

To download this infographic with full color, check out:
http://www.theunderdogcode.com/bookresources

Step 1– Distinguish It By Saying "Gotcha!"

In the dictionary, to "distinguish" means "to make noticeable or point out a difference; to set apart."[6] Whenever you catch yourself saying something you know you shouldn't be saying, the first step in the D.E.F.Y. method is to make it noticeable. When you do this, you set it apart in your mind. This is known as "distinguishing". Distinguishing our limiting beliefs is the ability to catch ourselves when we are forming a negative meaning or interpretation. Basically, just say "gotcha!" out loud. This is so important because, if we ignore it, limiting beliefs will grow like weeds in a garden and ruin your life. The best way to stop negative interpretations is through the initial process of distinguishing them. Now, here's the kicker. If you resist doing this, they will persist. Resistance leads to persistence. But there's good news: In the moment you distinguish your limiting beliefs or negative thoughts, they start to lose their power over you.

Step 2 – End the Story and Become a Perspective Detective

Good detectives are experts at analyzing the facts of what actually happened at a crime scene. They do this by separating the story from the actual facts. By now we know the limiting belief lies in the story. But, when you can eliminate the story you have about what happened, the limiting belief will automatically disappear. This will create the space to create a new perspective on the whole situation. Obviously, your goal as a Perspective Detective is to create a new perspective that will empower you to move forward, and with velocity.

Step 3 – Flip it 360 Degrees

One way to create a new perspective or empowering belief is to flip the old one 360 degrees. For example, if your old belief was, "I don't have enough time," just flip it into, "No, I have plenty of time." When you catch yourself saying, "I can't do that," just flip it 360 and say, "I can do it and I will do it now." When you catch yourself saying a negative comment that steals your power, just flip it into something that empowers you. It's really that simple. Just remember you are the one who created the limiting belief, and if you created it, you also have the power to create a new one. The late philosopher Nikos Kazantzakis once said, "Since we cannot change reality, let us change the eyes that see reality."

Step 4 – You Got This Statements + 1 Action

Now that you created a new empowering belief, the next and most important step is to take action. One way to build confidence around taking a new action is by declaring the phrase "you got this" with your name following after the statement out loud, then declaring the action you intend to act upon. Declarations should be announced out loud. They empower and shock your nervous system into action. Simply put, declaration precedes action. And, in the words of a successful, blind, entrepreneur, who manages a 6 billion dollar investment firm and is one of two to hold a jiu jitsu black belt in the world, "declaration procedes leap".

Here are a few examples:

- You got this, <u>your name here</u>, now call that person.
- You got this, <u>your name here</u>, now go to the gym.
- You got this, <u>your name here</u>, now call those 10 prospects.
- You got this, <u>your name here</u>, now go create your business plan.

"This is what I meant when I said 'you got this statements.' Nothing replaces old conversations better than action. It becomes the driving force behind your new empowering belief. Taking massive action on this new belief will create off the charts results in your life."

He looked at me expectantly. "Now, let's see how the D.E.F.Y. method applies to you. So, Richie, going back to your limiting belief about being afraid to fail. Let's think for a moment and see when you came up with that belief. Can you recall a moment in your childhood when you were really upset? It's really important to determine and dig really deep to find out at what point of your life you created this limiting belief."

"I'm thinking," I replied.

"Don't worry, take your time. Just pick the first incident that comes to mind."

"Oh, I can remember this one incident when I was seven years old. I was on my couch at home watching my favorite cartoon when my father and mother walked in screaming at each other in Spanish. Like, I remember Dad cussed out Mom really bad, and what really pissed her off was when he called her a *puta*. At that point, Mom coughed up a nasty spit and let him have it! So, he retaliated with a punch in the face. She collapsed and started crying, and was completely powerless against his attack. All I remember was Mom saying, '*Te odio desde lo más profundo de mi Corazon*' (I hate you from the bottom of my heart). You better leave my house before I call *la policia*.'"

"So, what did you make that mean, Richie?" asked Mr. Rodriguez.

"What did I make it mean? Hmmm," I furrowed my brow as I thought. "I guess I made it mean that if my father was a nobody, I certainly would also become a nobody. A worthless nobody. But now that I think about it, I made the decision right then and there not to try to become successful, because I felt it would just be a waste of time. I realized that I didn't consider myself worthy."

"Aha! So, that is the day your limiting belief was born. After all I have shared with you thus far, has anything opened up for you?"

"Yes," I said as I breathed a deep sigh of relief. Suddenly, my shoulders felt light and everything seemed clear. "What comes to mind is that up until now, I've carried an interpretation I created, and it's no wonder I don't try to get good grades and why I never give my full 100% effort at anything I do. I made a decision that day to really never try to fulfill my potential, out of the interpretation I created that I was a nobody and worthless."

"Exactly," replied Mr. Rodriguez with a big grin.

"I also realize that they were just having a fight and it had nothing to do with me, but somehow I made it mean something that only existed in my mind until today. Mr. Rodriguez, I am willing to let go of that limiting belief once and forever."

"Great! I like that, Richie. So, let's follow the D.E.F.Y. method to create a new belief. One that empowers you. You ready?"

"Yes, sir. Let's go for it. Never felt so ready!"

"Well, you just took care of Step 1: You distinguished and identified your limiting belief. Step 2 is to separate the story from what actually happened. All that happened was that your mother had an argument with your father. Those are the facts. Now, the story you created is that you would never amount to anything because your father was a failure; in other words, if he were a failure, then you surely would be a failure as well. That was the meaning you gave it. So, what are you going to make it mean? Because we both know that once you change the meaning, you also change the belief."

"Hmm... umm. I'll make it mean... huh, I'm thinking..." I bit the inside of my lip, trying to come up with an answer.

"Deep down, you know the answer. You're just afraid to let it out. Remember, the truth shall set you free from your limiting beliefs. Don't think so much, just flip it 360 degrees—which is Step 3. So, at your core, who are you really?"

"The truth is I am a loving, caring, dedicated and powerful man! And that is who I am."

"Awesome! That is who you are at your core. Yes, you are a true champion at your core and it is unleashed when you get to the truth of who you really are. Really great job, Richie! Now, my suggestion is to be in action about it. Step 4. Making bold declarations and taking massive action will build confidence in this area. This will help in erasing the old belief once and for all. Every positive action taken in this area will strengthen the new belief. Your new results—no matter how small they may seem—will create a new, positive conversation in you that will strengthen the new belief. Richie, the most successful people around today took the most action in regards to what they believed in. Not taking action weakens the new belief muscle, and eventually it will start to break down again. A cell without proper nutrition turns into bacteria. An expensive cruise liner left at the harbor will eventually rust without maintenance. A brand new car, left in a garage for years without attention, will corrode and be considered junk. The same happens with our beliefs; we feed them through our actions. Does that make sense?"

"It makes all the sense in the world." I was nodding along as he spoke.

"Can you see how you will experience different results from today on as a byproduct of doing this exercise?"

"I sure can." I grinned again.

"All I am coaching you to do is to be aware of the everyday events that are taking place in your life. Just because someone screams at you or does not honor their word, does not mean you should make it mean something that it doesn't.

"From today on whenever something negative occurs, you will automatically hear my voice in your head saying, 'Richie, don't make it mean something'. Just being aware of this distinction will allow you to be more powerful in your daily choices."

"I really get it. This is some good stuff, Mr. Rodriguez."

"Hold your horses, young man, it gets even better!" He grinned at my enthusiasm. "Now let's really observe this impact on a larger scope. The 'Life Gap Scale.'" He grabbed a notebook off the desk and quickly drew a diagram on it.

The Life Gap Scale

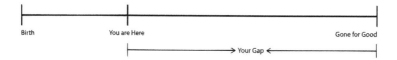

"This scale represents all the years you have on earth. As you can see, I marked your age on the scale with the arrow. Let's assume God granted you health until the age of 75 years old. The gap in the middle represents your time left here on planet earth. That could be one more year or sixty years, only God knows. Now, what will determine what you contributed to your family and to the world from today 'till your last day on earth will be a direct result of what limiting beliefs you were able to leave in the past and what new, empowering beliefs you were able to create in the present. As I always say, leave your past in the past way before you pass. Whatever happened in the past does not matter anymore, all that matters is what are you going to do today that will make a true difference. The ability to live a quality life of total abundance will be in direct proportion to how many empowering beliefs you were able to form during the gap. Now the sad part is that most people will give up their entire lives because of the negative, disempowering meanings they give to life's events. Interestingly, the gap closes so quickly and they don't get to live life at the fullest. When we pass all that represents what our life was is just a simple dash. On our tombstone it will say:

1. Your name
2. Who you were married to
3. Possibly the name of your children
4. The year you were born
5. A dash between your birth date and your departure date

"Richie, all that matters is what you fill that dash or gap with. And guess what, it's going to go the way you say it will go. What are you going to write in the empty chapters of your life that have

69

not yet been written? Will you be one of those people that walk around with a dead soul in a healthy body, or are you going to be the one? The chosen one!"

- The one who brings a cure to an 'incurable' disease?
- The one who creates a mission to end child abuse once and for all?
- The one who creates programs to help the homeless?
- The one who fights for world peace?
- The one who fights for a healthier and greener environment?
- The one who inspires others who have lost hope?
- The one who helps restore unconditional love in broken families?
- The one who creates community programs to enhance the quality of their fellow neighbors and their children?
- The one who sets an example of achieving extraordinary success by not divorcing their principles and virtues?
- The one who writes a book that will bring awareness to the world through your passions?
- The one who sings music to calm and enliven the spirits of those that are badly waiting for it?
- The one who creates a movie or documentary that sends a message so powerful that it transcends generations?

"Are you going to be the one, Richie?" Mr. Rodriguez asked, with a look so intimidating that even the bravest lion would run.

*****

"To this day I still remember that conversation, Darnell, because I took a deep breath, looked him in the eye and said out loud 'I am the one! I am the one!' As you can see, I took that conversation so serious that to this day I still live my life like that. Learning how to create empowering beliefs has helped me develop the rich mindset I have today. So, there you have it. Darnell, are you going to be the one?"

"Yes, I will be the one. Now I know why my dad suggested I talk with you. I'm speechless, bro."

"Not a problem, Darnell. When I was broke and frustrated, I

promised God if he blessed me one day, I would do my part and pass on the blessings. Consider this paying it forward."

"Hey, I really appreciate it."

"So, what has opened up for you?" I asked casually, attempting to mask my burning curiosity.

"This whole conversation made me realize why Obama, who is just like me, became the first black President in the United States."

"Okay. I am interested in hearing where you are going with this," I smiled.

"I am not sure if you've noticed, but Obama overcame many obstacles because he had an empowering belief that it could be done," Darnell said.

"Ah, now I can see you got it," I said enthusiastically.

Darnell continued, "You're not just 100% right, you're 1,000% right. Richie, up until Obama became president, nobody ever thought we would have a black President, with a black wife and black children, in the White House. I am pretty sure there were times Obama had doubted himself, but his *belief* in himself was so strong that it empowered him to press forward, regardless of the negative comments from the press, the negative comments from his own party, and even the negative comments from his own people. Not to mention all the death threats he received.

"He could have accepted the fact he was too young and inexperienced to become President, but nothing stopped him because, as you said before, his beliefs were not limiting, but empowering. From this conversation, I am starting to see how his empowering beliefs became the engine that fueled his passion to become the first black president of this great nation.Obama stepped into the belief of Martin Luther King, Jr., 'that a man should not be judged by the color of his skin, but rather from the content of his character.' He decided to feed himself that belief, and as a result of that, we have the first black president of the United States of America. When Obama became president, they interviewed him and asked him if he ever thought beyond his wildest dreams that he would win the elections and become the 44th President of the United States.

"His reply was that 'yes', he truly believed 100% that it was going to happen. It occurred because he became impregnated with the belief and he let that cook in him not for just nine months, but for many years. And as he let that cook in him, his whole DNA and cellular structure became one where he created a movement. A movement that filled stadiums. A movement where he inspired people to believe in him because he pronounced that he was going 'to be the one' to take this country and lead them into the biggest rescue since the great depression. Through this movement he was able to create all of this because of one important thing–a strong empowering belief that it could be done. The rest is history."

"Preach it champ! Don't stop, Mr. Motivational Speaker. Now you got me fired up," I cheered.

"Yeah, man, my mind is finally opening up. I'm looking forward to creating a rich mindset by putting in practice everything you have shared so far. This information you shared is so deep. The more I hear from you, the more I like you."

"The reason you like me is because, somehow, you see yourself in me. I'm just a mirror, Darnell, of what you can become and what's possible."

"I so look forward to getting back home tonight so I can share with my dad what I learned today."

"You're going to do that?" I said in sheer surprise.

"Yes, I am going to talk to Dad, because I noticed from this conversation how much drama I give him and it's all because of what I make things mean."

"Darnell, that's amazing, I am so impressed. You're a good kid."

"Thanks. It's because of you that I'm developing a powerful mindset and becoming a champion."

"Yes, but you are also very good at taking the coaching. You'd be surprised at how many people let their ego get in the way."

"I guess I am a champion, and I didn't even know it."

"You sure are! Everyone has one inside. It's just up to each of us to unleash it and let it loose."

"So, Richie, did Mr. Rodriguez ever share the code with you?"

"No, as he said he wouldn't, but he did help me discover it. I actually discovered it in the application of the success principles he shared with me. And if you are thinking I am going to tell you what it is, you are wrong my man. You will have to go through the same transformative process I went through to transform my mindset, habits and beliefs. As I shared with you earlier, Mr. Rodriguez is of the belief that when you take on these success principles wholeheartedly that process will lead you to discover it for yourself."

"Okay, well I see it has helped you, so I am also willing to go through the same process. I promise to apply these principles constantly as you share them with me." Darnell said.

"That's good to hear, champ."

"So, Richie, at what age did you start working for Mr. Rodriguez?"

"I started working for him when I was fourteen years old."

"In what ways did he challenge you?"

"Hmm, now you're making me think."

Chapter Four

THE WORST DAY OF MY LIFE
AND WHAT I LEARNED FROM IT

"Your definition of failure and success will determine your actions."

— Richard Fenton – Speaker/Author

"Darnell, let me tell you about the worst day of my life. But before I share that story, let me give you some context. After a year of working with Mr. Rodriguez, his positive influence really started to rub off on me. By the following summer, I was his right-hand man. I was the person in the store meeting with the vendors and pretty much making the decisions on what to buy and how much to buy. He showed me how to become a great negotiator at a young age. He even helped me open my first savings account. He chose the bank in East New York, over on Pennsylvania Ave. and Jamaica Ave. Today, if you drive by the place, it's still there—it just has a different name. That bank was about 15 blocks from my house. Mr. Rodriguez always said the farther the bank was, the better. I also promised him that I would save a small portion every week from my paycheck and that I would give a portion of it to my mother to help around the house. Mr. Rodriguez really didn't care how much I deposited into my account. All that he cared was that I deposit something, so I could get into the habit of saving. He always said that the most successful people around today all started saving at an early age.

"I remember collecting my paycheck on Thursday evenings. Without fail, I would ride my bike over to the bank on Friday afternoons to deposit my paycheck and withdraw the amount I would give my mom and put aside what I needed to get by for the week.

"I rode my ten-speed through rain, snow, sleet, 98-degree weather and even through different gang territories just so I could cash my check. I dressed as bummy as I could and even my look was unattractive, all designed to not call attention from local gangs. The last thing I needed was a knucklehead robbing me for my hard-earned cash. Every bike ride was different from the previous. You never knew what to expect. 'On the way, I often witnessed different gang members exchanging hand signs, and spray-painting the names of all their homeboys on the walls.'[7]

"Running out of money terrified me, so you can imagine how glad I was to see Friday come around every week. Somehow being in this predicament always made me stretch my money. Looking back, those were the best days of my life. Everything I know today is a direct result of what I learned back then. Yep, those were the good old days."

"Yeah, you can say that now but, back then, I'm pretty sure you didn't say that," chuckled Darnell.

"Well, you're right. They were rough but, somehow in life you tend to enjoy the journey more than the destination. Speaking of challenges, here's one I'll never forget. On that day, God really stretched me—boy, oh boy, was I scared."

"Tell me what happened." Darnell sat up and looked at me expectantly.

"It was the Summer of 1991, on a hot August day. As you know, Darnell, New York summers are something out of this world. For some reason, crime goes up, there are way more killings and we always seemed to be busier at the store trying to catch young kids coming in to steal stuff. I came to work early that day so I could get out by 2 p.m., because Diego had told me the day before that our cousin Edward Muñoz was coming home from the Gulf War. He left to the Marine Corps in 1990 and we hadn't seen him since. They were going to give him a surprise homecoming party in my uncle Jose's backyard, over on Hendrix St.

That day, the first thing I did was rush to the basement because I had to break all the boxes down and then tie them up so they'd be ready for the garbage man the next morning. When I entered the basement I heard one of my favorite merengues playing on the radio from *El Mayimbe Fernandito Villalona*. In my dominican slang, I sang along to the song when I started cutting up the boxes—"*Porque mande mande quien mande, en el mundo siempre habrá buena gente, mala gente, el que niega, el creyente, sabio necio, indiferente, tabaco y ron. tabaco, tabaco, tabaco. tabaco y ron. tabaco, tabaco, pero tabaco, tabaco y ron*". Just when I was in my flow I heard Mr. Rodriguez calling me to come upstairs."

"What is it? Can it wait ten more minutes?" I yelled back.

"No! Shut off the radio and come upstairs now," he hollered impatiently.

"Okay, I'll be right there," I groaned.

I ran upstairs and picked up some orange juice in the new store fridge. By now I was sweating profusely from the basement heat and I was thirsty from all that singing.

"So, what is it?" I asked, poking the straw in the juice box and taking a sip.

"Look, I need you to go to Jetro for me."

"Jetro?" I couldn't believe it.

"Yes, you heard me right," he said, nodding sharply at me.

"But... but... by myself?" My eyes widened in shock.

"Yes, by yourself. Do you accept?" Mr. Rodriguez demanded.

I felt like I had to accept, that I really didn't have a choice. "I think I can do it," I said, my voice cracking. Jetro was the main supplier to all the grocery stores. It was one huge warehouse. "But what happened to Freddy? Why don't you send him?"

"Freddy's wife gave birth last night and he can't come, so you will have to go so I can stay behind."

"But I can't drive that good." I stalled for time, trying to get Mr. Rodriguez to see it wasn't a good idea.

"Look young man, you drive well enough." He held the van keys out to me and glanced at the clock on the wall, "You best get going, if you want to leave early today. That way, you can make your family get-together in time."

Little did I know, that he was testing me.

I sighed as I took the keys from him and went outside, dragging my feet in despair. As I walked over to the van, I was wondering why he was making me do such a thing. I had all these questions running through my head. The door of the van felt so heavy as I opened it. The first thing I did was roll down the window—the AC hadn't worked in a couple years and the summer heat had built up in the van. As the air cleared a little, I stared out the windshield. I felt the weight of the world on my shoulders. I sat there for a good three to five minutes, then took a deep breath and said a quick prayer to God to calm my nerves. Mom always said that whenever she was nervous she would pray to God. She said that God's ways are better and higher than our ways. As I sat there, I heard my mother saying what she often said to us: that no matter what we go through in life, no matter how many disappointments we suffer, we will always be the apple of God's eye. He will never give up on us. After I prayed, I wiped the sweat off my face then noticed that my pants were wet. Crap! I was so nervous that I had sat on my orange juice and didn't even realize it. Hopefully, my pants would dry before I got there so people wouldn't think I'd peed myself. Then, I summoned up my courage, started the van, and took off. Till this day I don't know if the van was trembling because it was so old, or if it was because of my nervously shaking hands.

On the way there, all I could think about was how crazy Mr. Rodriguez was for doing this to me. How dare he! I kept thinking, he's lost his mind! "He's lost it," I kept muttering. I hope I don't let him down. Not to mention that he gave me an envelope with $4,500 in cash. To me, that was all the money in the world. Certainly this was a huge responsibility. What would a cop think if he pulled me over and I had no license and this huge amount of cash? The more I thought about it, the more nervous I became. When I arrived at the Jetro parking lot, I felt like I had arrived at the White House in Washington, D.C. As I opened the heavy, squeaky van door my knees were still shaking, so much so that I hit my knee on the way out. "God! Ouch! Aargh!" I screamed. I limped and cried, while yelling out loud, "This is all Mr. Rodriguez's fault, I hate you... I hate you!"

Then, as the throbbing in my knee dulled, I had a defining moment. Suddenly, the sky opened up—it probably didn't really, but it sure felt like it had. I started to notice all the drama I was putting myself through and realized how I had chosen to interpret this event. I said I can choose to interpret this event in a way that empowers me or in a way that disempowers me. What I really understood was that it's in our most difficult moments that we are presented with an opportunity to choose how to interpret life's events. So, I decided to turn this into an opportunity and prove my leadership. That's what I chose to make this event mean.

After giving it some thought, I knew Mr. Rodriguez would have never given me the keys to the van unless he saw leadership in me. I took ahold of myself and said this is a great opportunity to show how much of a reliable and powerful leader I am. Today is the best day of my life. Today is an opportunity to grow and expand. Boy, was I feeling good. Unbeknownst to me, I was actually starting to develop a powerful mindset. I guess all his positivity was rubbing off on me. I picked up my shoulders, raised my head and walked inside Jetro like I owned the place. I headed toward Paul, the manager who was expecting me. Mr. Rodriguez had called him earlier and he actually had my order all ready to go.

"Hey, Richie, how you doing?" He greeted me cheerfully.

"Feeling like a million bucks!" I grinned at him, my newfound positivity beaming out of me.

"Wow! You really don't hear that today from young guys like yourself." He handed me the compiled list of the order.

"Well, I ain't like most guys, I'm a champion." My stance, though I didn't realize it then, was a powerful one, with my arms loosely crossed and my feet planted solidly on the floor.

Paul looked me up and down, then grinned at me, "Okay, Mr. Champion. Let's take this order to the van. Is Freddy waiting in the van?" He started walking toward the parking lot.

"No, he isn't," I replied.

"So, who's the driver?" He turned and waited for me to follow him, his face creased in confusion.

"You're looking at him," I said proudly, standing even taller if that was possible.

"Ah," Paul got a knowing look in his eyes, "So you're the young man Mr. Rodriguez has been telling me about."

"What has he told you about me?"

"Good stuff, Richie. He really believes in you, kiddo." As Paul said this to me, I felt taller than the New York Twin Towers. We proceeded to load the van. I paid him after I inspected the whole order. Mr. Rodriguez always said that a good leader inspects what he expects[8]. When all was clear I made sure he stamped my receipt so it read, "paid". This would be my first business transaction. Paul helped me reverse so I wouldn't hit a truck that had parked close behind me. I maneuvered that van like a pro.

When I drove off I, couldn't help feeling like King Kong on top of the Empire State Building. I decided to drive by my old neighborhood so my friends could see me as the champion I was and not as the loser they thought I was all this time. When I approached my building on Sutter Avenue, I saw Stevo and, boy, was he surprised to see me driving a van. I asked him where Diego was and he told me he was at the corner store. When I arrived, I saw Diego's back as he was spraying some graffiti on the corner building of Sutter Avenue and Euclid Street. These graffiti markings had been there for as long I could remember. Over the years, people sprayed over the old ones. Names upon names. Nobody ever erased them. They represented a culture, pain, and often death[9]. As I drew closer to Diego, I saw him painting a 'rest in peace' graffiti drawing with Jorkey's face and name on it. I could not believe my eyes. I immediately pulled over to Diego.

"Is this for Jor... Jor... Jorkey?" I stuttered. I was referring to my long childhood friend. Even though we haven't seen much of each other lately he was still one of my best friends. Diego walked over holding a paint can in his hand.

"Hey, what you doing here, bro? I can't believe Mr. Rodriguez loaned you his van," Diego said.

"Hey, forget about that. What happened to Jorkey? Tell me now!"

Diego shrugged. "Unfortunately, Jorkey is taking a dirt nap. He just happened to be at the wrong place at the wrong time, Richie."

I felt like exploding with anger. Instantly, tears rushed down my face. They blurred my vision. He said it so cold and showed no emotion. The streets can certainly do that to you. I could not believe what I was hearing.

"Diego, please, be more specific," I screamed.

"Richie, calm down, bro. Okay. This is how it all happened. Last night, he was coming into the building and the elevator was not working, so he decided to take the stairs. As he headed to the eighth floor, he ran into some bloods who were on the staircase smoking weed. It all happened so fast and he really scared one of them. Richie, you know nobody really uses those stairs and they're always dark and smell like urine most of the time. One of the gang members asked, 'Yo, why you trying to scare me like that?' Jorkey laughed at his comment and bumped him when he was trying to get by. In a blink of an eye, the blood member attacked him. In the middle of the scuffle a few shots were fired. They all ran and left him there dying in a pile of blood," Diego sighed and shook his head.

"So, who found him?" I asked, desperately crying.

"It was Rosa from apartment 6A. When she heard the Jorkey screaming for help, she came down and found him unconscious in a pile of blood."

"How do you know so much about what happened, Diego?"

"One of those dumb blood members told a friend of mine how it all went down. He also said that he didn't intend to do it, but Jorkey intentionally bumped him and everything went downhill from there."

"So, is your friend going to testify against those guys?"

"Now what kind of question is that Richie?" He sounded exasperated at my question, "If he did, he would become a rat, and you know what happens to rats in the hood."

"Well, that sucks big time. That ain't fair!"

"Unfortunately, the rule of the law is pushed to the side by the code of the streets," Diego replied.

"That's messed up, bro." I took a shuddering breath and tried to compose myself. "When is the funeral, Diego?"

"It's tonight at 5:00 pm, at the funeral parlor on Liberty Avenue. Hey, Richie, switching gears for a minute, I need a big favor," Diego said casually.

"What do you want?" I replied with a 'don't mess with me attitude.'

"Can you take me somewhere? It'll be quick, I promise."

"Come on, you know I'm working and Mr. Rodriguez is waiting for me. Plus, you know I'm not supposed to be driving and I don't even have a license. I'm sorry, but I can't take you anywhere!"

"Richie, when was the last time I asked you for a favor?" His voice was cajoling, reminding me that we're brothers and brothers are supposed to help each other.

"So, where you going anyway?" I asked, mostly out of pity.

"I want you to take me to the sneaker store over on Liberty Avenue to buy those Michael Jordan sneakers that just came out today. I want to wear them tonight for this hot date."

"Jorkey is dead and all you are thinking about is buying the latest pair of Jordan's sneakers?" I shouted at him.

"Hey, man, if you are going to take it out on me, then forget it," Diego retorted.

"Don't give me that guilt trip. It ain't gonna work."

"Come on, bro. Do me this one-time favor," Diego begged. His puppy eyes were convincing.

"Alright, alright," I mumbled under my breath. My voice echoed in my head. I finally agreed, but all I could think was 'I hope I don't regret this.' I unlocked his door and waved him over, "Let's make it quick before I change my mind."

"Sure thing, bro. I promise it will be quick."

*****

"Wow! What a tough day. On the one hand, I was happy my cousin Edward was coming home from the Gulf War; on the other, it was sad and emotionally draining because of Jorkey's death. Darnell, isn't it ironic how Edward survived the Gulf War but Jorkey couldn't survive the streets of his own neighborhood?"

"Yes, that is pretty ironic. So did you make the funeral in time?"

"I'm getting there. Just listen to the rest of the story because it gets better. To make things worse, the cops pulled me over."

"They did?" Darnell's eyes got wide.

"They sure did. When I heard the police siren, my heart froze. When they commanded me to pull over from the loudspeaker, it just confirmed it was the worst day of my life. Of course, that's apart from the day my father was arrested. When Diego heard the siren, he got very nervous and started cursing in Spanish.

Coño bro, why today of all days!"

"Diego, please calm down, don't make things worse." A terrible thought occured to me, "Oh no, please don't tell me you have drugs on you." I turned to look at him, my eyes wide.

"No, I don't—I have something worse than that...."

"What? Hurry up and tell me, they're approaching us."

"I have a gun, you idiot!"

"What? Are you crazy, man! I'm not going to prison, bro! I'm not cut out for that. Do you see these skinny arms? These wet noodles will prevent very few prison rapes."

"Just relax, bro. You are not going to prison," Diego replied. "Besides, who told you to drive by the precinct?"

"How was I supposed to know you were loaded?"

"Just relax and let me do all the talking," said Diego.

"Oh my God, we are definitely going to jail," I whispered desperately to myself.

As the two officers approached the window, all I remember hearing was, 'license and registration, young men.' The cop that approached my window was a very tall white guy, the kind you see in the movies. His uniform was neatly pressed and his chest inflated, either because he had his bulletproof vest on or maybe because he had a big chest. Either way, I was terrified. I didn't notice it at first, but I was clenching my fist so tightly that my knuckles turned pale white. I couldn't concentrate.. Then, I heard him say, in a horrible gringo accent,"*Vamos rapido, necesito su licencia y registración.*"

"I don't have a license sir, but here is my registration and insurance card," I responded, unable to make eye contact. I thought he would handcuff me on the spot. "Sir, if you'll just let me explain—"

"Who does all that merchandise belong to?" he asked harshly.

"That's what I was going to tell you, sir."

"Well, I'm waiting, young man."

Then I told him the whole story of how Mr. Rodriguez needed my help and how I decided to help him. As a last resort, I said, "Look, can you just give us a break? I promise not to drive again until I get my driver's license."

"Yeah, give the kid a break!" Diego said in a demanding voice. I felt everything was going well until Diego jumped in.

The cop leaned in real close and spoke in a quiet, serious voice. "Do you guys have any illegal possessions? Drugs of any type, or weapons?" He demanded.

"No, sir," I replied, with my knees shaking under the steering wheel.

"Can we go now?" Diego intervened with a Brooklyn attitude. What an idiot. I could not believe this dummy actually said that. Thick drops of sweat rolled off my forehead—I felt like I was in a forest fire with nowhere to turn.

"Somehow, I don't believe you. Please step out of the van." Then, he asked us to stand still while he searched us both.

"By now, my heart was about to pop out of my skinny chest. As he searched Diego, he found the gun tucked away tightly below his waist. Immediately, he handcuffed the both of us. I must admit, Darnell, having those cuffs on makes you feel helpless. I kept saying to myself, 'why is this happening to me? I know I'm not a criminal.'"

"What about the merchandise in the van?"

He said he would call Mr. Rodriguez so he could come and pick up the van. I can only imagine the shock Mr. Rodriguez would have when he got that call. The cop took us to the local precinct. When we got to the precinct, he stuffed us in a small cell. There were three men lying on the ground. Diego asked for food, but they just laughed in our faces. It was horrible. In our cell, there was a smelly dude who seemed to be on medication and, occasionally, he would fart. His farts really smelled horrible—it made us feel like throwing up. As a matter of fact, I think I did once or twice. That night, I could hardly sleep with that nasty odor.

The next day, we went down to central booking and saw the judge. He ordered us to be sent to Rikers Island. I knew the worst was yet to come. Rikers Island was a jail for local offenders who were awaiting trial and could not afford or were not given bail from a judge. Typically, people who go to Rikers were sentenced to one year or less, and those temporarily placed there are pending transfer to another facility[10]. It was literally a jail on an island. Only one way in, and one way out.

When we got there, two cops took us through the processing stage in the reception area. I felt like my world had been turned upside down. I kept on thinking that just a few hours ago I was working in La Familia Grocery Store, and now I was in jail for who knows how long. I sounded like a crazy man repeating things like: I know I'm not a criminal; I'm not a thief or a murderer. I don't belong here. I know I don't belong here. Why am I here? What would've happened if I had decided not to pass by my neighborhood? These questions kept running through my head. Then, I would not have seen Diego. I surely would not be here. These thoughts drove me crazy. I was feeling so much hatred towards Diego and that hatred was eating me alive. 'I know all about hate. It starts in your gut, deep down in your gut. It stirs and churns, and it rises. Hate rises fast and volcanic, it erupts hot on your breath. Your eyes go wide with fire and you clench your teeth so hard you'll think they will shatter.'[11] No matter how hard the situation was, I needed to calm my emotions, because if I didn't, it would drive me crazy.

When I awoke from my daze, the correction officer (CO) told me to take off all my clothes and personal belongings. Talk about feeling weird. Then they searched our bodies to make sure we were not bringing anything into jail. We were forced to wear orange sneakers and an orange jumpsuit. Later, I would find out that if you were under the age of 18 then you would have to wear this color and those who were older got green uniforms, to distinguish different age groups. Beige was for the people who were adolescents and green was the color for adults. We were also issued a green cup to get our juice at lunch. We were informed that if we did not bring our cups to the chow hall then we would not get anything to drink. Then, the CO's took my fingerprints and a mugshot. It made me feel like a real prisoner. Throughout this whole process I just kept staring Diego down. Whenever he saw me looking at him he would just look away out of pity.

Once processing was over, we were taken to building C76—a number I would never forget. When we arrived, we went straight to our cell in section C. Section C was a huge, open room, often referred to as 'dorms' or 'bubbles'. They call it a bubble because about fifty inmates were all in a room surrounded by plastic walls, with only one way in and one way out. There were two correction officers stationed at the entrance, and two inside the bubble as well. They monitored the inmates 24 hours a day.

When we were released into the bubble, all I remember was Diego saying, "Hey, just walk behind me."

"What?" I replied in a confused state.

"Don't ask too many questions, just walk behind me and shut up!"

As we walked into our housing unit, it went from noisy to silent real quick. Diego strutted in, like he meant business. He wanted everybody to know he came from the streets. Three tall African American guys approached us, and before they could say a word, Diego started swinging. It all happened so fast and, before I knew it, I was pulled into the fight, too. It got nasty, and my adrenaline got the best of me. I swung like a wild ape trying to protect its babies. Diego was head-choking one of those dudes, when the CO's came in and separated everybody. They did not punish us since they knew this was customary of all new inmates—it was just a way to gain respect in your new house. If you did not do this, you'd end up being taken advantage of for the rest of your stay. I never knew this, but I learned soon enough the ways of survival in Rikers. I must say, I really hated my new life beyond belief.

Then, another guy approached us, walking with a weird strut. He dragged his right foot and swung his arms around like a wild gorilla.

"Yo, what's up, Diego?" He called out.

"You know me?" Confusion interrupted Diego's cool expression.

"Sure, you're Steve's friend, right? Remember, I used to go out with his sister, Chuchi."

"Oh, yeah, that's right," Diego nodded, thinking. "You're Speedy; am I right?"

"Good memory!" Speedy grinned.

"What they got you in here for?" asked Diego.

"They caught me stealing a car in Howard Beach three weeks ago, so now I have to pay with time."

"How much time did they give you?"

"They said two years, but if I behave good they might cut it in half," Speedy replied. "Hey, follow me over this way."

He walked us over to two empty beds. There were two foot lockers in front of the beds. We were supposed to put our belongings into them. I still could not believe that just a few hours ago, I was on top of the world, and now I felt like the world was on top of me. I kept thinking about how I could keep myself in a positive mental mindset, just like Mr. Rodriguez always shared with me. But it was hard to be positive with a bunch of criminals surrounding me.

"Hey, Richie, come over here and play some dominoes with us." Diego waved me over as he followed Speedy to a different area of the bubble.

"Nah, I think I'll stay here by my bed."

"Ok, whatever," replied Diego with a careless shrug.

"Wait, wait one sec; hey, Spike..."

"No, it's Speedy." He turned to look at me.

"Yeah, Speedy. What can a person do around here to kill time?"

"Well, the only way you can ever escape reality in this hell hole is when it's bedtime. Other than that, you have to either read or workout to kill time because a man can go crazy in here and sometimes you may even feel like you're going to explode. Like they say in here, 'you either learn to do time or time will do you!'"

Speedy started to walk away again, then seemed to think better of it and faced me and Diego again, "Oh one more thing. Let me tell you some of the rules we inmates all know here, otherwise known as the 'block rules.' If you don't follow them, then you are truly headed for trouble." He started counting off on his fingers. "First things first, always lock your locker. Even if you just walk 15 feet to play dominoes, or go to the bathroom, trust me, somebody will steal your shit."

"Steal what shit?" I asked.

"It could be your toilet paper or maybe your green cup. Remember if you don't bring that cup to the chow hall, you will not get your juice. Trust me, you will look forward to that juice like a kid waiting to see his toys on Christmas day. Secondly, eat fast and do not look at anyone when you are eating. It avoids a lot of trouble. Thirdly, never get into a fight with someone when you are making a call. Those handsets are very heavy and the phone cords are very long. I have already seen two people get badly hurt by picking a fight in the phone area. Lastly, don't go to the bathroom alone. Try and go with your brother or me when you can. A lot of weird things have happened in there so it's always best to have someone on the lookout for you." As he gave me all the rules, he saw I had the thousand-yard stare.

"That's usually the look people have when they go crazy. It's as if they are staring at something that is a thousand yards away," Speedy continued.

"Is there anything else I should know?"

"Well there's more, but that should do for now."

*****

Darnell whistled in awe. "It sounds like you went through a lot in there," he said.

"'A lot' is an understatement. I hated every second. It was an experience I will never forget." I shook my head slowly.

"So did Mr. Rodriguez come to visit you while you were in there?"

"He sure did. He came to visit me seven days later. All I remember is one of the CO's calling out my name. When I approached her, she said, 'Richie you have a visitor.' At first, I thought it was mom and my little sister, Jennifer. As I approached the visitor's room, I saw Mr. Rodriguez from a distance. My heart was pounding from embarrassment. He looked me straight in the eyes."

"How you holding up Richie?" Mr. Rodriguez asked as he gave me his love hug.

"Under the circumstances, I'm okay, sir. So, how are things back at the store?"

"Everything is under control. Lucy's boy, Ricky, is helping out until you get back. I must admit, it's not the same without you."

"I know; I also miss being there with you guys." I began to tell him how it all went down and how I was sorry for putting him in so much jeopardy.

*****

"So, did he reprimand you, Richie?"

"No. I thought he would, but he said he forgave me and that we would talk more about this at a later time. Since I knew Mr. Rodriguez very well, I thought that he would have one of those man to man talks with me, but he probably felt that wasn't the right time."

"What you mean is that he probably was going to scold you, not have a simple talk," said Darnell.

"Well, Mr. Rodriguez didn't look at it that way."

"So, how did he see it? Please educate me, Richie," Darnell asked sarcastically.

"Mr. Rodriguez saw it as an opportunity for coaching."

"Coaching! Why coaching?" Darnell almost laughed.

"Why not! Darnell, did you ever hear this saying by the late actor and poet, Ben Johnson? 'He that is taught only by himself has a fool for a master.'"

This time Darnell did laugh. "No, I've never heard that before."

"Well, you see some people think that they don't need help. As a matter of fact, they don't realize they need help. They truly go at it alone and when they fail, they don't have anyone to guide them out of the dark hole they've dug themselves into. Darnell, why is it that people don't like to ask for help?" Darnell shrugged and I continued without waiting for a real answer. "The truth is that they have a big ego and they don't like to be told what to do. Can you imagine how many people fail just because they can't set their ego aside?"

"I never thought of it that way." He admitted.

"Did you know the first step for an alcoholic to begin recovery is the willingness to recognize he has a problem and the humility to ask for help? It takes real courage and maturity to do both. The bigger your goals, the more help you are going to need, it's that simple.

"So, if you want to go somewhere you have never gone before, it will require you to become a person you have never been before. Now you could try to become that person through trial and error, or you could benefit from someone who has been there and can take you there quicker. Darnell, which sounds better: Do it yourself or have someone guide you so you can get there quicker?"

"Quicker sounds better, but I still think that many times we can do it without help from anyone. I've heard of real smart people who have done everything on their own."

"Darnell, don't be fooled. No champion has ever achieved great success without the help of another. No professional athlete would dream of going a day at it alone. Okay, I have an important question for you that will make you think a little more about this: What is the single, most important thing all champions have in common?"

"Let's say persistence, dedication, and focus. Yeah I think that's it," replied Darnell.

"All of those answers are good, but the one thing that all champions have in common is that they all have a coach. Mr. Rodriguez once said that he overheard the CEO of Home Depot say this when it comes to coaching: 'I believe that people, unless coached, will never reach their personal best or realize their true potential.'[12] He always said that being coached allows you to step outside the problem so you can see it from a different angle. Once you see it from a different angle, your coach will then suggest a solution you would have probably never thought of on your own.[13] When you allow yourself to be coachable, you are giving yourself the gift of growing and benefiting from wisdom. Conversely, when you are not coachable, you are depriving yourself from a world of new possibilities."

"Okay, you've convinced me." Darnell took in my words, thinking them over carefully, then nodded. He turned his attention back to my story. "So, if he didn't reprimand you, then what did he say?"

"Ah, yes. Well, let me get back to that. This is what he said..."

*****

I waited with trepidation as Mr. Rodriguez looked me straight in the eyes. He didn't speak, and while he appeared calm, I couldn't quite tell if he was disappointed with me or what. I'd never felt more scared in this moment—not even compared to being in the van with Diego after learning he was packing heat.

"So, Richie, what do you do in your spare time?" asked Mr. Rodriguez.

I sighed. "Well, I've been so depressed that all I do is sleep and watch TV."

"Why don't you consider working out?"

"We started working out, but we would get very hungry afterwards, so we just decided to do push-ups once a day."

Mr. Rodriguez looked at me intensely, then said, "Richie, are you at peace with your past mistakes?"

"Can't say I really am." I replied.

"Richie, you need to be at peace with your past because if you aren't then you lose who you really are at your core. When you choose to regret what you did in the past and live in the past, a piece of you stays back there."

"So, how do I rid myself of these horrible thoughts and feelings that are constantly invading my mind?" I said, my voice tight with unshed tears.

"What are you making this event mean?"

I knew what I wanted to say. At this very moment, I felt scared, I felt like a failure, and I couldn't seem to sum up the courage to let the words out that I wanted to express. I didn't want to show weakness to Mr. Rodriguez, yet at the same time, I knew he was here to help me get something positive from this mess I got myself into. After a few seconds of silenced passed by, I mumbled, "I don't know, sir."

"Well, just think about it for a moment." His eyes shined with excitement as if nothing was wrong. I felt safe in his presence, but I still felt horrible inside. Finally, I spoke up.

"I guess I feel like a failure."

"How's that working for you?" His voice wasn't sarcastic or anything, he genuinely wanted to know how I felt about everything.

"What do you mean?" I didn't understand what he was getting at.

"In other words, how does that make you feel?"

"It makes me feel horrible." I kept my voice quiet, but I wanted to shout. Of course I felt horrible!

"Does that interpretation empower or disempower you?" Mr. Rodriguez's voice was level and it helped me stay calm.

"I feel totally disempowered!"

"Okay, so what are you going to do about it?"

"Well, I don't know," I said, feeling a little bewildered and scared.

"You don't know?" Mr. Rodriguez asked, clearly not believing that for a second.

"Well...I do, I guess." I admitted quietly.

"Come on, Richie. I'm not going to throw you a pity party and I'm certainly not going to buy into your drama. Just take responsibility and ownership for what happened and stop complaining. Blaming or complaining never produces any results and never will. Complaining puts all the power out there, which leaves you feeling powerless and acting like a victim. You can bring the power back in when you stop blaming and start taking responsibility and ownership for everything that happens in your life—and I do mean everything."

"Okay," I nodded, starting to see where he was going with this. "I guess I can start taking responsibility and ownership for what happened." I took a breath and thought about the events that had landed me here. "Wait a minute—you're right. I take 100% responsibility for what happened."

"Great, so glad you did. Now, the final step is to create a new interpretation. What could you create that would totally empower you in the face of this big challenge?"

"I guess I could interpret this as a learning experience."

"So, what does that look like?" His voice was encouraging, uplifting.

"I could choose to learn from this and also learn as much as I can while I'm here. I could... I mean, I *will* go to the library everyday and read books to educate myself. Any suggestions?"

"Suggestions about what?" asked Mr. Rodriguez.

"Suggestions about what kind of books I could read?"

"To answer that question, I will have to ask you another question. What do you want to do for the rest of your life? What are you passionate about? When you can answer this question, you will know what types of books to read."

"Oh, that part is easy. I want to be a successful businessman like you. I also want to be a big real estate developer and investor."

"Great!" He grinned at me. "In that case, Richie, there are two categories of books I'd like to recommend to you. The first category is about personal growth."

"Personal growth—what's that?"

"As my good friend, Manny Goldman, the author of 'The Power of Personal Growth' once put it, 'At its core, Personal Growth is proactive learning. Here's a metaphor to describe it: 'you can water a plant or wait for it to rain.' Each action or reaction has a very different outcome. When you water a plant, you are proactively providing the resource required for its growth. The same concept applies to your life. You can either create the life of your dreams or settle for what you get. Personal Growth is a personal journey about becoming aware, obtaining knowledge, and learning from every situation in life. Personal Growth speeds up the process of taking in and absorbing wisdom fully so you don't have to learn through repeated trial and error.' "[14]

"That is amazing. I never knew that," I said with a big smile. "So, what is the other category of books that I should read?"

"Those would be how-to books."

"How-to books?"

"Yes, books that will show you a step-by-step process on how to do something specifically. If you want to be a real estate investor, you will have to read books that will show you the specific strategies that will get you those specific results. These books focus on proven methods and systems so you can shorten the learning curve."

"That sounds great! I can't wait to start."

"Now, here's the secret—when you start reading these types of books, don't ever stop reading or stop learning new things that will empower you."

"You mean I have to do this forever?"

"Richie, I once heard from philosopher and motivational speaker, Jim Rohn, that success is not something you pursue, it is something that you attract by the person you become."

"And how do I become that person?"

"That's a great question," Mr. Rodriguez said. "You do it by making a commitment to a concept called CANI!"

"CANI?"

"CANI is a concept that Peak Performance Speaker Tony Robbins came up with. It stands for 'Constant and Never-Ending Improvement'. CANI is a principle designed to encourage you to make small incremental improvements daily, and in doing so, you will be forced to find a way to go beyond your current set of self-imposed limitations. If all you did was improve one tiny aspect of your life every single day, you would achieve mastery in uncommon time. Tony likes to say that we only learn our limits by going beyond them. This is exactly what Constant and Never-Ending Improvement offers us; it's an opportunity to go beyond our limits by taking simple but consistent actions.[16]

"Richie, when you commit to CANI, it will allow you to experience quantum leaps. Simply put, quantum leaps imply an 'explosive jump' in your personal performance that puts you far beyond what you thought you were capable of. It's a formula for stunning advances in achievement and realization of your dreams. The concept is one of exponential gains rather than incremental progress. You might compare it to multiplying instead of adding—it means a geometric progression in your effectiveness."[17]

"This is totally outstanding, Mr. Rodriguez!"

"It is. So, what did you get out of this conversation?" he said, as though he was testing me.

"You just reminded me of a critical point: how we choose to interpret life's horrible events is really important. The more I adjust myself to thinking this way, the better interpretations I will make about my life. Like you said, I just have to continue exercising that muscle."

"You got it, Richie, that's really good."

"I also learned the importance of personal growth and the long-lasting effect it will have on me. That was totally awesome when you said that success is not something you should pursue, but it is something that you attract by the person you become. I also got that we must read how-to books because you could have all the confidence in the world, but if you don't know specific how-to strategies, then it's like throwing darts while being blindfolded. Lastly, I really got your message on CANI. When you said that, you hit it on the nail! Constant and Never- Ending Improvement will always keep me at the top of my game. It's a sure way to experience quantum leaps in whatever I do." Before I could continue, the CO came over and interrupted us.

"Time's up, gentlemen."

"Well, goodbye Mr. Rodriguez."

"See you soon, kiddo," Mr. Rodriguez said as he began to wave goodbye.

"Wait, could you just give me one quick minute?" I asked the CO.

He glanced at the clock on the wall, then back at me, sizing me up. "Okay. But, hurry up."

"Mr. Rodriguez, I just want to thank you for the positive influence you have had on my life. I promise when I succeed, I will share everything I learned from you with the world. This is the gift I will repay to you." As he came to give me a hug, he whispered something into my ear that was so uplifting.

"He said, 'Richie, I believe in you and your dreams. Don't ever let me down.' After he said that, I summed up the courage and thanked him for being like a father to me. Then I whispered back very softly, 'I love you, Mr. Rodriguez, and just know that I will never, ever let you down for believing in me!'

"I love you, too, kiddo! Richie, I have to go," he said as we both teared up and he gave me one last hug.

*****

"So, is this your way of paying back Mr. Rodriguez?" Darnell asked enthusiastically.

"Yes, you are 100% right! He gave me a gift, and now I want others to have it as well. Darnell, I've learned that receiving a gift is the best gift back to the giver. And because I received his gift, it created the space for him to want to give more. It's hard to explain, but that's just how it works.

"Darnell, if you want to experience a new level of joy, just learn to become a giver. It brings peace and happiness to your soul. I once heard from a good friend that those who receive a lot in life once gave a lot. When you give part of yourself, you give to yourself. Giving makes your life complete. Most people focus on just taking and not giving. It's time to start shifting our attention from how much can I get to how much can I give. You will never be truly fulfilled as a person until you master the art of giving. Now here's the kicker: When you give, do it without expecting anything in return.

"You might say, 'but Richie, I don't have anything to give.' Sure, you do! You can give a smile, a hug, or some advice to a friend in need. As long as you come from an authentic place and speak from the heart, any message you share will make a difference."

Darnell was nodding at me. "Now, I see why you are the way you are. Richie, I promise you that someday I will share with other people everything you have taught me and become a person who contributes and serves."

"Awesome. That's all I ask."

"So Richie, what happened after Mr. Rodriguez left?"

Chapter Five

THE COMPLAINER VS. THE CHAMPION

"Unfortunately, science has failed to create a technology to look into a human being's heart and measure their drive and passion. Especially to measure their will and desire to succeed. Consider this the next time you underestimate the tenacity of an underdog."
— Edward R. Muñoz – Speaker/Author –
"The Underdog's Code to Riches"

As the guard escorted me back to my room, I kept thinking about the inspirational conversation I'd had with Mr. Rodriguez. Suddenly, my environment didn't look so bad. It's as if something had shifted in me. I asked the guard if I could go to the library and pick up some books. He said I could during my next break, which was in two hours. Those two hours were the longest two hours of my life. I was excited about learning how to become a successful entrepreneur, and knew that focusing on my personal growth would be my ticket out of the ghetto.

When I returned to my bubble, I wrote Mr. Rodriguez a long letter thanking him again for believing in me. I poured out all of my feelings and emotions into this letter. I also wrote down all the goals I was committed to achieving in my life. I must have written for at least two full hours, because by the end, I had written nearly ten pages. I tried to record everything I could think of that I wanted to accomplish in my life.

That day, I wrote down thirty-eight goals. Just looking at the list really fired me up. They were so real to me. This was the beginning of my new life. One of the pages included a note I wrote to my mom. I asked Mr. Rodriguez if he could personally take it to her.

I asked him to do it because I knew if he took the letter personally to her, he would say something to make her feel better. Mr. Rodriguez has a way of influencing those people in his presence.

*****

When the bell sounded, it meant break time. I sealed my envelope, put a stamp on it and rushed to the library. As I was leaving, Diego stopped me.

"Hey, where you going?" He asked.

"I'm going to the library." I gestured vaguely in the direction of the library.

"Library?" Diego scoffed.

"Yes. Something wrong with that?" I said defensively.

"Why you going there?"

"I'm going to pick up some books to read."

"C'mon…don't waste your time with that. Come with us, we need one more guy on our basketball team."

I shrugged, "Nah, go without me."

"Let's go guys, my brother's being a weirdo," Diego said as he walked on, shaking his head and rolling his eyes.

When I arrived at the library, I asked an inmate working there where they kept the self-help books. He pointed to the top corner, way on the top shelf. It was kinda high for me. I wondered why the books were placed in such a hard-to-reach area.

I returned to the desk the inmate was behind. "Hey, why are the books all the way up there?"

He shrugged and glanced in the direction he had pointed me, "Nobody reads those books in the joint. You're actually the first in a long time."

"Are you kidding?" I couldn't believe it.

"Why are you so shocked? Look around you. You're in jail," he smirked.

"I don't know. I just thought more people would be reading this stuff."

"Well, you're right. More people should be reading this stuff. Maybe then the books would be placed on a lower shelf," he smiled.

"Don't worry, I'll see to that."

I climbed onto the fragile ladder to choose which book I wanted to read. From then on, each time I visited the library, I borrowed three books at a time. My days went fast. All I did was read, until I could no longer keep my eyes open.

The first book I read was, *Think and Grow Rich* by Napoleon Hill. Wow—what a classic! They next book I read was *Never Give In*, a biography about Winston Churchill written by Stephen Mansfield. These two books awakened the sleeping champion in me. They literally transformed my thoughts, feelings and actions. It was absolutely amazing. Suddenly, I found myself talking and thinking differently. The more I read, the better I felt. It actually helped me to be optimistic in an increasingly negative environment. The whole jail was separated and controlled by gangs. It was actually safer to belong to one so that you weren't seen as a loner. Most inmates thought I belonged to Diego's gang, so nobody really messed with me.

One day I approached Diego with a book in my hand. I told him I wanted him to read it.

He never did. Instead, he said, "Hey, are you crazy? Get that away from me."

I followed him, waving the book at him, saying, "Don't you want to learn how to be positive in your life? This book has really inspired me to think differently about life's circumstances and how we can choose to be powerful—no matter what life throws at us."

"Oh, now you're getting too philosophical on me," he said. "Look, Richie, I ain't like you and I certainly don't like people telling me what to do. Call me stubborn if you want, but that's just me."

"Diego, why are you so hard-headed? Don't you ever want to change?"

"Maybe someday I will, but for now, I am very comfortable being the way I am." He waved a scolding finger in my face, "So don't you try to change me, bro. It's not going to work. And stop talking all that philosophical crap to me around here; people are going to think I'm as crazy as you."

I was hurt by his words, but shrugged it off. "Okay, your loss, Diego."

Slowly but surely, we were drifting apart. I focused on developing my mind, thoughts and habits. I wanted to have a rich mindset—just like Mr. Rodriguez. On the other hand, Diego was set in his ways. It was a weird relationship. We were bound by blood, but separated by our beliefs and values. I focused on developing a rich mindset, and he focused on getting rich. Mr. Rodriguez always said if you focus on developing yourself first, the money will follow. However, the sad part is that 95% of the world tends to do the opposite. It's no wonder they end up working for the 5% who chose the path of working on themselves first.

*****

Later on that evening, Diego came up to me. "Hey Richie, I have some bad news for you."

"I'm a grown man, just give it to me straight." I crossed my arms and looked him in the eyes.

He backed away a little bit from my stare, then smiled at me, "Take a chill pill, dude. It's actually good news. I was just playing around. I confessed to all the charges and took 100% responsibility for everything that happened."

"You did?"

"Yes, I did. So, as of tomorrow morning, you will be a free man. They are processing your paperwork as we speak."

I was both sad and happy. The last twenty-nine days were a scary roller-coaster ride I would never forget.

"So, how much time did they give you?"

"They gave me two years, but if I behave good, it could be less."

"Man, that is depressing, bro." I shook my head sadly.

"Yeah. Well, that's just the story of my life, Richie. You got a good head on your shoulders and you sure don't belong in here. So go out there and go for your dreams. I know I'm hard on you, but I think deep down inside I act that way because I'm jealous."

"Jealous!" I shouted incredulously.

"Quiet down—don't get too excited." He laughed as he shushed me. Then his voice got somber again, "Well, yes. I think I'm jealous because I see you as a natural leader and you're, like, everything I'm not," Diego said as he slouched back against the jail bars.

As I continued to stare at him, Diego continued, "Please, just let it be, for once don't fight me—just accept my words as the truth."

"Thank you," I said, lowering my eyes and letting any potential argument leave me. It was the first time I'd ever heard Diego say something positive about me.

*****

What really happened in that moment was Diego choosing defeat, and passing me the baton so that I could finish the race as the winner. He did not want to be the winner. He didn't even want to try—at least, that was my interpretation. I stood there quiet, and looked him straight in the eye for about five seconds.

The feelings that moment gave me sure were strange, and I didn't have the words to describe what I felt. My eyes welled with tears, but he pretended not to notice. He opened his mouth to say something, I heard him stutter, but no words came out. And then he took off. It really broke my heart to see him so miserable. It was probably for the best, because two men crying in Rikers would have been an opportunity for others to ridicule us mercilessly.

I quickly regained my composure, but then began to experience an array of mixed emotions. My shoulders tensed up and I was worried my stomach was going to send back the last thing I'd eaten, so I decided to go to bed early to try to calm my nerves.

The next day, I jumped out of bed and did 250 push-ups. Then, I leaned on the edge of my bed and fully extended my right leg and kicked my left leg in the air. Then, I pushed off the edge of the bed, up and down, 100 times until I could do no more. Boy, oh boy, did that burn my triceps! Next, I took off my t-shirt and replaced it with a dry one. As I flipped a towel around my neck, I took a quick glance at my Herculean chest and arms. The last thirty days of hard work really paid off. I began to imagine all the smiles and glances that would soon come my way. Yep, my chiseled body was a shrine to be worshipped.

Out of nowhere, the CO appeared and snapped me out of my daydream. "Richie, get your stuff and follow me young man, today is your last day on the rock." That's what Riker's Island is known as, by those in the hood. As I left the room, a few of the guys said, "Good luck Richie, we hope to never see you in here again." I looked back to say goodbye to Diego, but he looked the other way so the other inmates wouldn't see him tear up. As I was leaving, I felt really sorry for the ones who had just arrived. Just yesterday, three young dudes rolled in because they were caught trying to rob a supermarket. I felt sympathy for them because I knew they would be locked away for quite a long time. People just don't think of the consequences of their actions. They just think, 'I'm tired of being broke.' Sometimes they just get caught up with the wrong crowd; before you know it, they are in so deep that prison or death becomes inevitable.

When I walked outside, Freddy was waiting for me with the store van.

"Where's Mr. Rodriguez and Mom?" I asked.

"Your mom couldn't make it. She couldn't find anyone to take over her shift for the afternoon. She's really happy for you, Richie. She told me to tell you that she left you lunch on the kitchen table. As for Mr. Rodriguez, he said that if you wanted, you could take the rest of the week off and come back to work on Monday with a fresh new attitude."

"Come on, Freddy, were those his exact words?"

"Of course he said that. You should know him real good by now," Freddy chuckled.

As we drove off, I kept looking at the trees and watching all the kids play in the streets. I sure did miss that. You tend to miss even the smallest things when you are incarcerated. It felt great to be free. It's crazy how thirty days can seem more like a year when you are locked up and confined from having so many of your normal, everyday privileges. I decided to go home and just take a break from everything.

When I arrived, my little sister, Jennifer, jumped all over me. She was so glad to see me, but also sad because Diego was not beside me. The first thing I did was take a long bath. Just the thought of taking a bath without having to look over your shoulders to see who was checking you out was so relieving. Then, I ate the meal Mom made especially for me. She actually made my favorite: rice and *gandules* (beans) with *pollo frito* (fried chicken) and her special homemade potato salad. It was the best tasting food I'd had in a real long time. Especially compared to jail food, which had no seasoning at all; the guys even put jelly into their juice so that it would taste sweet. Now you can imagine why I was all over Mom's food. I kept lickin' my fingers and murmuring, "Mmmm, mmmm". Boy was it good! I washed it down with some homemade cold iced tea.

After this great homemade meal, I took a long power nap. I

felt like I was in heaven. You don't sleep much when you are in Rikers because you're always wondering if somebody is going to sneak up on you. You tend to sleep with one eye open and one eye closed. Don't ask me how I did it, because I wouldn't even begin to know how to answer.

*****

When I woke up, Mom was in the kitchen reading a book.

"Hey, Mom. What you doing?"

She looked up at me, over her book. "How about a hug first, then ask me what I'm doing."

"Sorry, Mom." As I got closer, she stood and held out her arms, fully extended. I can't remember the last time we hugged with so much intensity and love. Mom hugged me so tight I could barely breathe. After a few seconds, I slowly released, and as I looked over at her face, I noticed how swollen her eyes were and how many tears were coming down her cheeks.

I looked at her with concern. "Mom, I'm alright. Why are you crying?"

"Richie, why are you asking such a dumb question?"

I gave her a small smile. "Sorry for asking, but I'm okay, Mom. So, please, stop crying, will ya?"

She looked me in the eyes and sighed. "Richie, the past thirty days were the worst days of my life, even worse than when your dad went away to prison. I know Diego is lost in his ways and, hopefully, he will see the light someday, but you Richie, I really was surprised that you got caught up with that. I know you don't have a hostile bone in your body. I have big expectations for you."

"Mom, I just happened to be at the wrong place at the wrong time, but I can assure you that it won't happen again. Besides, I, too, have really high expectations for myself and my life."

As I said this to her, I could see she was having a hard time handling it. I decided to briefly change the subject, and the cover of the book lying on the table caught my eye.

"Now, can you tell me what you are reading?"

"This is my..." but before she could finish, I read the title out loud, "History 101."

She crossed her arms and gave me a stern look I knew too

well. "Yes, that is exactly what I was going to say before you interrupted me. Can I continue?"

"Yes, ma'am, sorry."

"When Mr. Rodriguez dropped off the letter you told him to personally deliver, we had a nice chat. That conversation really inspired me to start taking responsibility for my life. I immediately decided to enroll myself into York Community College and get a degree to become a social worker."

"Mom, sorry to interrupt again, but he had the very same conversation with me. Recently, I've also decided to take my life in a new direction. I'd like to share what I learned with you when we get a chance, but for now keep moving ahead. I must admit that I really like to hear you talk like this. It's so inspiring."

"Thanks, Richie! Yeah, he told me he had that talk with you. Mr. Rodriguez has unwavering faith in you. But enough kudos. Let me finish my story."

"Go for it, Mom. Fire away!"

"Seeing my two sons in jail really made me think. Instead of blaming you two for what happened, I decided to take responsibility for it. It's my fault I never set a proper example. But all that is going to change. It is clear that I need to set an example around here, and the only way to create a better future is by not letting my past stop me from taking action in the present, regardless of my problems. I've noticed that the more I think about my problems, the more depressed I become, but when I think about my goals and aspirations, I get really excited. I have come to realize that I can't change my past. What matters is what I do today to make my future different. And in order to have a bright future—full of dreams and possibilities fulfilled—I need to focus on accomplishing my goals. And that, my son, is what I am focusing on; I suggest you start doing the same, or you will end up just like your brother and dad."

"Okay, Mom, I got it. Wow! I have never seen you so fired up. Your determination is contagious. I knew Mr. Rodriguez would inspire you, but this is a total transformation."

"Richie, if it's one thing I have learned in life, it's that you can't inspire anybody unless you are inspired yourself. You can't love anyone, unless you first love yourself. You can't tell someone else to do something until you first do it yourself. You must be the example for humanity, so humanity can be an example for you."

Mom was on fiya! For the next few hours, I told Mom of my experience in jail and how I, too, was seeing a new light. I told her about my new goals and aspirations and that I was also very excited about her new possibilities. We both laughed and spoke in a way that we never have before. After that day, I never saw my mom in quite the same way. Somehow, I related to her not only as my thirty-four-year-old mom, but also as my best friend and someone that I looked up to.

*****

During the next few days, I took it easy, went to school, did my homework and just relaxed. On Monday, I returned to the store after school for my first day of work. Everyone was so happy to see me. When I saw Mr. Rodriguez, I was both happy and nervous. I really did not know what to expect.

"Hey, Richie, it's good to see you," commented Mr. Rodriguez.

"Thank you, it sure feels good being back." I smiled widely at him.

"Well, let's get back to work, everybody, so Richie can get back into the swing of things." He patted me on the shoulder and gestured to a corner of the store, "Richie, why don't you go ahead and start unpacking those boxes over there so we can start stocking those shelves."

"Sure thing, boss," I replied enthusiastically. It sure felt good to be back at the store. I must admit, I got tired quickly because I had gotten out of the habit of working and I was accustomed to sleeping a lot. Either way, I preferred this to Riker's Island a thousand fold.

At the end of the night, Mr. Rodriguez came over to me. "Richie, could you come by my house, tomorrow after school? I want to give you something."

I nodded. "Okay, sure thing, boss."

On my way home, I couldn't help but wonder what was it that Mr. Rodriguez wanted to give me. He had never asked me to go to his house before, and just the thought of that was making me real nervous. I kept thinking what he could possibly have up his sleeves this time. Was he finally going to reveal the oh-so-famous code? Hopefully he would, because he had made me promise him that I would never ask. Mr. Rodriguez lived only five minutes from the store, and had been living there for over thirty years. People still wonder to this day why he never left the neighborhood.

On the following day, I headed over to his house after school. As I approached the house, I noticed that it was of average size and was well-kept. It really showed pride of ownership. When I approached the door, Mrs. Rodriguez came out and said, "Come around to the back, Mr. Rodriguez is waiting for you." Walking to the back made me feel like I was in the Brooklyn Botanical Garden. It was a slice of heaven. There were all sorts of flowers and plants all over the place. I especially loved the aroma of all the flowers. They calmed my nerves and the rainbow of colors generated a sense of peace and tranquility in me. It was soothing, to say the least.

Mr. Rodriguez was swinging on a hammock under a grapevine. As he stood up to greet me, I accidentally kicked the pitcher of lemonade he had on the ground.

"I'm real sorry, Mr. Rodriguez." I knelt to pick it up.

Mr. Rodriguez held out a hand to stop me. "Please don't worry, Richie. It's only lemonade. So, how was your week?"

"Very relaxing, I must say. How was yours?" I asked, a cool breeze rustling around us, swaying the hammock.

"We've been pretty busy at the store and we have also been repairing some apartments that were recently vacated."

"Apartments? What apartments?" My brow furrowed in confusion.

He went on to tell me something I never knew. It just so happens that the twenty-four unit building where the store was located belonged entirely to him. He also told me about the other properties he owned. It's weird, but I never knew this other side of him. He was way more successful than I could have ever imagined.

After explaining this, he looked me in the eyes. "You're probably wondering why I invited you here, right?"

"Actually, I am." I tried to contain my nervous energy, thinking—hoping—that he was finally going to reveal the code.

"So, are you curious as to what I have for you?

"Yes." I bounced a little on my toes.

"What do you think it is?" He smiled at me.

"I really have no idea." I gave a tight smile back trying to not reveal my interest in finally learning the code to riches he had talked about with me a few years ago.

"Here's the first clue: it is not the code."

"It's not?" My eyebrows creased in confusion again and I stopped bouncing around.

"No. It's a gift of knowledge. You already know I am never going to share the code with you. I made that clear the first time I brought it up."

When he said that, I immediately thought to myself, 'here we go again.'

"Now, Richie," Mr. Rodriguez continued, "I know you're disappointed I didn't reveal the code—I can tell by that funny look you have on your face. But, it is a beautiful gift that will bring eternal joy and abundance in all the areas of your life. It is a gift that never stops giving. Would you like that?"

"I sure would, sir!" I said, pretending to be happy but hiding my feelings because I really thought I was going to finally learn the code.

"Great! I want to share a conversation my grandfather had with me when I was just about your age. He was a powerful leader and a successful businessman as well. Unfortunately, he passed away, only a year after we had this talk." As he said this, he reached into his wallet and handed me a picture. "Go ahead and take a look at him." The black and white photo was torn and delicate. I thought it was going to fall apart in my hand.

I grinned at the almost familiar face that looked back at me. Faded as the picture was, it was easy to see the family resemblance. "Mr. Rodriguez, now I know where you got your good looks from."

"Thanks, you're not so bad yourself," Mr. Rodriguez chuckled. "Coincidentally, we talked right in this yard, on a hot summer day just like this one. The garden looks just as beautiful today as it did back then."

"In this backyard? You mean to tell me...?"

He nodded. "Yes, this used to be his house. It was passed down over the years and I could never sell it. This house holds great sentimental value and it represents so many memories."

"Oh, now I understand." I looked around the yard again, thinking of what it must have looked like when Mr. Rodriguez was my age. Then I turned my attention back to the photo. "So what was his name?"

"Go ahead and look at the back of the photo and see for yourself."

I turned the delicate photo over. My breath caught in surprise. A name was neatly written in carefully precise letters. Richard Rodriguez. "So, his name was Richard?"

"Yes, that's correct. But everybody just called him Richie."

As he said this, my heart skipped a beat. "Are you for real?"

"Does it look like I'm kidding, young man?" he replied with a big smile on his face.

"Okay, now this really feels weird," I said, "but tell me more about your grandfather. I really want to know everything. I'm super curious!"

"Richie, the talk my grandfather had with me was a conversation about 'choosing to be the victim versus being responsible for your actions.' I think it's the appropriate time to have this conversation, considering you just came out of jail. Unfortunately, many people choose to be a victim of their circumstances." He sighed.

"Circumstances... what do you mean by that, exactly?"

"Okay, circumstances are those things that life throws our way to take us off course. Just another word for obstacles or problems."

I nodded. "That's what I thought, but I just wanted to make sure."

"So, as I was saying, many people choose to be a victim of their circumstances. When you choose that mode, you become angry, depressed or both. You start to experience a loss of hope. A victim is someone who always sees hope as something beyond his control. Let me put it another way Richie, victims have a negative way of viewing the world[17]. Whenever something goes wrong, the victim's mind starts to experience a chain reaction. As they run into additional obstacles, they make them mean something that's totally negative. Then they search for all the reasons to justify why they're so unlucky. Finally, they end up experiencing less creativity, less enthusiasm, less power, less effectiveness... and before you know it, nothing seems to work."

"Mr. Rodriguez, if we constantly fall into this downward spiral and victimize ourselves along the way, why is it so hard for most people to take responsibility for their actions?"

"My grandfather told me that most people do not want to be responsible because it makes them feel uncomfortable. It doesn't come easy to most people because they have been playing it safe for most of their life. If they choose to take responsibility, it means that they will have to be vulnerable and hold themselves accountable for their actions. Just the thought of this idea scares most people. The first reason why people resist responsibility is because it's in their nature to resist. We are resistance-machines and it is our natural inclination as human beings to resist anything that is uncomfortable. Most people don't realize that they are resisting taking responsibility in the first place. The second reason why people resist is because it may represent a failure in some way. What if they took responsibility and then failed at it? Now, that would be devastating—or that's what they think, at least. Richie, that is the one thing all people hate: to fail. They don't like to fail in their relationships, businesses, in school, and this list goes on. Yet they are miserable and ain't doing nothing about it. It's almost like they are in a trance and they don't even realize it."

"So, how can we snap out of it?"

"Okay, that's a good question. So let me tell you a story that can maybe shed some light on this. Many years ago, I was on a local boxing team."

My eyes widened. "You were, Mr. Rodriguez?"

"That's right—and I was pretty good, I must say. I was in amazing condition back then and I always trained extremely hard for my fights. So, one day my coach approached me because an opportunity had arisen to fight the infamous 'Heavy Hands Raul'. This was a very important fight because if I beat him, I would earn the right to take on the champion in my lightweight division."

"So what happened?"

"That evening, I went home and I told grandpa about the news. I also told him that I did not feel ready to challenge him and that I was going to decline the opportunity to fight 'Heavy Hands Raul.'"

"So, what did your grandpa say?"

"He told me the only way I would ever know if I was truly great at boxing was if I stepped into the ring and actually put my gloves on to fight. I admitted to him that I was scared, and he reminded me that this fear was normal. He said that the first step to being a champion in life is to take on challenges that really strike fear into you.

"Next, he asked, 'Did someone force you to become a boxer?' I said 'No.' 'Did anyone put a gun to your head and make you do it?' I said, 'No!' 'Exactly! It was your choice. So, if it was your choice, don't make yourself the victim now. Take responsibility for your choices.'"

"So, did you fight him?" I was completely sucked into the story now.

"I sure did!"

"Did you win?" I didn't think my smile could get any bigger.

"No, he knocked me out in the first round and made me see stars for days."

My smile dropped. "Okay, so what's the point of your grandfather's story, Mr. Rodriguez?"

"His point was that a champion always gets into the ring, no matter what. That's how you take responsibility for your life, even if you're scared beyond measure. It doesn't matter if you win or lose. It's not even about how you play the game. All that matters is that you play the game. That you get into the ring. That you play full-out. That you give it your all. Now, you may lose often—and you probably will—but if you continue getting into the ring, there will come a day where you will win. Once you do win, that win will give you confidence, experience and momentum."

He looked at me steadily, his voice getting quieter so I had to really focus on his words. "Richie, the ring is just a metaphor for your life. It's normal to be nervous and scared, but it's worse if you just watch others take action while you sit back and take no action. That's what victims do. They sit back and complain, but take little to no action. They have all these reasons and opinions of how things should be done, but there is no follow through to back up their statements. However, when you jump into the ring of life, your talk instantly translates into action. Now, you're no longer talking about the game; instead, you are in the game.

"So, this is what my grandfather meant when he said that most people have all these problems in life, and all they are doing is making themselves the victims by complaining all the time. Meanwhile, there are others that choose to do something about it. I really commend those people who are making huge efforts to take on challenges such as saving their marriages, businesses and health. I consider these people the champions of our society because these are the few who are willing to give up their reasons, pride and judgments. They are just pushing all that to the side and jumping into the ring regardless of the outcome. Now, if you get into the ring, one of two things will happen: you will either win or you will lose. That's okay. Either way, remember that you weren't sitting back and waiting for something to happen. You were willing to put yourself on the line and create something from nothing."

"So, how can I create something from nothing?"

"Richie, it's simple; Grandpa always said the first step in being responsible is nothing more than accepting you are the cause and the creator of your failures and your successes."

"I am?"

"Yes, you are. I bet up until now you have been telling yourself that you can't cause your success to happen and, if this is the case, you have definitely developed the victim mentality. When this happens you are operating from the victim mode.

"However, the key to being responsible is the realization that you can cause things to happen! Never forget this," advised Mr. Rodriguez, his voice rising with passion. "Richie, repeat that out loud three times!"

"Repeat what?"

"Please repeat what I just said."

"Okay, Mr. Rodriguez, I can cause things to happen, I can cause things to happen, I can cause things to happen!"

"When you said that out loud, how did it make you feel?"

"Really awesome!" Even my spine had straightened when I said that.

"Do you know why it makes you feel awesome?"

"No, I don't."

"It's because when you speak like that, it's not you doing the talking; it's your inner champion who's doing the talking. He comes out when you declare out loud your commitments and your dreams."

"That's powerful. I never looked at it that way."

*****

After witnessing Darnell's reaction to the story of Mr. Rodriguez's grandfather, I decided it was the right time to impart a powerful piece of wisdom. I could see that Darnell was 'getting it', and his confidence was growing with each new story I recounted.

Mr. Rodriguez continued, "Okay, here's the philosophy my

grandfather shared with me. He said, '*We are born with the complainer and the champion inside of us*.' The complainer is the little negative voice in your head. He is called the complainer for a simple reason—he's always complaining. If we allow him to complain all the time, he will start to affect your attitude. If not handled right away he will negatively impact your happiness, productivity and your desire to succeed in life.

"You know it's the complainer talking when he says:

- Don't do that
- You are not good enough
- You know it won't work
- You'll never rise any higher
- You can't succeed
- You don't have what it takes
- You've reached your limit
- You know what happened the last time you tried it

"But the good news is that we also have a champion inside us and he is the positive voice that reminds us of how great we are. You know it's the champion talking when you hear him saying:

- If he/she can, so can I
- It's a done deal
- It's just a matter of time
- I know you can do it
- Let's do it now
- You are perfectly able
- You are close to your breakthrough

"As you can see, Richie, both the 'complainer' and the 'champion' exist within you. I bet you would like to know where they live."

"Yeah, where do they live?" I asked.

"The champion lives in your heart. Have you ever heard someone say: just follow your heart, your heart knows best, or he has the heart of a champion? It's because this is where the champion lives. The champion is committed to you being powerful. He is a force for good. He is a force to be reckoned with. When he shows up, you are bold, courageous and persistent. He is constantly thinking of goals to achieve in the future, he talks in a positive manner and he comes up with impactful ideas to fulfill that future. He is constantly pushing you out of your comfort zone and empowers you to be your best!"

"That is powerful, Mr. Rodriguez! So where does the complainer live?" I asked one more time, waiting impatiently for his next words.

"The complainer lives in your head, Richie. He does not want you to go beyond your comfort zone. He lies around in your head to cloud your judgment whenever you come up with a good idea. Have you ever noticed that people who are depressed rarely speak? It's because they keep all their problems in their head and try to solve everything on their own. It's like entering a jail cell with a 300-pound dude waiting to kick your butt. If you stay too long in your head, he will eat you alive. It is real hard to talk yourself out of a problem when you are having a conversation with the complainer, because his number one job is to complain rather than create solutions or possibilities."

It was at this point in our talk that Mr. Rodriguez pulled out a sheet of paper with a diagram displaying two huge circles in the middle and filled with words. Mr. Rodriguez then began to explain in more detail the meaning of this diagram and the amazing things that could happen when we choose to operate as champions as opposed to complainers.

A Champion Commits To:

Power Based

A Complainer Commits To:

Fear Based

To download this infographic with full color, check out:
http://www.theunderdogcode.com/bookresources

"Let's talk a little more about the complainer so I can explain my next point. Like I said a few minutes ago, the complainer lives inside your head and the complainer's sole job is to control your life and keep you small. He does not want you to move out of your comfort zone. His job is to protect you from harm's way. This is how he keeps you small. He's like the overprotective mother who doesn't want to see her child get hurt or feel embarrassed. He is a default mechanism inside you. He's always running on automatic in the background without you noticing he's there. Just know that he is not who you are. He is a space that fills your being whenever you are in doubt or in fear. Richie, do you get what I'm saying?"

"I think so," I replied somewhat hesitantly.

"That's what I thought." He nodded. "Let me repeat it again. The complainer is like a default mechanism inside you. He's always running on automatic in the background without you noticing he's there. Just know that he is not who you are. He is a space that fills your being whenever you are in doubt or in fear."

"So you mean to tell me that I am not the complainer? You mean, that's not actually me?"

"No, it's not you. Look at it this way. We are human beings, right?"

"Of course, what kind of question is that?" I raised my voice quizzically.

"Just bear with me, son. The 'human' part of the word is the flesh that's on our skin right?"

"I suppose. So, what is the 'being' part of the 'human being'?" I asked.

"It's real simple. The 'being' part is an equally important space and you fill that space with who you are choosing to be. So if you say you are love, this is exactly what shows up in your life. In that moment, this is what your space—or your being—generates in the world and to all those around you. If you are being vengeful, then that is what shows up in your life. Whatever you declare who you are being, that is what fills your space. What enters your space is going to dictate what you see, how you feel, the actions you take and the results you will end up having."

"Okay, that makes more sense now. As a matter of fact, it's starting to make a lot of sense."

"Now, let's talk about the negative impact the complainer may have on your life. When you let the complainer run you, it affects the quality of your life. Interestingly, he shows up when you are being doubtful, fearful or in any negative state."

"So, let me see if I got you right. Whenever I am being fear that is what is in my space, or being as you call it."

"Right," replied Mr. Rodriguez. "So, if I choose to fill my space with...

- Aggression
- Anger
- Betrayal
- Blame
- Cowardice
- Depression
- Cynicism
- Dishonesty
- Envy
- Greed
- Hatred
- Intolerance
- Irresponsibility
- Jealousy
- Pessimism
- Pride
- Resentment
- Revenge
- Sadness
- Selfishness
- Skepticism
- Distrust

"Then that is what fills up my space and that is who I get to be.

"Richie, I remember a time when the complainer was a big part of my life. I had just opened the store, and felt like I was hit with obstacles day in and day out—when I managed to handle one challenge, three more were piled onto my plate. But rather than continue to complain, I decided to flip my perspective and treat each obstacle as an opportunity to learn and grow, both personally and professionally. I knew that if I continued to let the complainer rule my life, he may end ruining my life.

"So, instead of letting something else rule your life, Richie, you can take control and choose to fill your space with…

- Love
- Power
- Courage
- Leadership
- Boldness
- Heroism
- Devotion
- Acceptance
- Valor
- Excellence
- Determination
- Authenticity
- Integrity
- Humility
- Honor
- Passion
- Honesty
- Compassion
- Perseverance
- Dignity

"Then that is what will fill up your space. In this space, you Unleash Your Inner Champion. (www.UnleashYourInnerChampion.com) In this space, you operate at your best.

"Oh, one more thing…when you choose to live from these positive ways of being, get ready for a different you to show up. Now, you show up powerfully. These powerful ways of being end up positively impacting your career, business, health, family, relationships and other areas of your life that are important to you. This is why it is so crucial to constantly create new ways of being that are going to empower you in the present. This is the first step in causing things to happen. It starts with creating how you want to show up in all areas of your life."

POSITIVE
WAYS OF BEING

WHICH IMPACTS YOUR:

CAREER
BUSINESS
COMMUNICATION
RELATIONSHIP
WELL-BEING
HEALTH

"If you don't create how you are going to show up, you will most likely default to doubt, fear or some other negative state. And these are the very states where the complainer loves to reside."

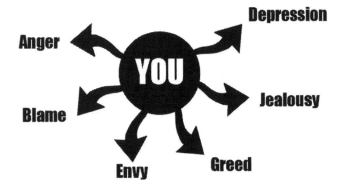

NEGATIVE WAYS OF BEING

WHICH IMPACTS YOUR:

CAREER
BUSINESS
COMMUNICATION
RELATIONSHIP
WELL-BEING
HEALTH

"Richie, here's the bad news: The complainer will never stop doing his job until you actually tell him to stop. He leaves your space when you make a verbal declaration out loud of who you are choosing to be in the moment. This is why I am inviting you to always choose a powerful way of being. It all starts with a dynamic verbal declaration. When you make these declarations out loud, your inner champion is unleashed. It's like you get a sudden burst of energy; all of a sudden, you find yourself feeling happy, creative, outgoing and unstoppable. It is a miracle when it happens—miracles that you can choose to experience on a daily basis. The 'victim/responsibility' distinction, or let's call it the 'complainer/champion distinction', lives or dies with each choice we make."

"So, what you are telling me, Mr. Rodriguez, is that I can choose which mode to operate in?"

"That's exactly what I am telling you. Make the choice, and you can start to reap the rewards that the inner champion will generate in your life. Now, if you refuse to choose which mode to come at life from, the complainer will take over by default, like I mentioned a few minutes ago."

I pondered this for a minute. "Can I ask you a question?"

"Sure thing, shoot."

"Is there a way to condition ourselves so we can spend more time operating in positive ways of being, as opposed to negative ways of being?"

"Yes, there is. You must choose the ways of being that will empower you to become unstoppable in the areas that are important to you, then intentionally maintain it over a long period of time. Let's choose bravery, for example. If you practice being brave long enough, it will start to become a new way of being. But if you keep practicing being brave over an even longer period of time, then bravery will become your default. You can literally train yourself into any way of being through intentional repetition."

"Wow, that completely blew my mind! So. intentionally choosing to repeat bravery—or any way of being I choose—will become my new default. I love it!" I shouted.

"Here are four steps that you can use to condition yourself into these new ways of being. It will help you operate at your optimal level and greatest consistency. I call it the 'Unleash Your Inner Champion Success Cycle.' "

Here Are The 4 Steps:

1- Distinguish your negative thoughts by saying "GOTCHA!"

2- Flip it 360

3- Voice your new commitment out loud

4- Repeat for 21 days

"Richie, what you need to know is that the complainer will always be running in the background. Mostly, the complainer goes unnoticed. The best way to stop him is by saying, 'Gotcha!'

"Saying the word 'Gotcha!' will not only cause you to laugh at first, but will help you to acknowledge your negative thoughts. Have you ever heard the following phrase: 'What you resist will persist, but when you let it be, it will set you free?' Resisting your negative thoughts will give them power to consume and control you. By acknowledging your negative thoughts, they become less significant and you will be able to interrupt them in a humorous way.

"For example, if you know you have to work on a school assignment and notice the little voice in your head saying 'nah, I'll do it later', be aware that that's him doing the talking—not the champion. If you know you have to be somewhere at 7:00 pm and the complainer says, 'What's the hurry, five or ten minutes late is no big deal.' Just notice the complainer is doing the talking, not you. The secret is to choose your conversations and ask yourself: Is this my complainer talking or my champion talking?

"After saying 'Gotcha!', just flip your negative thoughts 360 and immediately voice them out loud: 'No, I am not going to do that assignment later, I am going to do it now.' Or, 'I'm not going to be late, let me hurry up so that I can be on time.' By catching yourself and saying 'Gotcha', flipping it 360, and then voicing out loud your new commitments, the complainer vanishes. Once again, your champion is unleashed. In these examples, you can see the complainer is doing the talking and the various ways to flip it 360."

The Complainer	Flip it 360	The Champion
• It's not my fault		• I take full responsibility
• Someday		• Let's do it now
• Not now		• Right now!
• This can wait		• I will do it now
• I can't		• I can
• I am uncertain		• I am certain
• I guess I should		• I must and I will do it
• I am a loser		• I am a Champion
• I'm too busy		• I have plenty of time
• I never have enough money		• I am a money-making machine
• I have such a bad memory		• I have a great memory
• I'm not smart enough		• I am a world-class leader
• I'm lazy		• I am proactive
• That's too hard		• I'm the person for the job
• I want to give up		• Game on!

The Complainer	*Flip it 360*	The Champion
• My past always brings me down		• I'm over it. I am moving on.
• I think poorly of myself		• I have high self-esteem
• I will never achieve my dreams		• If it's got to be, then it's up to me

"When you start to flip your negative thoughts and declare your new commitments out loud, you will find yourself getting into massive action. The results will appear lightning-quick. The last step in the 'Unleash Your Inner Champion Success Cycle' is to condition your mind to consistently flip negative thoughts to positive thoughts with lightning speed. It is very important that you do this, Richie. If you do not do this, then you will be at the effect of your negative thoughts for the rest of your life. Since it takes twenty-one days to form a habit, I want you to flip your negative thoughts 360 for twenty-one days. Repetition is key for the formation of the new habit."

"What is a habit?" I asked.

"Reverend Dr. Mike Murdock once said that 'a habit is any action, conduct or behavior that you do over and over again'[18]. Anything you do once is called an action, but if you repeat it over and over, then it tends to become easier. This repetition process will create and reinforce the habit. This is the reason why I want you to do it for twenty-one days, as it will instill a new way of being in you. It will also install a new habit in you. He went on to say that "the secret to your success is always hidden in something you do daily."[19]

"The Reverend also said that 'your habits are vehicles. They will take you into a desirable or undesirable future.'[20] and he added, 'It is important to understand that what you are doing today is creating a permanent you, because what you do habitually will determine who you become permanently.'[21] But remember, Richie, that becoming a master of your habits will take a lot of hard work and dedication. I believe you have it in you to become a champion, and this is why I'm sharing my wisdom with you."

He leaned back in the hammock and smiled at me. "So there

you have it, my friend. What do you think of my 4-step process to liberating your champion?"

"I love it! I can now see how, over time, I will be operating mostly as the champion and not the complainer."

"Bingo, now you got it!" Mr. Rodriguez smiled triumphantly.

*****

"Darnell, now you know how I have conditioned myself to become the champion I am today."

"Yes, sir. I can now see the importance of choosing to operate as the champion versus the complainer. One has a very negative effect and the other has a positive ripple effect on everything you do."

"You hit the nail on the head, Darnell. But never forget that if you choose to live an extraordinary life, you don't get to choose the obstacles that will come your way. However, you can choose who you will be in the face of your obstacles."

"I love it. I simply love it. So, how did this conversation impact your life, Richie?"

"It made me realize that life is a choice and it's up to me to decide my future. My dad chose to sell drugs, and his brother chose to be the best he could be in the military. He's actually a decorated Sergeant Major. My brother, on the other hand, chose to follow his father's footsteps, but I choose to follow my dreams."

"You sure did, Richie, and you knocked it out of the park, if I might add. So what was the first step you took to make your dreams a reality?"

"The next day after this conversation with Mr. Rodriguez, I went ahead and signed up at my local college. I wanted to major in business administration. Over the next four years, I enrolled and participated in courses such as business law, operations, statistics, introduction to finance, business communication, strategic management, accounting, economics, and computer classes. Basically, anything related to how the business world worked.

"But, I must say that I learned more about business just by working side-by-side with Mr. Rodriguez. The ironic part is that Mr. Rodriguez never even went to college. He did say if he had to do it all over again, he would have gotten a degree in business administration. Often, he proclaimed that knowing the big picture of how the business world works allows you to form your own picture of how you are going to make it work for you."

Darnell interrupted me. "But Richie, I also want to be a businessman; I'm just not sure if I want to go to college."

"It's important to recognize the value of a college education. I would hope you would reconsider before making a final decision. Getting a college degree under your belt will certainly help you speed up your success in the entrepreneurial world. Now, I am going to say something that many would consider pretty radical."

"Shoot! I'm all ears."

"For what it's worth, here goes. College isn't the only vehicle to financial success. Did you know that you could also go to 'Darnell University'?"

"Darnell University? What's that?"

"Going to Darnell University means you would be taking a stand for what you are committed to at that moment. You do this by making a commitment to read books and attend seminars on topics that will help you succeed in your area of choice. The difference between today and your future is information. If you don't learn anything today, tomorrow will be just like today. This means you don't have a future... just a longer today[20]. This is why it is important to keep learning information that will help you achieve your goals with velocity.

"I once heard that if you read ten books on any given subject it will put you in the top 1% of knowledge level in the world in that specific area. If you take this head-on, in no time you will know 99% more than most people in the world on your subject. Since you said you want to become a successful entrepreneur, you will need to focus on learning key skills like business management, leadership, negotiation, communication, sales, customer service, accounting and marketing, just to mention a few.

"If you commit to this process and take it on like your life depended on it, I can promise you outrageous results. But in order for it to work, you must commit to making it work 1000%."

Darnell grinned. "That sounds great—but if it is that easy, why don't most people do it?"

"The truth is that most people are not disciplined enough to do it. Bottom line—they have no desire to do it because they don't believe they can. For the few who do believe they can, they simply lack the integrity to stick to it. This is why so few people are self-made millionaires. However, what a college or university provides, besides a great education, is accountability. It is set up in a way where you have to physically be there at certain times to learn your course topics. It also provides a learning and supportive environment where your intellect is accelerated.

"Richie, all of this makes sense, but what if I had the commitment and the integrity to follow through and commit to learning those skills on my free time?"

"If you do, then hallelujah to you, young man. Fortunately for you, we live in times where there are more self-made millionaires than ever before. They became millionaires because they do the things most people would never do. That is why they made it in the first place. Now it is important to remember that the end result we all seek is to educate ourselves against ignorance. However you do that is up to you. Ignorance is what keeps you in poverty. Darnell, do you know the difference between being poor and poverty?"

"I can't say I do, Richie. What is the difference?"

"Being poor is just a temporary state in which you live in. It is not a permanent state, if you decide to pursue an education or master a skill. It is recognizing that you have to take responsibility for your greatness. Poverty, on the other hand, becomes a permanent state of being once you become the victim of your circumstances and decide not to pursue an education."

"Man, that's intense." Darnell stated.

"Conversely, having an education is the foundation for what you are out to create in the world. Without this foundation, success can become an illusion or a fantasy. A proper education guards you against a life of economical struggles. Simply put, education leads to developing a new skill. Mastering the skill positions you as an expert. Positioning yourself as an expert breeds demand, and the more you are in demand, the more money you will make. All the people who are financially wealthy reached this point because they are experts at what they do, and experts are always in demand. Is this making any sense?"

"It most certainly is, Richie!"

"Can you see how it all started with an education, whether through college or through attending Darnell University?"

"Yep! True that. I must say that this conversation has inspired me to attend college. I sure could use the accountability. And on top of that, I am also going to attend Darnell University because there are a few courses outside of college that I know I need to eventually attend if I want to achieve my goals."

"Good for you, champ!" I replied enthusiastically.

"So, how did you get started in your first business?"

"That's a great story, Darnell, and a long one, I might add. Let me share it with you after I finish my business meeting. We're entering Boston right now and we're just ten minutes away. For now, I need to mentally prepare for what I expect to accomplish from this meeting."

"So, Richie, what is this meeting about?" Darnell pressed on with more questions.

"I am meeting with my lawyer, the owner of a huge lot I want to purchase, and the bank representative who will provide the financing. If all goes well, I plan to build fifty-two houses and make a nice profit on the upside."

"Upside, what does that mean?"

"Don't worry. I'll explain later. Oh, and one last thing, if you do speak, make sure to use at least one of these three keywords in your communication with a big grin on your face—"

"A grin?" Darnell interjected.

"Yes, a grin is sort of like a big smile, and it goes a long way. It says a lot about your confidence and self-esteem."

"So what are the three words?"

"They are 'Please,' 'Thank You,' and 'Excuse Me.' These three words demonstrate you have character and that you are not ordinary. Often times, being polite will take you a lot farther than coming across as a jerk. You can't imagine how many deals I've negotiated and won, all because I was respectful in my business practices. Got it?"

Darnell thought for a second, then cheerfully replied, "Got it!"

Join my Weekly Motivational E-Newsletter and Receive the Exclusive Interview I did with a Self-Made Billionaire

Text keyword: freeaudio to 66866

In my weekly e-newsletter, I cover topics such as entrepreneurship, personal growth, wealth creation, and many more. More importantly, you will gain access to a wide variety of strategies to empower and inspire you to design your destiny, based on what you want and what matters most to you.

Chapter Six

5 WEALTH PRINCIPLES THE WEALTHY LIVE BY

"Do not focus on building wealth without first focusing on building self."

— Edward R. Muñoz

"Making money is easy when you have the right beliefs, habits and values."

— Edward R. Muñoz

(The story has shifted over to the perspective of Darnell in the beginning of this chapter)

It was a blistering hot summer day in Boston. I was sweating buckets in my oversized suit. I dragged myself into the conference room only to see perfectly trimmed eyebrows with eyeballs to match staring straight at me. I bet they were probably wondering why such a young person who was this poorly dressed would even bother entering the room. As I sat in the back of the conference room, I looked out and saw people filling the room, wearing power blue suits, red ties and sporting classic pocket squares. Not to mention, they all carried fancy briefcases, had perfectly groomed hair, manicured fingernails, and seemed to have the exact same laugh. It weirded me out a little. Still, I got the impression that I was in a room with some extremely powerful people. I was curious to watch Richie in action—I wanted to see his negotiation skills in practice. Everything felt like it was happening in slow motion, just like in the movie *The Matrix*. This was all new to me and I couldn't help but visualize myself filling these seats one day.

Richie's performance impressed me. It was nothing like I had imagined. I had a picture in my head of Richie being aggressive,

129

bold and persuasive. Instead, he spent the first thirty minutes asking others about their families and how they were doing. He asked many questions that had nothing to do with business for what seemed like an eternity. But people naturally seemed to connect with him, and just loved the way he spoke. I loved the way he listened.

During the meeting, he only spent about 25% of the time talking, and the remaining 75% of the time listening. As a matter of fact, this reminded me of what Richie once told me about the concept of listening. He said, "Active listening is taking the time to capture and then process the information." Once you take the time to process the information that you received, you need to connect it with your emotions, past experiences, and sentiments. According to him, you should only give feedback once you have gone through this complete process.

It was one thing to hear Richie share these bits of wisdom with me in the past, but it was a totally different experience to see him in action. When it came to listening, he was a pro. I also observed how he kept his cool when the pressure was building up during the negotiations stage. At one point, the owner of the lot, Mr. Bruns, and his lawyer got upset about his proposal.

Mr. Bruns stood up and screamed at the top of his lungs. "You're crazy, Richie, if you think I'm going to accept your offer. It's not fair. How could you offer me $5,100,000 for this lot when you know I am asking five and a half million? Come on, I thought you were a serious buyer. Why are you wasting my time?"

"Mr. Bruns, you are a smart man. Let me pay you the compliment of being blunt. I did some research, and I think you are asking way too much for your piece of land. It has to be a win-win proposal for the both of us. So while I generally prefer to negotiate, this is my last and final offer, sir," Richie said with conviction.

Mr. Bruns stormed out of the room, and I thought for sure the deal was dead. The whole room went quiet for at least twenty seconds. While the meeting was in recess, I heard Richie quietly whispering to his lawyer.

"Don't worry, I always like to low-ball them, because if you don't, you will never know just how low they will go. My rule is to make an offer that may seem downright embarrassing to present to them. You know you've made a good offer when you feel weird about presenting it; let him cool off, and I'll come back with my final counter-offer," Richie said under his breath.

"Your strategy sounds good, but we are dealing with the big fish now and we need to close this deal—preferably without looking like amateurs. I sure hope you know what you're doing," Richie's lawyer proclaimed.

Finally, Mr. Bruns returned to the meeting. Richie walked over and offered him a seat. He calmly sat across from him then leaned forward, smiled, and in an apologetic manner said, "Mr. Bruns, please excuse me if I offended you earlier. In no way was this my intention. However, after doing my numbers, I think the offer I just made you is reasonable, and must make sense for you and me. If you would please accept my offer, we will get the ball rolling and end this meeting early. What do you say?"

A long fifteen seconds passed, and to everyone's surprise, Mr. Bruns finally answered him. "Okay. Give me $5,150,000 and you've got a deal. I need the extra $50,000 to pay off a small loan."

"Great! You got a deal." Richie and Mr. Bruns shook each others hands.

Roughly five minutes later, contracts were signed and the deal was sealed. Richie's lawyer could not believe his plan actually worked!

After everyone cleared out, Richie placed all his files into his briefcase. He invited his lawyer friend to accompany us for a quick bite before hitting the road, and he happily agreed. When we got to his Porsche, I jumped in the front seat and enthusiastically shouted, "Shotgun." The lawyer laughed and said, "I was going to follow your lead anyway." Richie named a restaurant, the lawyer nodded, then we sped off, the lawyer close behind.

When we arrived at the restaurant, it was packed. Fortunately for us, the host recognized the lawyer, so we got a table fast. After we sat down, Richie asked me what I thought about the meeting.

I considered what I had learned before responding. "You know, during the meeting something clicked for me, Richie. Don't ask me when, because I wouldn't be able to tell you. Everything felt so right. I literally visualized myself doing what you did in there for a living. Right then and there, I decided I was gonna spend the rest of my life surrounded with champions. I realized that only a champion could truly raise another champion, and if I wanted to be a champion, I needed to be around visionaries like you all the time."

"That's right. Just know that there's always a champion who came before to inspire a future champion to achieve something extraordinary. This is why I always surround myself with powerful people. I like to call it the 'Power Circle.' Having powerful people in your circle will always keep you playing at your best."

"Thanks Richie, I can't wait to form my own 'Power Circle'."

"Don't be surprised, Darnell, if that time comes sooner than you think," Richie replied.

*****

We said goodbye to my lawyer as we reached our cars. He was headed back to his office and Darnell and I were headed back to New York to avoid the traffic jam around the George Washington Bridge.

As we started on our way, I noticed Darnell silently staring out the window. I was about to ask him what he was thinking about when he spoke up. "Richie, when did you get inspired to start working on your first deal?"

"Darnell, I will never forget that day, because it all happened on my 19th birthday. Mr. Rodriguez took me to eat at my favorite seafood restaurant called the Lobster Box in City Island. Their food is out of this world, and they have majestic views of the Long Island Sound and Sag Harbor.

When we arrived, Mr. Rodriguez said, "Hey Richie, don't be shy, order whatever you want."

"Are you sure?" I cut my glance to the prices on the menu.

"Yes, I am sure," Mr. Rodriguez laughed.

I ordered my favorite—a broiled lobster tail, a baked potato and a side of King Crab Legs with lots of butter. I washed it all down with a glass of ginger ale. Yes, I totally love seafood and at 19, I had a big appetite. I must say the food was delicious. After the meal, I remembered looking out the window and seeing the giant yellow orb of the setting sun just beginning to kiss the horizon line of the Sag Harbor[23]. I was so stuffed that we decided to go on a walk and watch the sunset. The view was spectacular, and the scene was picturesque. From afar I could see the NY city skyscrapers. The beautiful buildings pulled me in. The water was a pristine blue and glistened with our every move. At one point we walked over to the railing and within the next 15 seconds we watched the sun rapidly melt, then disappear into the most breathtaking purple-orange haze from the warm glowing waters[24]. We walked for another twenty minutes or so, soaked in all the beauty the harbor had to offer, and then headed back home.

As we got into the car, Mr. Rodriguez said, "Richie, I have to make a few stops along the way. Is that okay with you?"

"Sure thing, boss." I stifled a yawn, content and comfortable in Mr. Rodriguez's car.

The first stop was at a three-family brick corner building in downtown Brooklyn.

"Hey, Richie, come with me, it won't take long."

"Coming, boss," I said, following closely behind him.

As we entered the property, I saw Mr. Rodriguez travel from apartment to apartment collecting rent. After we left the building, we passed by a few more of his properties to collect rent from other tenants. He had so much cash, that he had a hard time fitting all of it in his pockets. He even started handing me some of the cash, so I could put it in my pockets.

As I walked through these hallways, I felt both awkward and awesome knowing my pockets were stuffed with cash. I had so much cash, that I had to put some of it into my drawers and socks. I was so excited, I almost tripped going down one of the stairs. To this day, I still don't know if Mr. Rodriguez planned to collect the rent with me on purpose. Regardless, it pumped me up.

Oh, and it didn't end there, because after he finished collecting his rent, we went to his house to store the money since it was Sunday and banks would not be open until the next day. When we arrived, Mr. Rodriguez's wife came over to congratulate me and she mentioned that several tenants came by to drop off their rent as well. I was so amazed and couldn't believe what I was witnessing. Mr. Rodriguez, literally, had created a money-making machine.

"Can you help me count this money and do some bookkeeping before you leave?" Mr. Rodriguez asked.

"Sure thing, Mr. Rodriguez." As we started marking things in his big ledger, I heard the doorbell ring every few minutes like clockwork. Each time the door rang, all I heard was ka-ching, ka-ching, ka-ching! In all, six more tenants came by to drop off their rent. I couldn't take it anymore, so I asked him, "How could I build my own real estate empire? I can see here you have collected twenty rental payments today alone. That's..." I couldn't think of the right word, "that's a crapload of money. That's about as much as Diego keeps around the house—except this is clean money. I want to earn this the honest way, just like you. Can you show me how?"

"Of course I would like to show you, but I can't right now."

"You can't? What do you mean you can't?" My jaw was twitching in frustration, but I tried not to let it show.

"Well, I shouldn't say I can't, because I can, but let's just say I choose not to." Mr. Rodriguez continued making notes in his ledger, not making eye contact with me.

I took a deep breath. "Mr. Rodriguez, with all due respect, I am getting very impatient. Why is it that you are choosing not to share your wealth-building strategies with me?"

"Don't take it personally, Richie." Mr. Rodriguez replied in a calm manner.

"Too late, I already did." I retorted.

He chuckled at my snark. "Look at it this way, young man: I couldn't show you how to write without first teaching you the ABC's, right?"

I shook my head, agitated. "Translate, please."

"I cannot–and will not–show you how to create wealth without first..."

"I know, I know, the right beliefs," I interrupted.

"You're correct, Richie, but that is not what I was trying to say. I was going to say, 'without first teaching you certain key wealth principles.'"

"Okay, then tell me—I am all ears." I sat back and stared at him imploringly.

"Hold on, young man, now is not the time to have that conversation, it's too late at night to get into this. Besides, you will also have to prove yourself first."

"Prove myself! What do you mean by that?" I blurted out.

"I'm not going to get into that right now." He remained infuriatingly calm.

"So, how will I know when I am ready?"

"You won't. But I will," Mr. Rodriguez smiled at me.

*****

As I headed home that night, I continued to think about how long would it take for me to be ready, and I was so excited that I could hardly contain myself. When I got home, my cousin Paul was over visiting Diego. He had just gotten out of jail for the third time in the past six years.

"So Richie, how ya doing?" asked Paul.

"I'm great, really, really great Paul," I replied.

"So what's new?" Paul asked.

"A lot, but I can't talk much now. I have to take a quick bath, and meet with some friends in 45 minutes to work on a paper that's due tomorrow in school."

Diego scoffed, "Paul, leave Mr. Businessman alone, he's always in a hurry. Even when he went to visit me in jail, he was never there for more than 15 minutes."

"So, you complaining that I only went to see you for 15 minutes or so? How long did your friends visit you for?"

"That has nothing to do with this." Diego glared at me.

"Paul, he's complaining, but none of his friends ever went to see him. Only mom, sis, you and me. So if you don't have anything positive to say, just shut up!"

"You shut up! So you're the boss now, Richie?"

"No, never was and never will be, just tired of hearing your negativity. Sorry Paul, but I have to run now—at least I want to do something positive with my life." I took a quick bath and, in 20 minutes, was out the door.

*****

During the next few weeks all I could think about was the feeling of all that cash in my pockets. Every time I heard the doorbell ring in my house, it sounded like the ka-ching going off in my mind's cash register. Ka-ching, ka-ching, ka-ching! But what did Mr. Rodriguez mean when he said 'I wasn't ready'? That I had to prove myself? What did that mean? Did he mean I was too young? Did he mean I wasn't smart enough? At that moment, I realized those were all limiting beliefs and the complainer was making it mean something that didn't even exist. So I chose to end the suspense once and for all.

"So what did you do, Richie?" Darnell asked excitedly.

"I needed to confront Mr. Rodriguez and ask him face to face what he meant when he said I wasn't ready. My gut told me I was ready, and he most certainly needed to hear that from me."

So, I decided to go to his other supermarket over on Hendrix Street. I knew he usually went there on Thursdays to oversee things. When I arrived, Mr. Rodriguez was in the meat freezer, going over inventory with the store manager.

As I walked down the perfectly neat rows of merchandise, my heart began beating faster and my palms started sweating. When I got to the back, something told me to forget it and just turn around. For a quick moment I thought, 'Richie, what are you doing here? You know Mr. Rodriguez does not like to be interrupted when he is working.' Then, suddenly, I realized it was just the complainer doing his thing. I quickly shut him up, flipped it 360 and proceeded into the freezer, despite being afraid and nervous.

Mr. Rodriguez looked up when I entered the freezer. "Hey Richie, what are you doing here? Is everything okay?"

I gulped and caught my breath. "Oh, yes. Everything's okay. I just wanted to have a talk with you."

He glanced back down at his work. "Well, I can't now, but come by on Sunday afternoon and we can talk then."

"Sunday!" I groaned.

"Yes, Sunday." Mr. Rodriguez's voice was firm.

I persisted anyway. "Can't it be sooner? It's pretty important."

Mr. Rodriguez sighed and looked back up at me, "Well, unless this talk is an emergency, it'll have to wait."

I paused. "It is really important, but I guess it's not an emergency," I admitted.

"Okay, now that we are clear on that, can you leave me alone? I have a lot of work to do."

"Okay, see you around 3:00 pm," I said.

"That sounds perfect, young man," Mr. Rodriguez smiled at me, but in his eyes I saw the message, 'please leave, kiddo. You're bothering me.'

I was starting to get extremely impatient at this point. I was so eager to know the secret to his wealth, and I wondered why he kept me waiting so long. After all, what was the big deal? I knew deep down in his heart I was like a son to him. So why was he continuing to make me wait!

The next three days lasted an eternity. Something was happening inside me, but I couldn't describe what I was feeling. Mom even noticed. She kept asking me if I was okay, and if there was something I wanted to talk about. I repeatedly told her I was fine but mothers can always tell when something's wrong with their kids. She knew I was not acting like my normal self. I couldn't stop thinking about the other day when I had my pockets stuffed with all that cash. The more I thought about it, the more I wanted Sunday to arrive.

I glanced at Darnell, who was watching me attentively. "Mr. Rodriguez really helped wake up the entrepreneur in me. Darnell, have you ever heard the story of the goose who laid golden eggs?"

"Oh, that story, yes, that's where this goose kept on laying golden eggs. Until one day someone wanted to kill the golden goose to get all of the remaining golden eggs."

"That's correct. Now, do you think that was the right thing to do?"

"I don't know." Darnell shrugged.

"Just think it through for a moment."

"Well, of course not, Richie!"

"Why?"

"Because if you kill the goose, it won't produce more golden eggs."

"Exactly, that's my point! You see, Mr. Rodriguez had many golden gooses and they produced golden eggs consistently for him, which in turn provided him with a great lifestyle. This is why I was so anxious and eager to learn all that he knew."

"Okay, I get it. Come on, Richie, please finish your story. We're about 90 miles from NY and I can't wait to hear the rest."

*****

"Let's see—the next day after I spoke to Mr. Rodriguez, I remember asking Diego to lend me his car so I could go on a date. Normally, I would take the train, however, this time I really wanted to impress this girl. At the time, Diego had a brand spanking-new 1994 soft-top cherry red mustang convertible. It had low performance tires, a hooked up car kit that was simply badass, and some really cool rims. I knew how protective he was with his baby he called 'Rosa'. But I just had to take a chance and ask him."

That Saturday evening, he rushed in around 7:00 pm to get something, and before he rushed back out, I hollered, "Diego, hold up—I need to talk with you."

"Well, follow me down; I'm in a hurry." Luckily, when we entered the elevator it was empty. As he walked in, he nodded his head in an upward motion, then cracked what seemed to be a smile.

"So, what do you need?" asked Diego.

"I need a huge favor! I need to… to… tooooo…." I hesitated.

"Yo, stop stuttering and just tell me, will ya!"

"Okay." I took a deep breath. "I want to borrow your car." At this point, I was sweating *la gota gorda*. For what seemed like an hour, time stood still.

Then he screamed, "My car! Are you crazy? Come on Richie, you know I don't lend my car to anyone."

"Come on, do me this one-time favor." I pleaded.

Diego narrowed his eyes at me. "Why do you need my car?"

"I got a hot date tonight with Cindy, this pretty Boricua who has some killer legs, a curvaceous figure, dark brown eyes, bee-sting lips and curly black hair to die for. I just met her, and I really want to impress her. C'mon, you know I have a clean driver's license."

"Richie, she sure sounds like a hottie, but, truth be told, your emergency is not my emergency. The answer is no!"

"Come on, we are brothers, and I've always been there for you the few times you needed me."

"So now you're rubbing it in my face, huh? Okay, look—I will do it this one time, but don't get used to it."

I pumped my fist in true New York style. "Thanks, bro."

Once we arrived on the ground floor of our building, he told me to drop him off at "the office", which was really his drug spot. As I peeled away, he dropped the soft-top. It was so cool to see the sky and the stars from where I was sitting. My hair tossed around playfully like it was in a breezy volleyball match with the wind. Through a tuft of hair dancing in front of my eyes, I could see the vibrant rays of a declining sun. To top it off, my eardrums thumped to the loud music coming from my brother's custom-made music system. Then Diego decided to change the radio station and ran into his favorite song—Juicy by Bigge Smalls, the Notorious B.I.G. He turned up the volume and the jam pumped and vibrated throughout the car. We danced in our seats, sang the song out loud, looking like two kids just having a good time. Off we went in unison:

'Uh, and if you don't know, now you know, uh

You know very well who you are
Don't let em hold you down, reach for the stars
You had a goal, but not that many
'cause you're the only one I'll give you good and plenty

I made the change from a common thief
To up close and personal with Robin Leach
And I'm far from cheap, I smoke skunk with my peeps all day
Spread love, it's the Brooklyn way
The Moet and Alize keep me pissy
Girls used to diss me
Now they write letters 'cause they miss me
I never thought it could happen, this rappin' stuff
I was too used to packin' gats and stuff
Now honies play me close like butter played toast
From the Mississippi down to the east coast
Condos in Queens, indo for weeks
Sold out seats to hear Biggie Smalls speak
Livin' life without fear

Puttin' 5 karats in my baby girl's ear
Lunches, brunches, interviews by the pool
Considered a fool 'cause I dropped out of high school
Stereotypes of a black male misunderstood
And it's still all good

Uh...and if you don't know, now you know.'[21a]

Man, oh man, that sure was a good time. In no time we arrived at the office. When he exited the car, he turned back before I could peel out and said "Look Richie, don't drive fast, don't eat in my car, and you betta' make sure you pick me up at 1:00 am."

"Sure thing, bro," I said, as I slowly pulled out from his spot.

That night was so awesome. I felt like a king. The Ka-ching King; at least, that is what I kept repeating to myself. Cindy totally loved the car and we had a great time. We went out to dinner, talked, and little by little, I started to fall in love with her personality. But as much fun as we had, I had more fun driving her around in this cool car. I loved how I felt when I tugged the corners and revved her up.

That night, I decided I was going to use the money I had originally saved to buy a cool convertible. I knew that a similar car in an older version was in the $8,000 range. So, I decided to come up with a plan to borrow the remaining $4,600 I needed from Mr. Rodriguez.

✶✶✶✶✶

Judging by the look Darnell shot me when I said that, it was clear that he'd picked up on something questionable about my plan.

"But there was only one problem, Darnell."

"What was that?"

"My greatest challenge would be convincing Mr. Rodriguez to lend me the money. Originally, the purpose of saving that money was so that I could use it towards the down payment of my first home. Since I had a change of heart, I was going to tell him that I needed a car first. Then, I would save for the purposes of purchasing my first piece of real estate. I knew if I wanted to convince him, I needed to come up with a solid plan. So, the plan I was going to present him was:

1. Work extra hours at the store
2. Pay him interest on the money I would borrow from him
3. Get an extra job if needed
4. Buy the property after I graduate from college

"This sounds like a good plan, Richie. I don't see what the problem could be." Darnell interjected.

"Well, everything sounded good in theory, Darnell, but now I had to convince him in person."

Sunday came real quick, and as I walked over to his house, I could not help but feel nervous about our conversation. When I arrived, Mr. Rodriguez was waiting for me in the den. He was swaying back and forth in his favorite rocking chair while listening to the song, *Mona Lisa* by Nat King Cole. He looked so relaxed, and this made me even more nervous because I knew what I had to share with him went against everything he had taught me.

"How are you doing, Mr. Rodriguez?" I greeted him softly.

"I'm doing fine, young man. I bet you're probably wondering why I denied telling you my wealth-building principles. Isn't that why you are here?"

As Mr. Rodriguez spoke, I broke into a sweat. If he only knew I was going to ask him if I could borrow $4,600. Boy, am I glad I dodged that bullet! Instead, I replied, "Yes, that's one of the reasons. So, why did you take so long to share your strategies with me?"

"Now, come over here and have a seat," he said, welcoming me to a dark brown couch covered with embroidered pillows. Mrs. Rodriguez's lovely handiwork, no doubt. "I wanted to see just how hungry you were. I wanted to see how far you would go without me telling you."

"So you mean to tell me you were testing me all this time? That never crossed my mind," I said a little angrily, yet surprised at the same time.

"I must say, you definitely beat the last guy who asked me these same questions."

"How long did that guy take?"

"Let's put it this way Richie—I'm still waiting for him to come back and ask me." We both chuckled.

"I don't know about that other dude, but I'm definitely ready to learn how you made all that money in real estate."

"Hold on now, Champ. Before I show you the strategies to make millions in real estate, first I need to teach you how rich people think when it comes to building wealth. Only when you learn how the most successful people relate to money and how our mind views wealth can I teach you the strategies of creating your own wealth. Making big money in real estate requires a complete mindset shift, one that will only happen if you want it bad enough and are willing to do whatever it takes to create your own success."

"Can't you see how hungry I am to learn, Mr. Rodriguez?" I replied desperately.

"Yes, I can see that you're hungry, however your results and your ability to take consistent action will be your two biggest challenges."

"You leave those to me. Don't you forget that I have the underdog mindset. I'm ready, willing and able to do whatever it takes to make it happen."

"Only time will tell," replied Mr. Rodriguez.

"Why don't you believe in me, Mr. Rodriguez?"

"I do, but you still have to prove it. Success is a roller coaster ride with many ups and downs. Most people quit during the downs—that's why there are so few people in the ups."

"Okay, game on. I love challenges. You'll see." I grinned confidently at him, "I just hope God grants you enough health so you can see all of my progress and successes in action."

Mr. Rodriguez laughed, and then went on to share his wealth-building principles with me.

<u>Wealth Building Principle #1</u>: Don't Chase Money. Attract It!

"Richie, did you ever hear the story about a boy who tried to get a stubborn donkey to pull his cart?"

"I can't say I have."

"He invented a really smart way to get the donkey to go forward. His solution was to tie a carrot to the end of a rope attached to a stick. The carrot would hang in front of the donkey. The carrot was positioned in the donkey's sight, but out of reach. Every time the donkey would see the carrot swing within his reach, the faster he would go[25]. The carrot is just a metaphor for the things we want in life, and the donkey, of course, represents us going after our dreams. This is exactly how we act in life—we spend our lives chasing the carrot and looking for happiness, only to find out happiness is not there. So we take off again chasing the next carrot, only to find more of the same in a different form.

"Look at it this way, Richie: I bet when you were a child in middle school, you probably thought, 'When I graduate middle school, then I'll be happy. I know that in high school I will be very popular. Yep, that's when I'll be happy.'

"Then, when you arrived at high school and felt intimidated by all the seniors and great players on the team, then you thought, 'Oh, this is definitely not it. I know when I become a senior that will be it. Those seniors are way too cool.' Then you became a senior and you thought, 'Oh, this is definitely not it. Now I have all this peer pressure to do all sorts of things, I'm just so confused. I really don't know what I'm gonna do with my life.'

"Then, one day you thought, 'Oh, I know, when I go to college that definitely will be it. I will get to be on my own, experience being totally independent and most of all; I'll be away from my parents. That will totally be it.' But when your first week in college passes by, you realize, 'Oh, this is definitely not it.' Now, you have a lot of homework, long papers to do and all this stress to keep up with your new demands. You then start to doubt if you really made the right decisions in the first place.

"Then you get a glimpse of hope with this new idea: 'I know! I'll get into a relationship. That'll definitely be it.' So, you get into a relationship and you're madly in love. Then, you start to notice all these other gorgeous people who were not around before are suddenly very much interested in you. 'Oh, this is definitely not it'. You find yourself asking if you really want to turn down all of these opportunities. 'I know, I'll just be single again.' When you become single again, you realize that those same gorgeous people are no longer interested in you, you start asking yourself, 'What happened, where did I go wrong? Oh, this is definitely not it.'

"Then one day you come up with another great idea: 'I know, I'll go get a job so I can make money and buy anything I want. That will definitely be it.' So, you go out and get that job, only to find out that it wasn't all you dreamed it up to be. You find yourself thinking, 'Holy crap, what did I get myself into? What?! No summers off, only two weeks of vacation, and worst of all, I have to wait until I'm 65 to retire?! Oh, this is definitely not it. I know, I'll get married and settle down and have a family. Yes, that will definitely make me happy.'

"Then, you get married, and find you are arguing more than ever. Every topic leads to a heated argument, one that you never seem to win. Now you have to take out the garbage before going to bed, wash the dishes and fold the laundry before going to bed. Oh, this is definitely not it. 'I know, I'll buy a nice car, furniture and a new house. Yep, that for sure will make me happy. That's definitely it.' Then, you buy the house, only to have all this constant influx of new bills and high interest payments. And you once again catch yourself thinking, 'Oh, this is definitely not it.'

"Yet you find yourself pressing on, and then say, 'Oh, I know! If I have a child. that will definitely be it. That will certainly, without a doubt bring me a lot of joy. Yep, this time I know 100% that it's what I want.' Then, you have your first-born, and this baby changes your life forever. Your baby inspires you and gives you another reason to live. You're super happy! But your happiness doesn't last long. Pretty soon, you find yourself waking up several times in the middle of the night to a crying baby. Then, you have to change the diapers, buy new clothes, invest in his/her future, and you say, 'Oh this is definitely not it.'

"Richie, many people spend their whole lives getting some place they think will be 'it'. Yet once they arrive there, they quickly get bored when they find out it's not as big or amazing as they imagined. The mistake is they spend their whole lives trying to get somewhere other than where they are right in that moment. And if these people are somewhere other than where they are right now, they will have trouble getting all they want out of life. Instead, they become a character in a fiction story that they created about their life.

"What I want you to take away from all this is that you first have to be happy with what you have. Realize that happiness is where you are, not out there somewhere. Learn to appreciate all that you have, and consciously make a choice to be grateful for it. Once you learn to appreciate what you have, then and only then should you attempt to go after other things in life. The big difference now is that you're not chasing the carrot looking for happiness—you're just chasing it because you know you're capable of achieving more.

"In this scenario, you will no longer have to chase after money to make you happy, but rather to improve your quality of life. Instead of coming from a space of need, you will be coming from a space of gratitude. And when you come from a space of gratitude, you will attract abundance.

"Another way to attract wealth is to follow a principle from the late philosopher and motivational speaker Jim Rohn, who used to preach when he was alive, 'Success is something you attract by the person you become.' He expanded on this concept by saying, 'You must be willing to first become more so you can attract more.' I love his philosophy, because you are not going to put the attention on the carrot; instead you are going to put the focus on growing inwardly so you can attract outwardly all that you desire. Doing so will give you access to more money than you can possibly imagine."

"That is so true, Mr. Rodriguez—I can certainly see how following this wealth-building principle will definitely help me attract money instead of spending my entire life chasing it for the wrong reasons. I will never, ever forget this. Thank you so much for this gift; I am truly honored to have you as my friend, coach and mentor."

"Thank you for your flattery, young man," Mr. Rodriguez chuckled. "Let's move on to Wealth Building Principle #2."

<u>Wealth Building Principle #2</u>: The average person loves to spend their money. The wealthy look for ways to invest their money.

"You see Richie, every individual defines money differently. But what money truly means lies just under the surface. Consider that money is not what you see, but rather the images you create in your mind. You invent your own story about money and assign a meaning to it, whether you realize it or not. In that meaning lies your relationship to money. This is why the problem you have about money is not the real problem—the relationship between you and your money is the real problem.

"Most people have a poor relationship with money, and it's no wonder they're always broke or in high debt. This also points to why they don't invest, as many people relate to money solely as a tool to buy things. When their paycheck comes in, that money immediately goes towards their bills, followed by their wants and needs. The average person rarely think about tomorrow—all they think about is how they are going to spend their money today. Their relationship to money is to cover the necessities (household, car, utilities, rent, mortgage, etc.) in order to get by. So they see money as a means to live instead of creating a relationship to money as a powerful tool that you they can use to create wealth."

"If you were to ask the average spender what they need money for, you might hear one or more of these comments:

I need money to go on vacation.
I need money to pay my mortgage.
I need money to pay my rent.
I need money to buy some new clothes for the upcoming wedding.
I need money to buy new rims for my car.
I need money to buy my kids some new toys.
I need money to buy myself a new toy (motorcycle, Xbox, PlayStation, jet ski, etc...).
I need money to buy my boyfriend/girlfriend the watch they wanted the other day.
I need money to pay off my credit cards.

"When people with a spending mentality see the word 'investment', they might offer up the following resistance:

Something I'll do someday.
I'm too broke to even think about investments.
You need to spend money to make money.
I don't know anything about getting rich, so why even try.
I don't know anyone who can teach me.
I know nothing about managing my money, and every time I try, I mess it up even more.
It sounds too difficult.
That's not for me.
That sounds like too much work.

"So, would you like to have a breakthrough in this area of your life?" Mr. Rodriguez asked.

"I sure would. That's why I'm here."

"Great! Let's start out by analyzing the difference between two types of mentalities: The 'Spender Mentality' and the 'Investor Mentality'. Then we'll look at how each relates to money and the impact these two ways of thinking could have on your life.

"Richie, there is so much great stuff I want to share with you, but there is only so much time in a given day. **I just finished creating an entire guide, entitled 'The Spender Mindset vs. The Investor Mindset'.** I want you to take a look at this guide first thing when you get home tonight, and write down a reflection of each mindset and how you can use them to take action in your life right now." He handed me a pamphlet and tapped the cover as he spoke.

To take advantage of this valuable guide, visit:
www.EdwardMunoz.com/FreeGuide
(No Email Is Required - Immediate Download)

Wealth Building Principle #3: The Spender has a 'Job Mentality'. The Wealthy have an 'Investor Mentality'.

"Richie, how many times did you hear your parents say that if you got good grades then someday you would get a good job?"

"All the time. I still hear it."

"Exactly; we were brought up with the notion that if we got good grades, someday we would have a solid job that could provide us with security and a great lifestyle. Now, our parents meant all the best, and they are just doing what their parents taught them. This consistent message is what I like to call the 'Job Mentality'. And, if you really think about it, there is no longer such a thing as 'job security'. In order for a job to be considered a good job, they would have to guarantee you would never be fired. But, we both know that will never be the case.

"When you have a 'Job Mentality', everything you think, do, and want revolves around that job. If you want to go on vacation, you have to ask your boss for permission. If you want to leave early, you have to ask for permission. Your cell phone bill is paid from your paycheck that came from your job. Your monthly utilities are paid by your paycheck. Your monthly groceries are paid by your paycheck. Your credit cards are paid by your paycheck. Your rent or mortgage payments are paid by your paycheck. Your vehicle and car insurances are paid by your paycheck.

"Now, what would happen if one day, the unexpected were to happen, and you got laid off or fired? How would you continue to live without a check coming in on a weekly basis? How would your family eat? How will you pay your bills? This is exactly what happens when your whole life revolves around your job. Essentially, a 'Job Mentality' means your lifestyle is 100% reliant on your paycheck. You are also completely at the mercy of your employer.

"When you have a 'Job Mentality', you are trading your time for money. In other words, you are selling your time so you can pay the bills and take care of your responsibilities. But this also comes with a huge cost if you do it for a long time. You start to neglect your health, spend less time with your family, and miss your kids baseball or soccer practices. You forget to change the brakes on your car—and before you know it, you are stuck in the rat race." He took a breath and looked at me, "I'm sure you get the message by now."

"Kind of. So, are you saying that I should not rely on a job for the rest of my life? That I should start my own business like you?"

"Now that would be your choice, and that is not what I am suggesting."

"So, what exactly are you suggesting?" I asked, somewhat confused.

"What I'm saying is that you can't depend on one source to make a living. You can still keep your job if you love it. But adopting an 'Investor Mentality' is simply finding different ways of creating multiple income streams should the unexpected occur. The 'Investor Mentality' has various income streams and comparatively few expenses.

"Often, investors say you are not going to achieve all of your dreams through your job alone, but you can achieve it through your investments. Think about it—if your investments brought in more money on a monthly basis than your paycheck, would you really want to continue working for someone else? Did you know this is a great formula for early retirement?"

"What did you say? Can you say that last sentence again?"

"Ah! Now I got your attention, huh," Mr. Rodriguez laughed.

"Yes, you did!" I laughed too.

"You can choose to retire when your monthly income generated from your investments is more than your monthly expenses. This type of income is known as passive income, or money that comes in every month without you having to work for it."

"That is so powerful, yet so simple."

"Yes it is, young man. Another reason why I encourage people to develop the 'Investor Mentality' is because they gain leverage through their investments. Having an investment portfolio will allow you the opportunity to multiply your time instead of exchanging time for money. Now, the money generated through your investments will afford you sufficient time to do as you wish, buy what you wish, and go where you wish."

Wealth Building Principle #4: The 'Investor Mentality' Champions create their own wealth. Complainers complain about their lack of wealth.

"Richie, the wealthy are always on the lookout for their next big investment opportunity. They wake up everyday thinking where they can find the next deal to be made. They know there are so many opportunities out there because the average person is just too lazy to go out and do something about it.

"They are simply comfortable in their current situation. Jumping out of their comfort zone just doesn't seem like a responsibility they're willing to take on. They are so stuck in their own world that anything outside of the norm just sounds too difficult."

"The Complainer's world is a world of reaction, while the world of the Investor Mentality Champion is all about creation. If you took the letter 'C' out of the word rea**C**tion and put it at the beginning of the word, you would have **C**reation. Many times, all you need is one small shift like this."

$$rea\underline{C}tion \longrightarrow \underline{C}reation$$

"The Complainer's typical day is going to work, then going back home, then going to work, then going back home, then going to work, then going back home. They get so caught up in a world

149

of reacting, that they forget how to create. Then they complain about all their money problems, yet they do nothing about it. Living in this mode actually numbs and inhibits their potential and greatness.

"Richie, did you know most of the properties and businesses I have today are a direct result of me creating those opportunities for myself?"

"How did you do that?"

"It all started when I was a teenager. Back then, I would drive around town putting my name on every property or business I wanted to someday own."

My face wrinkled in confusion. "Your name on it? What do you mean by that?"

"Okay, let me explain what I mean. I used to wake up at 3:00 am every morning and headed over to the bread factory in Jamaica, Queens to pick up the bread I would distribute. Back then I was nineteen, and I worked for Mr. Lonzo, who owned a bread route in Bushwick, Brooklyn. He was an old fashioned Italian in his mid fifties with a rough beard and a heavy accent. Whenever we drove around town, I would try to spot a business or a building and say, 'That's going to be mine, and that's going to be mine, and that corner building will be mine one day.' Mr. Lorenzo thought I was totally crazy. Yet without even realizing it, I was creating the very things in life I wanted. I did so by dreaming, visualizing, voicing out loud and thinking consistently about what I wanted to accomplish. This strategy became my formula for creating multiple opportunities and successes in my life.

"The reason why most people don't do this is because they can't envision a future where this could happen. But if they only knew that creating wealth starts by just voicing out loud what you want from the universe. It's only when you express your dreams and wishes constantly to other people with conviction that the universe aligns with you for the realization and fulfillment of that request. Suddenly, people, events and other circumstances will show up out of nowhere to help you fulfill your goal.

"You will also start to notice how, out of nowhere, you will meet people who have the exact same goals and dreams as you do. Or, it might come in the form of a call from someone out of the blue with a great business opportunity. It might sound crazy at first, but it's just how the wealthy operate. They create a universal realignment for themselves just by doing this. This simple method starts to pull everything you so dearly want directly towards you. This creates what I like to call a 'readiness state'. Once you feel you have reached this state, you must consistently take action and be ready to attract the opportunities you created for yourself. Just keep in mind, Richie, that no amount of money or opportunity will ever appear until you are ready on 'the inside'. When you are ready internally, it will eventually appear externally. It's a universal law.

"So, if I were you, I would first become clear with what it is that you want in life, then go out and light up the world by declaring out loud what you are setting out to create. Oh, and don't forget to back up your words with action. You can declare all you want, but success isn't miraculously going to appear at your doorstep. You have to work hard for it, and be willing to take massive action to surpass your goals. Never forget that declaration creates the possibility but action makes it a reality.

Wealth Building Principle #5: Investor Mentality Champions do not live inside a world of 'Scarcity'; they live inside a world of 'Abundance'.

"Most people are afraid to invest because they look at their bank account and say, 'how can I become an investor if I am always broke?' First, you should know you are not your bank account. Most people feel excited when they have a lot of money in their savings account, but when their account is low, they create an interpretation or story that they are not good at playing the money game.

"When you start making yourself the victim of your circumstances, you become powerless and your attitude and thoughts are reflected in your bank account. It's important to know that any mistakes you made in the past in reference to money were just an event that occurred, nothing more, and nothing less. What happens is we start to create interpretations of those events, and these interpretations stop us from creating and taking action in the present.

"Another reason why so many people are financially broke is due to their relationship with money. Whether on a conscious or unconscious level, they believe that money is scarce. Yes, you heard me correctly—scarce. They think there's not enough to go around. Their whole mindset is based on scarcity. It's all happening around them, yet they are too blind to see it.

"Let's take an example: If you are an aspiring actor who lives in a world of scarcity, you might say something like, 'Oh, there's just too much competition out there.' If your goal is to become a professional basketball player and join the NBA, you might say something like, 'There's so many great players out there who are way better than me.' If you are one of those people who wants to become a real estate investor, you might say something like, 'Oh, that's too hard. Besides, I've heard so many horror stories of investors trying to flip homes, only to lose their money.' You see, Richie, these are perfect examples of a scarcity mentality.

"What you need to consider is the rich and wealthy have a different mentality and relationship when it comes to money. They don't think of it as being scarce. Instead, they understand that money comes from a space of abundance. That is why some people lose all their money, only to come back and make it all back again in a short time. It's because they always think in terms of abundance!

"In this new mental space, they look forward to reinvesting and actually attract what they think. When you think about it, the world is full of abundance everywhere we turn. Two thirds of the earth is full of water, we have all the air we will ever need to breathe, and every day new businesses are created. So why limit ourselves, our resources or our potential when we live in this world of abundance? I challenge you to expect abundance, and when you do, that is exactly what will show up in all areas of your life."

*****

"So Richie, did you ever ask Mr. Rodriguez to lend you the money?" Darnell asked.

"Of course not, are you crazy? After we had that conversation, everything I ever thought about money shifted for me. To this day, I still use those 5 Wealth Building Principles to create and build all my wealth. Man, am I glad that I had Mr. Rodriguez in my life."

Darnell looked at me with his shiny eyes, full of sweet tears that were about to burst, and said, "Richie, I am so glad that you are a part of my life."

"Back at you, kiddo," I replied, my smile shaking and my breath catching in my throat. "You're a fine young man, and I see an amazing leader about to emerge in you. I can't wait to see how you progress in your life's journey."

As Darnell regained his composure, he asked, "Richie, after you learned these principles, what did you do with all that knowledge? What was your first step in creating something from nothing?"

Chapter Seven

ALL IN

"If you can't fly then run, if you can't run then walk, if you can't walk then crawl, but whatever you do you have to keep moving forward."

— *Martin Luther King Jr.*

That same evening, I went home to share what I learned from Mr. Rodriguez with my mom. I walked into the family room, and found her knocked out on her favorite recliner with her reading glasses slipped down to the tip of her nose, a couple of hardcover textbooks sitting on her lap, and a yellow highlighter still in her hand. I softly awoke her with two tender kisses on her forehead, and she immediately started swatting as if it were a fly or mosquito. Quickly, my mom realized it was me. While I put her slippers on, she gave me a weak smile. I helped her get off the recliner and gave her a goodnight hug.

Since we both worked and went to school, we did not see each other for the next three days. On the following Thursday evening, I got home early because I had no school. I couldn't wait to eat the *pollo frito, con arroz y habichuela* (fried chicken, rice and beans) she told me she was going to prepare for dinner.

"Hi, Richie, how are you doing?" She smiled at me as I entered the house.

"I'm pretty good, Mom, just a bit tired after a long day at the store." I yawned, then gave her a hug.

"So, how's school going, son?"

"It's good, just can't wait for it to be all over. One more year and I'll be graduating. I can't wait for that day to come, Mom. I have so much to tell you about the meeting I had with Mr. Rodriguez last Sunday."

Before I could explain, Diego walked in and interrupted us as he set his beer down on the kitchen table. "Hey guys, look at my new tattoo, isn't it cool?" Diego said, taking off his shirt and showing us the Tupac cross he'd just had tattooed over his right shoulder.

"Why on earth are you getting more tattoos; you already have three!" Mom yelled.

Diego shrugged nonchalantly. "My boy over in Howard Beach gave me a freebie, so I took advantage of it."

"Yeah, yeah, what you really mean is that you gave him some of your special medicine in exchange for your tattoo—isn't that right, Diego?" Mom shouted, folding her arms across her chest and glaring fiercely.

Diego looked the other way and avoided answering the question, taking a sip from his beer instead.

"Why do you sell drugs anyway, Diego?" I asked.

"I do it for the greater good. I bring jobs to the community," Diego replied sarcastically.

"Well, why don't you think about the smaller good and stop bringing those dirty jobs to the community. We'd be better off without the likes of you," I said, glaring back at Diego.

This time, Mom jumped in and said, *"Quiero saber cuando vas a dejar de vender drogas?* Yeah, when you are going to stop selling drugs?!" she screamed at the top of her lungs. I'd never seen her so pissed off.

"C'mon, Mom, stop talking all that shit!" Diego screamed.

"You betta stop disrespectin' me. Look me in the eyes when I'm talking to you. I demand you treat me with respect, for the way you treat me is how you will treat your future wife." Mom blurted angrily.

"Stop giving me advice, you ugly bitch! I'm never getting married anyways." Diego replied, trying to be a macho man.

Diego didn't know what he had coming to him as my mom raised her hand to slap him. He grabbed her by the wrist, and flung her onto the table. The beer bottle flew off the table and hit the wall, shattering into a bunch of little razor-edge pieces. For a few seconds, it rained glass. Unfortunately, they landed on Mom.

I jumped at Diego, enraged and landed a torpedo punch smack in the middle of his face. He counter-attacked with fury. I held my hands over my face to block his angry punches, but somehow they found their target. Luckily I landed a few, too. At one point Mom tried to separate us, and accidentally caught my elbow on her chin, knocking her back 3 or 4 feet. She stood up furiously, grabbed

Diego by the hair, and somehow separated us. To this day, I still don't know where she got that strength from.

Apparently somebody on our floor heard the screams coming from our apartment and called 911. Coincidentally, there were cops in our building investigating another case and they were notified to come to our floor within minutes of our fight. Before we knew it, there was a heavy knocking on the door. "Open the door, this is the police," the cops hollered. We let them in, but Mom refused to press charges. At this point, she was horribly disturbed—the last time the cops visited our home was when dad was arrested. Having them over again evoked all kinds of memories from the past.

When they left, Mom told Diego, "I want you to pick up your belongings and leave my house *ahora* (now)!" As she yelled at him, my sis, Jennifer, just sat in the corner and cried as she saw Diego pick up all his stuff. Mom pretended to be tough, but on the inside her world was falling apart. Looking back, it was the best thing she ever did. Diego had turned into a real mess.

On his way out of the house, Diego looked me in the eyes and said, "The only difference between you and me is that you have blinders. The good part is that they keep you focused. The bad part about having them blinders is that it's really hard to watch your back. That's all I gotta say!" Then he slammed the door.

*****

Darnell shook his head, "Man, that guy had serious problems. So, whatever became of Diego?"

"He became worse the moment he left home. I guess he really took it to heart. He became known as a real troublemaker everywhere he went. Nobody wanted him at their parties because he always started a fight. He developed a bad reputation real quick."

"It's sad to hear this, Richie. Your brother seemed to have the same potential that you did, yet he went in a completely different direction."

"Wait until you hear the rest of the story."

Rumor has it that one summer day, someone saw Diego doing some crazy stuff. Some kids on the block said they saw him walking to the corner bodega with no shirt on and low-slung jeans. On that day, he was sporting an oversized Yankee hat tilted to the side, while showing off his hardcore ripped muscles. When he entered the bodega, he would ask for the usual: a cigar and a 32-ounce bottle of Colt 45. Then he would turn the cigar into a blunt by removing the inside of the cigar and refilling it with marijuana. As he started to smoke his blunt, he noticed this guy was staring at him. The dude was standing next to another guy, who I assumed was his friend.

Without saying anything, Diego went up to the guy, who was much taller and stronger than him, and bitch slapped him across the face really hard. Notice I did not say punched him–I said *bitch slapped* him! He then stared the guy down, firmly pressed his index finger on the dude's nose and said, "Ya got beef with me? You want more of this, homeboy? Don't be disrespectin' nobody on the street unless you want to be killed." The two guys thought he was a lunatic straight out of Bellevue Hospital. So they quickly took off running.

Diego was on a rampage, and unstoppable by his own standards. Little did he know that his actions were setting him up to fail real big.

*****

"Richie, your brother sounds like a real terror. How did you put up with him?" Darnell interjected.

"Sometimes you have to let people go and figure things out for themselves. I tried my best to help Diego, but it was clear he didn't want to have anything to do with me. Anyways, let me continue with the story and you'll hear more about what Diego got himself into."

When Mom kicked him out, Diego went and rented a small one bedroom apartment just three buildings away from our building. He went out and hired more people to work for him. It went from two people on staff to eight on payroll. This is how he positioned himself to make some big loot. He had one guy watching the door to his apartment at all times, one dealing in front of the building, two girls packaging his products and two guys selling the merchandise on the corner of Mother Gaston Blvd and Dumont Ave, by Richard Green Playground Park. And the other two next to the #3 train by Livonia Ave and Rockaway Ave. With all this money coming in, he started buying up the world.

Overnight, he changed his whole wardrobe. He always wore nice clothes, but after tasting some success, his weekends consisted of going to Barney's and Bergdorf Goodman in his new money green soft top BMW convertible. He went from buying Michael Jordan sneakers to patent leather Pradas. He went from nice t-shirts to $500 Gucci V-neck T-shirts and vintage Ralph Lauren Polo's. His favorite jeans were either Dior Homme or Seven Jeans, and occasionally he would wear True Religion jeans that were usually in the $200 range. He would hold up his jeans with nothing less than a Gucci double logo belt. Did I mention he also developed a love for sunglasses? He had a big collection of Fendi and Gucci glasses in all colors to match his clothes and Yankee baseball caps.

I began to wonder: How could a guy who went from wearing average clothes to $1,000 outfits not get noticed? There is no way possible an average person living below his means, living in the projects could afford this lifestyle. Unfortunately, Diego gained entrance into a glittering world of luxurious trappings that had a trapdoor to failure. Pretty soon he was on everyone's radar, and went from being an underground drug dealer to living the life of a notorious drug dealer in Brownsville, Brooklyn.

Meanwhile, we were struggling just to get by. I knew Mom was stressed with Diego's drama, so my number one concern became to buy my first home. This way, Mom, sis and I could move out of this crazy neighborhood and into a better, safer area.

I started looking for my first home a few weeks after my 21st birthday. I contacted the same realtor Mr. Rodriguez used to buy several investment properties from in the past. His name was Augustine. Mr. Rodriguez referred him to me because he always said to work with a realtor who owns real estate himself. Augustine owned several properties, and knew how to identify a good deal. His area of expertise was commercial properties but, every once in awhile, he would help a customer who was referred to him with a residential property.

When we met, we hit it off immediately. Somehow, our impressions of each other were quite different when meeting up in person. I expected him to be in his mid forties based on the deep voice he had over the phone, and he expected a young Latin man in the late twenties or early thirties. Much to my surprise, he was only 29 years old. Originally from the Dominican Republic, he was well spoken for a man of his age. He was about 5"11' in height and of medium build. He was right where I wanted to be.

He was also very surprised when I told him that I was 21 years old. He was even more surprised at how much I knew about real estate and business in general. I asked questions like what would be my ROI (return on investment) if I purchased a house for X amount? What is the vacancy rate in the area? What is the average income per household in the area? How much rent are month-to-month tenants paying in the area for a 3 bedroom apartment? These questions made him realize that I was not the average buyer, and that he shouldn't underestimate me because of my age.

We started viewing homes in my price range on the days I had off from the store. Occasionally, I would take extra time off just to go see a property that really caught my interest. It sure was harder than I imagined. They were either too expensive or needed a lot of work, but I knew my investment of time would pay off, and I most certainly was not going to let the complainer win.

He was always saying, "So, you think you're going to able to afford a house? You don't have any experience. Are you crazy?" Every time he said something negative, I would shout out loud, "Yes I can, and yes I will. Why? Because I am a champion and I deserve it. That's why!" Or something of that sort. I was not going to let him get in the way of buying my first home. I had learned from Mr. Rodriguez that as long as I kept creating what I wanted out loud and taking massive action, it would be very difficult for me to fail.

Sure enough, one Saturday morning Augustine called to let me know this three-family property in Cypress Hills was back on the market. I especially liked this home because it generated a solid rental income and was centrally located on Highland Place. The best part was that it was just one block away from the YMCA, and was directly across from Highland Park. The area was also a lot better than Brownsville. Not to mention, I'd be able to attract higher quality tenants, and possibly raise the rent to generate even more income.

I told Augustine that I first needed to run the numbers by Mr. Rodriguez so that he could give me the okay since he was going to co-sign on the property. Mr. Rodriguez had agreed to co-sign, with the stipulation that in two years time I would take him off the deed. I assured Augustine that the deal looked good on the surface, but to just give me till Monday. He agreed that I should take my time and make sure I had all my bases covered.

I could not wait to surprise Mom with the good news. When I left Augustine's office on Jamaica Avenue, I rushed over to Mr. Rodriguez's store to go over the final details. After running the numbers, we agreed that it was a fair deal. I will never forget that day because my heart was pumping with excitement. I was envisioning my doorbell ringing, and the ka-ching going off in my mind's cash register. My life's work and sacrifices were finally about to pay off. I could already taste the sweetness of success.

I was so excited that I couldn't contain my emotions. So I ran like wildfire all the way home. When I finally got there, I decided to take the stairs—the elevator always took too long and I was way too wired to wait. I thought I was never going to get there. The last time I took the stairs was so long ago and it was because they were fixing the elevators. Not even the smell of old urine could affect me. I was too high on life to notice it, and kept focus on the great news I was about to share with my mom and sis.

When I arrived at apartment 16C, I rushed in with so much energy, I must have scared Mom. She thought something happened to me. She never saw me sweat so much.

"Oh, my lord, were you in a fight, Richie?"

"No, Mom. I'm okay. Can you please lower the radio?" I asked, trying to get some air and catch my breath. As Mom reached to lower the radio, Jennifer walked over with an anguished face and handed me a pink slip.

I took it, perplexed, "What's this? Why does it have the hospital's name on it?"

"Those are the results of my test," Jennifer replied in a sorrowful tone.

"Are you sick?" I tried to focus on the clinical words on the page.

"No, worse. I'm dying!" My little sis shouted.

"Dying from what?" I asked as my mind was trying to comprehend her words.

"Leukemia! The doctor said I have leukemia," she cried out. In the blink of an eye, one of my best days turned out to be one of my worst days.

I looked up at my mom, "Mom, how did this all come about?"

"Richie, you may have not noticed, but in the last few weeks, Jennifer was not her normal self. When I saw her health worsening, I decided to take her in to see what was wrong. That's how we found out about her condition."

I looked at the paper in my hands, then back up, "Don't you think we need a second opinion?"

"Richie, that is exactly what I was thinking."

The next morning, we took Jennifer to see a cancer specialist in another hospital. After some blood work, the doctors decided to do a bone marrow biopsy to get a closer look. Once the doctor received her results, he took us into his office and asked us to sit down. He explained that Jennifer had Chronic Myeloid Leukemia.

Before anyone could say anything, I shouted, "What is that?"

"Leukemia is a cancer of the blood cells," the doctor calmly replied.

"How serious is it?" Mom asked, her eyes filling with tears.

"We don't know yet. First, Jennifer is going to have to go through a series of tests to determine how advanced the cancer has spread. Then we can figure out the potential treatment options available," the doctor replied, gently and calmly.

While we continued to ask more questions, Jennifer just sat, motionless. Her body slumped in the chair, unable to speak until finally she looked up at me. Our eyes met, red and misty, tears streaming down our faces. I got up from my chair, kneeled down next to her and held her in my arms as we both started to cry.

*****

"I will never forget that day, Darnell. It was so emotional and heartbreaking. I felt totally powerless."

"I can't begin to imagine what you were going through, Richie. You've dealt with so much pain in your life, yet now appear more powerful than ever."

"That's right, Darnell. Dealing with everything life throws at you builds up your strength and resolve.

"When we arrived home, I tried to lift her spirits by treating my sis to her favorite—pistachio ice cream. But she said no. She wasn't in the mood. Now you know something had to be wrong for her to say no to some pistachio ice cream.

"As all this went down, I started to reflect on my own life, and realized that I should not wait to apologize to someone I offended, or to say 'I love you' or 'I appreciate you' to someone who I really care about. Unfortunately, if I leave what I want to say or feel for tomorrow, it may be too late. Life is too short.

"In fact, the more I thought about it, the more I realized love is just an expression, and it only exists when we express it. Notice how great people feel when you say 'I love you'. The experience of love is only felt in the moment you say it. On the contrary, when you suppress your inner feelings of love to another, you deprive yourself and others of receiving your affection.

"Darnell, the meaning I was going to attach to this difficult event was that I was going to allow myself to be more vulnerable and more expressive by sharing my love with those that are important to me. I was also going to let them love me as well."

"Richie, are you telling me that before all this ever happened you were not an expressive or loving person?" Darnell asked.

"I was at times, but most of the time I wasn't. It was really hard for me. I was tough and hard like a coconut shell. Before Jennifer got sick, I only let those I wanted in my coconut to taste my sweet coconut juice," I said, as Darnell started to laugh out loud.

"However, this difficult moment was like the ax that cracked my coconut. Now I had my sweet coconut juice to share with those I really cared about," I continued.

"That's cool! Now, you're making me think about places in my life where I could do the same."

"Good. I hope I've inspired you. Just keep looking inside yourself and see what opens up for you. So, to finish my story, as we walked back home, I told Jennifer that I loved her very much and that she meant the world to me. I promised I was going to support her and never let her down."

"So, what did she say?" Darnell wanted to know.

"She said, 'Richie, you're the closest thing I have to a dad, and I just want you to know how proud I am of you. When I grow up, I want to be just like you. You are the best thing that ever happened to this family.' I could not help but weep because I never knew this was how she felt about me. I wept out of sadness and joy at the same time."

"Did you ever end up buying the house over on Highland Place?"

"I actually decided to put it on hold until things cooled off. With Jennifer's fight against cancer, I didn't think the house was the right thing to focus on at that moment. As the months passed by, things got worse because Mom was taking off more and more time from work to go to Jennifer's doctor's appointments. One day, Mom called me at work and told me that she needed to talk with me right away. I pushed my bike extra hard that night to get home real fast."

"What did she ask you?"

"She was terribly concerned, because she'd fallen behind on all her bills, including the rent. Jennifer's leukemia had not only taken a toll on her emotionally, but also financially."

"Richie, do you think she wanted to borrow money from you?" Darnell asked.

"No, that wasn't it—she didn't know I had all this money saved up. The home was going to be a surprise. It was going to be my gift to her." I shook my head. "But then, she went ahead and laid more bad news on my lap. She went on to tell me that in two months, we were going to be evicted from our apartment if we didn't start paying the rent right away. The worst part was we could end up in a shelter if we did not come up with the late rent."

"Shelter! Did you say—shelter!"

"Yes, you heard me right. Let me get back to the story, young man, and you can ask all the questions you want when I'm finished."

Up until that moment, I had only heard of the word shelter in conversations outside of my family. Somehow, hearing my mother say this really terrified me, but I knew if I was terrified, she must be even worse off. The more she spoke, the stronger my headache became. For the first time in my life, I left her talking to herself. She kept talking, but all I heard was mumbling. I suddenly experienced the sensation of going color blind and feeling nauseous. I felt like my whole world was falling apart. I started thinking about how much my life sucked. Yes, I know that was the complainer talking, but I still kept on saying my life sucked.

I walked towards the window behind the kitchen table and leaned on the safety guards to get some fresh air. I looked up at the clouds and saw them moving fast, or was it that my mind's thoughts were racing really fast? I couldn't be sure. I looked down to the streets and everyone looked smaller than normal. Way, way down there I could see some kids opening the water hydrant to get wet in the summer heat.

A little boy took a bucket and was taking turns with a friend, filling up the buckets with water to then fill two big green plastic garbage cans. When they finished, they jumped into the garbage cans full of cold water to play and cool off. From a distance, I could see them shivering as they stood there splashing water at each other.

Some other boys were using the fire hydrant to spray cars that would stop to cool off. This was their idea of having fun and collecting tips in the process. It seemed boring to me. Or was I just bored of living this way?

I watched the kids play and kept talking to myself and repeating things that didn't make sense. Thoughts that didn't make sense to me anyway. Still watching the kids, I heard Mom's voice. She was filled with fear and despair. "Richie, what are we going to do?"

I didn't know what to say. I was still in a daze and I kept asking myself, 'Why me? Why me! Life isn't fair! I have a father who is in jail that I don't even know. My brother is a drug dealer, my sister has leukemia and my mother is depressed. And they all turn to me to solve their problems. Why me?' The feeling of being invincible as a teenager quickly vanished as I turned 21, and gave way to a series of battle scars, with each representing an old pain or wound from my previous life.

To top it all off, I found myself in a huge dilemma. Should I help Mom and take over the household responsibilities, or should I buy the property I'd been waiting to buy for the last five years?

"Richie, did you hear me?" Mom screamed in the background, interrupting my inner conversation. "Are you ignoring me?" she repeated.

"No, Mom. Look, I got you!" I replied playfully, turning to smile at her, hoping to ease her concerns.

"You got me? What does that mean?"

"As of today, I decided that I'm taking over all the household responsibilities. So, I am requesting that you call your boss as soon as possible and tell him that you will be taking leave for the next six months or so. If he can't handle that, then he should get another person to replace you. I want you to solely focus on school and taking care of my little sis, so that she gets better soon." I stood

165

up, grabbed her hands and said, "Don't worry Mom, somehow, everything's going to turn out just fine."

"'Turn out'; what does that mean, Richie?"

"It's like a roller coaster that has its ups and downs; when the fun is over, everyone on the ride wants to go again because they know exactly how the experience is going to turn out."

Mom shook her head at me, "Richie, the example was kinda over my head, but I think I get your point. Besides that, this ain't no roller coaster and we sure aren't in the Coney Island Amusement Park. I know you have the best intentions son, but how do you plan to catch up on all of my late payments. You can't handle it on your income alone. It's just impossible."

"Mom, I have something to tell you." Just as I said this, Mom jumped out of the chair and grabbed me by the collar.

"Please don't tell me you're also selling drugs because my heart won't be able to handle it," she cried.

"Please calm down. No, I am not selling drugs. The truth is, I have been saving up my money for the past five years."

"You have?" Mom said as she dried her eyes.

"Yes, I have. I was saving it because I wanted to buy my first house by the age of 21. I was going to give you the good news the day I found out Jennifer got diagnosed with leukemia. It just so happened that I was going to make an offer on a property in Cypress Hills, but after I heard the bad news I decided to hold off."

"Do you mean to tell me that you're going to use your savings to pay off my outstanding bills?"

"Yep. I'm also going to take care of all of the household expenses until Jennifer gets better."

"You are! What inspired you to do that, Richie?" she asked with tears in her eyes.

"I'm not going to let these problems drag us down because I know deep down in my heart I am bigger than them. The truth is, there is a moment in your life when you get sick and tired of being sick and tired. That's why I decided to be done with all this crying and all the drama that it brings. It's time someone took responsibility for everything that happens in this family.

"I've decided it's going to be me, Mom. So, without crying, drama or complaining, quit your job, stay focused on school and take good care of Jennifer. Let me worry about all the money issues."

"I never heard you talk like this, but I must say I like it. Okay, my young champion. As of today, I am passing you the family baton, until I can take it back."

"Darnell, that was the first time in my life that I took ownership of my problems instead of listening to the complainer. I decided to be in action and handle my responsibilities. The first thing I did was sit down at the kitchen table and go over all the outstanding bills. After adding them up, they totaled $2,831.23. When I saw the amount on my calculator, I started to panic. I began to doubt my decision to take on all the household expenses. How could I pay for everything? In a matter of seconds I went from fear to anxiety to doubt. Then I caught myself and remembered what Mr. Rodriguez taught me. I remembered not to relate to money as a feeling. Rather, I chose to relate to money as its actual form and nothing else. I took a deep breath, smiled and started writing checks. Back then, I did not have online billing like we have today," I smiled as Darnell laughed.

"After a few hours, I ate dinner, then took the elevator down to put the envelopes into the mailbox. As I walked towards the blue mailbox that was in front of my building, I saw your dad talking to some friends while leaning on his motorcycle."

"Oh, now you really caught my attention, Richie. What was my dad doing in front of your building?" Darnell interrupted, sitting up even straighter.

"Your dad was about to go ride with a few members of his motorcycle club."

"What kind of bike did he have back then? I'm super curious," Darnell replied.

"Man, his bike was badass. He sported a 1973 Harley Davidson Sportster."

"Wow, he still rides the same bike today when he's not working at the restaurant. I guess some things never change." Darnell chuckled.

"Yes, very true. When he saw me, he approached me and I opened up and brought him up to speed with everything that I was going through. Being the type of guy he is, he invited me to ride with the club. Since it was a while from the last time I went on a joy ride with him, it was hard to say no. I knew deep down inside that it would be therapeutic and good for my soul. So I shoved the envelopes in my back pocket and jumped in the back seat.

I popped on the extra helmet, and we took off to meet the other club members. When we united with them, we sped off into the night. There's something about riding a Harley into the night. It felt good and different. How else can I explain it? When we hit the highway, the pack leader increased his speed."

Fotolia_Motorbike_s_31064659

"Something happens at around 92 miles an hour. Thunder headers drown out all sound, engine vibration travels at the heart's rate, fields of vision funnels into the immediate and suddenly you are not on the road. You're in it, a part of it. Traffic, scenery, cops, cardboard cut outs blowing over as you pass. Sometimes, I forget the rush of that. That's why I love these long runs, the only problem is all the noise is gone, nothing else to worry about except what's right in front of you. Maybe that's the lesson for me to focus on today, to hold on to these simple moments, appreciate them a little more and there's not many of them left. Finding things that make you happy shouldn't be so hard. I know you'll face pain, suffering, hard choices but you can't let the weight of it kill the joy of your life. No matter what, you have to find the things that you love. Run to them. There is an old saying; that which doesn't kill you will make you stronger, but I don't believe that. I think that the things that try to kill you make you angry and sad. However, strength comes from the good things. Your family, your friends, the satisfaction of hard work and being responsible. Those are the things that will keep you whole, those are the things to hold on to when you're broke and full of problems.[26]

"After hangin' with the bikers, your dad dropped me off right in front of the building. I felt like a brand new person. My head was clear. That ride helped me confirm that I was doing the right thing in taking over the household responsibilities. I reached into my back pocket and pulled out the wrinkled envelopes that managed to somehow not fly away during the joy ride. As I walked towards the mailbox, I started to feel real good about taking responsibility for everything that was happening but I also knew that I needed a plan. When I was on the bike run I had all these ideas rush to me. One of those ideas was to approach Mr. Rodriguez and ask him for a raise. Yep. That would definitely help me out in this situation."

"Did you get the raise?" Darnell asked impatiently.

"Let me finish the story, Mr. Impatient."

"Okay, just go straight to it; will you tell me already!"

*****

The next day, I went to the store thirty minutes early to have a talk with Mr. Rodriguez. When I walked in, he was talking to his manager. After he noticed me, he quickly finished the conversation and walked towards me.

"Hey Richie, how's your sister? What have the doctors said about her progress?"

"She's still going through some tests. The doctor said it's too early to give us her prognosis. I guess he was afraid to give us hope should something happen, if you know what I mean."

"Yeah, I bet it's been pretty rough for you."

"Rough ain't the word." I shook my head.

"Richie, I can really sense the frustration and sadness in your voice. It must be really hard for the entire family. Just know that I am here for you 100%."

"Thank you, Mr. Rodriguez. That really means alot to me. It

169

sure hasn't been easy dealing with all this stress." I went ahead and told him I had taken over the household expenses so Mom could care for Jennifer. As I spoke, Mr. Rodriguez just looked at me as if he knew what I was going to ask him.

"Umm... this kinda brings me to the next topic. There is something you can do for me. I kind of, uh, well what I mean to say is I re-re...really need a pro... promo... promotion." I was so nervous that I stuttered to the last word.

"Did you say what I think you just said, young man?" Mr. Rodriguez crossed his arms.

"Well, sorta... you know times have been tough for me and it's been awhile since you've given me a raise. I was hoping you could promote me to be a manager in one of your other businesses. I think I've proven that I'm trustworthy, coachable and hard-working. So, what do you think?"

Mr. Rodriguez took a deep breath, stood silent for about twenty seconds and made the weirdest faces. Oh, my lord, I was bracing myself because I never knew what to expect from him. He was a totally unpredictable man. I was going to crumble right before his eyes if he did not say something really quick.

"Richie, the time has come," he said loudly and confidently.

"It has," I replied with enthusiasm. "Yep, I knew this day would come. I just didn't know it would be today. So, does that mean that you're going to promote me?"

"No, it means I'm going to have to fire you."

"*What!*" I almost fell off my chair, then I stood up like I meant business. "Mr. Rodriguez, what are you saying? I don't understand!" My voice cracked and I couldn't help but to start crying. I must have cried for about five minutes straight. He just sat there in silence and waited for me to calm down. I wanted to leave his office and never ever return but something inside of me would not let me. All I kept saying was this was so unfair, how could he. Is this a joke? He knows everything I'm going through.

Then, I heard him say, "Richie, please collect yourself."

"You see, Richie, I promised myself the day you asked me to promote you to become one of the managers I would fire you. The reason why I fired you is because if I make you one of my managers, you will get comfortable real fast. When most people get comfortable with their salaries they start to lose their drive, and I certainly don't want that to happen to you. I don't want to be responsible for killing your dreams."

"Can't you let me decide? Besides, you know I have pretty big dreams. God willing, nothing is going to stop me," I said with tears in my eyes.

"That's what you think. You will have to work longer hours, that also means you will have less time for school. Not to mention, you will have less time to pursue your dreams. The majority of my managers have been with me for more than ten years. They get paid enough to not quit. Believe it or not, this makes people quite comfortable."

"Mr. Rodriguez, with all due respect, can you give me an opportunity to prove you wrong? If you don't give me your support, my family could end up in a shelter soon. I only have enough to carry the household expenses for six months at the most."

"That won't happen, Richie, if you follow and execute my plan."

"So what is your plan?" I asked, feeling pissed off.

"I want you to consider going into sales." His voice remained calm.

"You want me to consider what?"

"You heard me."

I crossed my arms tightly in front of my chest. "First, you fire me and now you want to throw me into sales? With all due respect, Mr. Rodriguez, I think you've lost it. If you're trying to give me another lesson; please, this ain't the time for that."

"Hold on. Young man, did you know that most entrepreneurs started out as salesmen? In fact a high percentage of Fortune 500 CEO's also started out as salesmen."

"But I know nothing about selling," I said desperately.

"That's what you think. As a matter of fact, I know you would be a great salesman. Once you learn the art of selling, you will be able to use that in all areas of your life."

"So, why are you encouraging me to become a salesman?"

Mr. Rodriguez started tallying off on his fingers, "First of all, if you become a good salesman, opportunities to make big money are within your reach. You will begin to make more money than I could ever offer you. With this extra money, you will be able to buy all the properties you want. In sales, there is no glass ceiling. The possibilities are endless.

"Secondly, to become a great salesperson, you will have to overcome the fear of failure and rejection. When you develop the ability and mindset to overcome that, there is no project too big that can intimidate you.

"Thirdly, to become successful in sales you will have to master your communication, negotiating and marketing skills. These three skills are the pillars for any business to succeed and once you know them they're yours for life. Now that is priceless!

"And last but not least, being a salesperson is like being in business for yourself, but not by yourself. You will get the opportunity to build a customer base that you can use later on in life to sell them other products and services. If treated right, they will become your loyal customers and will follow you wherever you go. And you get to do it at the expense of your broker. He's the one who will pay the office rent, company advertising and other related company bills. All you have to do is go out and sell."

"Okay. "But what happens if I don't sell? Will I still get paid?

"No you won't, and that's the best part of it all."

"It sure doesn't sound like it," I said with complete honesty.

"Okay, look at it this way: if you knew you were not going to get paid this week, would you wake up earlier and work extra hard everyday?"

"I sure would!"

"That's exactly my point. All of a sudden, life has passion and urgency. These two ingredients are necessary to become successful in any endeavor. When you finally make a sale, it's like getting a month's worth of paychecks from me all in one check. Not to mention, all the growth that comes along with it. Once you start cashing in, you will be able to pay your bills a few months out until you really start building some momentum. Then you will be able to use all the extra money to invest and from there on the rest is history."

"Okay, now I see where you're coming from." I nodded.

"Richie, the only reason why I am encouraging you to go full force is because you already have a six months' reserve. If you didn't have that to back you up, I would have recommended you go at it part-time until you have saved six months of reserves before you went into it full-time. The real money is made when you can dedicate a full work day to prospect for new customers and work referrals, negotiate the deals you have on the table, return phone calls, handle customer concerns and then service your customers' needs. In case you didn't know, Augustine used to work for me."

"He did?"

"Yes, he did, about ten years ago. I also encouraged him to go into sales just like you. In his case, he had to go at it part-time because he did not have six months reserves like you do. I am very proud of him and what he has accomplished since he got started. He would have never made the money he is making today had he ended up being one of my managers. Do you get the point, son?"

"Yes, I do. I'm just a bit scared."

"That's absolutely normal. But the secret to success is to be scared and still take action, regardless of your fears. And never forget that preparation can only take you so far–after that, you need to take a few leaps of faith."

"I know, you're right. You're 100% right," I replied with more enthusiasm. "Were you ever a salesperson, Mr. Rodriguez?"

"I sure was. I fell into it out of luck and necessity. Looking back, it was the best thing I ever did."

"So what did you sell?"

"I used to sell real estate back in the '60s. It all started when a real estate agent came by one day to give my friend's parents a presentation because they were thinking of putting the home on the market. I just happened to be over visiting that day. I was really impressed with the way the agent carried himself and with his entire presentation. He was young, positive, energetic and appeared to be very accomplished. He saw how involved I was with the presentation, and when he finished, he asked if I was interested in applying to work for his company. He mentioned he would put in a good word for me.

"So, I applied, got my real estate agent license and started working for them on a part-time basis, since I was still working on the bread route. At first, I just saw it as an opportunity to make extra money. But when I realized the real potential, I got really fired up. I will admit that the beginning was difficult. I felt challenged because I was doing something I had never done before. I even contemplated quitting several times but I wouldn't because I had so many big dreams. I knew that if I could just get going, I could use that money to invest in real estate and other businesses. Thinking about my dreams consistently is what kept me in the ballgame.

"Then everything changed the day I was introduced to Ernie Drucker. He became our new team leader. He showed me how to be a great salesperson, or consultant, as he used to say. I learned how to powerfully set up appointments, close a sale, listen by being fully interested in what people had to say, ask questions that would gear my presentation to elicit a 'yes' and, overall, how to be totally confident and effective.

"Within eleven months of working part-time, I had saved enough to quit my full-time job. I had set aside a sufficient amount of cash to carry me for the next six months. And that is when I really put the pedal to the metal. Within two years, I was the top agent in my company, and the following year I was in the top ten in my region.

"When I started generating all these profits, I invested in real estate right away. I noticed how my friends were buying expensive cars and wasting their money on vacations, clothes, and jewelry. I was more focused on investing so that my money could work for me, instead of me having to work for my money for the rest of my life. Seven years later, I decided to open my first business. As you can see, I went from an employee, to a part time agent, to a full time agent, to an investor, and finally to a business owner. And it all started because I jumped into sales and leaped 'all in'. It took courage, lot's of it...but in the end it was all worth it. Frankly speaking, it was one of the best decision I ever made.

"That was over thirty years ago, Richie, and I'm still benefiting from that experience. So as you can see, I was exactly where you are today."

"Wow, you have certainly changed my point of view about the world of sales," I said, feeling excited, confused, and nervous.

"Ever since I learned the importance of selling and becoming a good salesman, I created possibilities that provided many opportunities that exists only in the business world. I've made it my mission to encourage my friends and those I meet to either get into the world of sales or learn by taking several salesmanship classes. I see these sales skills as a tool to elevate your performance no matter what career you are in. Learning all the aspects of salesmanship can take you from an average performer in your career to a high performer. It allows you to grow in the ranks quicker, become more successful in getting your point across, leading groups to reach high volumes of sales, handling customer complaints effectively and compassionately, becoming a better speaker at company events and, in the end, making more money because you are now more valuable."

"That sounds great. I just don't know if I am ready."

"Who said that?"

"I know, it's the complainer," I replied while my voice dragged down.

"Correctomundo! Just get that every time you set a huge goal for yourself, he's going to have a panic attack. The way he sees it, you are now going into expansion mode and this really threatens him because he does not want you to go into expansion mode. Every time you want to expand, he will want to contract. His job is to keep you safe and small. It's his way of dealing with a threat. All you need to do is recognize that contracting is counter intuitive. So press on and be a champion, Richie. Champions will always continue to expand regardless of what the complainer is saying because, as motivational speaker Tom Peters used to say 'you can't shrink into greatness.'"

"Yes. You're 100% right. I'm just scared, that's all." I admitted.

"No, you are not scared, it's him that's scared. Just recognize it and take action in spite of his fear. This is called being powerful. Powerful people are not going to ever stop being afraid. The only difference is they don't let fear stop them from taking action. They actually sucker punch fear in the gut and go for it anyway."

I nodded. "Yep, I guess you're right."

"Richie, don't forget that fear is what you make it mean. The complainer, when faced with a challenge, will: Forget Everything And Run but the champion in you will Face Everything And Rise[27]. As you can see, it's all about how you choose to interpret fear."

"Okay, I got it! I'm going to take it on, in spite of my fears. I am going to face fear head on and rise to the challenge. I declare today that I will use this tool for the rest of my life whenever I am afraid of doing something that I want to do. I also declare to be open to your coaching, just like you took Ernie's coaching. So where do I start?"

"The first thing I want you to do is to remain coachable. Most people will be coachable as long as they like the coaching. But when it gets uncomfortable they tend to check out and stop being coachable. Never do that, Richie. If you do, you will fail miserably. The second thing you have to do is think about a product or service that you are passionate about. You can't sell something unless you are sold on it yourself."

"Oh, that's the easy part, I am very passionate about real estate."

"Great! There's your answer. The next step is to find a real estate office that is willing to train you. Generally, the way it works is they will pay you less in the beginning while you are getting trained. Your commission will increase as you start to sell more and depend less from your manager."

"Do you think I will make it?"

"Richie, that's not for me to decide."

"I know, that's up to me to decide, no, let me correct that. That is for me to create."

"Now, we're talking. Richie, all the training I have given you should be enough for you to be a millionaire for the rest of your life," Mr. Rodriguez chuckled, and I couldn't help but do the same.

*****

After listening to Mr. Rodriguez's powerful words of wisdom, the first thing I did was call Augustine so I could share the good news. I asked to meet with him because I had some very important news to share. We met later that evening, and I shared everything that had transpired from my conversation with Mr. Rodriguez.

"Oh my God, he got you too? I knew it was just a matter of time," Augustine said while laughing so hard he nearly fell backward on his chair.

"Augustine, quit laughing! I just want to know if you can train me. I really want to work in this company, but only if you train me."

"Well, I'm not a trainer."

"Yes, but someone took the time to train you once. So, now I'm asking you to do the same."

"Richie, you're really serious, huh?"

"Does it look like I'm playing around?"

"Alright, alright, I'll show you everything I know but if you don't do as I say and if I see you're uncoachable then I will quit at the drop of a dime."

"I got it! For the record, my nickname is 'Champ'."

"Okay, let's see if you can live up to your name. So, Mr. Champ, do you have a car?"

"No, but that is not going to stop me."

"What? How do you plan to sell houses if you don't have a car?"

"Look, I'll do whatever it takes to make it. I'll either meet the buyers at the properties or drive there with them. Don't you worry about that, you just worry about training me right and I will do the rest."

"Okay, but just know that I will be your assistant hands on trainer and the company sales manager will be your trainer as well."

"Okay, just make sure they hire me and train me and I will do the rest.

"You really sound determined, Richie."

"Determined is an understatement. I have burned all my bridges and there is no turning back for me now."

"What do you mean?"

"Did you ever hear Mr. Rodriguez's story about the point of no return?"

"No, I haven't."

"Did you know that when a naval ship leaves from the U.S. to Spain, it only carries enough fuel to make it to its final destination? At one point in its journey, it crosses the halfway point. Now if the ship encounters a mechanical failure after crossing this line, it would not have enough fuel to return to the United States. You see, once the ship crosses the point of no return, as I like to call it, the ship must continue its course.

"I bring up this story, Augustine, because I've crossed the point of no return and for me there is no turning back."

"Okay, I got it. Let's roll up our sleeves and get to work, Champ."

"Game on!" I replied.

After this conversation, he sat me down and gave me the rundown. The first thing I needed to do was go to school to get my real estate license. It required taking a 45-hour real estate course. Upon completion, I had to take the state test. If all went well, I could obtain my license within 45 days or so. When I was not in school, I headed to the office to help out Augustine with his deals. I got to see him in action and it really inspired me. The more I went, the more I knew I was cut out for this job.

Within 16 days of taking my NY State Licensing test, I received my NY Real Estate License. I was so excited the day Augustine told me his broker received the license in the mail from the department of NY State Licensing Division.

*****

"Richie, I never ever knew you were a salesperson." Darnell was shaking his head.

"I know. Then again, I never thought Mr. Rodriguez used to be a salesperson either."

"So how did you do in your first month? Did you sell a lot?" Darnell asked.

"No, selling was more difficult than I thought. I learned real quick that everyone wants the best deals in the market. I would spend all day scheduling appointments, only to have many of my buyers cancel at the last minute. Then, when I did get offers, the sellers would want too much and when I would go back to the buyers they usually never wanted to budge. Being in the middle was frustrating and the pressure was getting to me. Every step I took on the way to my appointments, I could hear the cling clang of the quarters jiggling in my pockets."

"Why did you have so many quarters in your pocket?"

"I had them so I could return my phone calls whenever I got beeped. Remember, Darnell, back then cell phones had just come out and I could not afford to have one. Having a beeper was the best I could do. To catch up with my schoolwork, I did most of my homework on the train to and from school and when I was on my way to my appointments. I worked like a slave, seven days a week. The words Augustine told me the first day he trained me kept ringing loud in my head every time things did not go my way."

"What were those words?"

"Well, from the moment we started working together, I told him how serious I was about trying out real estate. To this, Augustine retorted, 'You're not going to try real estate, real estate is going to try you!'

"After he made that comment, I told him that it was just a figure of speech and I reiterated that I was not going to only try—I was going to succeed, because I was 'all in' and there was no turning back.

"I also mentioned that even if I failed, I would never quit because being the underdog was something that I had become accustomed to. I added that underdogs are fueled by their failures and it only makes them stronger. A real underdog doesn't focus on the obstacle but rather the goal they are committed to achieving. They fight and continue pressing on until they win. Victory is their greatest motivator.

"Lastly, I knew if I didn't succeed as a real estate agent, we would end up in a shelter and that was one thing I was not going to put my family through. That simply was not an option. More than ever, I knew that I needed to act on faith and put into practice everything I had learned thus far from Mr. Rodriguez's teachings. I made it a goal to apply his success principles everyday. Hey if it worked for him, then it would certainly work for me."

"Richie, I'm at the edge of my seat and can't wait to hear the rest of the story. By the way, how long did it take for you to sell your first home?" Darnell asked.

"Ah, now that's an interesting story. Let me share it with you."

CLAIM YOUR FREE GIFT

I am so glad you made it this far. By now, you probably feel inspired to take over the world and conquer all your dreams.

I want to gift you a productivity course called "Unleash a Performance Explosion" for **FREE**. All I ask is that you take part in the #PhotoChallenge

Take a photo of your The Underdog's C.O.D.E. to Riches book cover in your favorite place:

- In your office
- By the pool or beach
- At a local Starbucks
- In front of a cool car Or
- anywhere you desire

Post it after you've taken your picture

In your Instagram Caption, tag @EdwardRMunoz and include #TheUnderdogCode #BookReview #Bookstagram #AwesomeBook
My Instagram handle is @EdwardRMunoz

In your facebook caption, tag @EdwardRafaelMunoz and include #TheUnderdogCode #BookReview #Bookstagram #AwesomeBook
My Facebook handle is @EdwardRafaelMunoz

TAG ME

Once you tag me, I'll send you a link to download the "Unleash a Performance Explosion" course for FREE.

Photo Credit: Fotolia_124974717

Chapter Eight

THE TEMPTATION TO
BE ORDINARY

*"Everything begins small. The skyscraper began with a
single brick, the giant oak tree with a tiny acorn. You are
just a portion of what you will be tomorrow."*
— *Dr. Mike Murdock, Author/Pastor*

"I caught my first glimpse of hope three weeks after getting my
real estate license. That day, I was with Augustine and we
were driving to view a home when I got beeped. I asked Augustine
to lend me his cell phone so I could return the call, but he was
too busy singing along to some hip hop song and bobbing his
head like he meant business. I had to practically scream to get his
attention. I found out a seller we presented an offer to had decided
to accept it. After I told him the good news, I was so excited that
I increased the volume of the car radio. As the hip hop pumped
louder through the speakers, we moved to the rhythm of the beat
and I sang out loud. We were celebrating my first of many sales.
Even though I wouldn't collect my first commission for probably
the next two months or so, it still represented major progress."

"So did you take off from there, Richie?" Darnell asked.

"Well, let me tell the story and you'll see!"

*****

I would not make another sale for two months. All the pressure
from home and sis was really getting to me. It just didn't allow
me to perform. I went from an all time high to an all time low.
Then, to make matters worse, one night when I arrived home,
Mom shared with me what the doctors told her about Jennifer's
condition. That really drove me crazy.

Turns out the cancer was starting to spread fast and that meant
my sis needed to get treatment quickly. Mom told me that, after
going through extensive blood tests, they noticed the leukemia

had worsened. She went from Chronic Myeloid leukemia to Acute leukemia. In this stage, the cancer cells multiply at a quicker rate. She would have to go through a series of chemotherapy to kill the cancer cells. She might even have to go through some radiation treatment which uses high dose x-rays to destroy cancer cells. The doctor said that even with this treatment, there was still an enormous possibility it could return—that's if her body could take it. The only way to really guarantee her life was to get someone who was compatible to donate their stem cells from a bone marrow transplant that, in turn, could rebuild her supply of blood cells that would boost her immune system.

"So how do we get a donor, Mom?" I asked.

Mom sighed dejectedly. "It's not that easy. She has to get on a national waiting list. And once on the list, she would have to find someone who is compatible with her blood type. The doctor said if they found someone, it would be like hitting the lottery since the odds were pretty slim. As you can see, it's a bit complicated."

"Complicated... but Mom, isn't there anything else we can do?"

"It's in God's hands right now. All we can do is pray."

"Is that your best answer?" I tried to keep calm, for Mom's sake.

"Look Richie, I'm more worried than you, after all she is my daughter," she cried.

"Yeah, Mom, I'm sorry, it's just really hard to grasp." I paused to steady myself. "So where is she?"

"She's in the hospital now. The doctors want to start her first chemotherapy treatment today. Just as the nurses were shaving off her hair, Jennifer was asking for you. Listen to me, I want you to pray for her."

I nodded quickly, "Yeah, sure thing, Mom. I'll continue praying until my knees wear out." Then I paused as the rest of Mom's words sunk in. "Did you say the nurses shaved off her hair; come on Mom, please tell me you're kidding? Why on earth would they do that?"

"When she starts her chemotherapy, she will end up losing her hair because the drugs are so strong that they kill off the bad cancer cells but the treatment also kills off the good cells, too. It just so happens that the hair cells are very fragile so they are the first to go. That's why she asked for you today. She really wanted you to be there for her first treatment.

"But... Mom, what will happen if it doesn't go well?"

"Then her last chance is a bone marrow transplant." Mom looked steadily at me. "Are you going to see her? I know she really wants to see you. More than ever, she needs you."

"Mom, I'm not sure. I'm really busy," I said. The truth was I could not bare to see her in such a hopeless condition. I was afraid of breaking down before her eyes; that was the last thing she needed.

*****

"Man, Richie, I still can't get over how poised you were through all of your life's ups and downs. How were you able to maintain your composure?" Darnell asked, eager to hear my answer.

"Truth is, Darnell, some days I wasn't able to keep it together. I tried my best to keep a strong appearance on the outside, and looked to my close friends to help me through the tough times," I replied.

I felt so desperate that day that I decided to call Anthony and told him I really needed to go out somewhere to get away from everything. I felt I was going to go crazy if I didn't, and we both agreed to meet at the pizzeria over on Livonia Ave, by the train stop. He claimed it was the best pizzeria in all of Brooklyn. Personally, I've eaten better pizza but I wasn't in the mood to argue. When I arrived, Anthony was hogging down two slices and a coke.

"Hey, Richie, what's up?" He mumbled, still chewing on his pizza.

I shrugged. "Not much, just hanging in there."

After he washed down the pizza with a swig of coke, he said, "Look, I know you're going through a lot, so after you called I thought we'd go down to the beach to break the everyday routine. Whad'ya say?"

"Sounds like a good idea," I replied unenthusiastically.

"The only thing is I left my car at the mechanic. They are doing some work on the transmission, so if you don't mind let's take the train."

"Yep, whatever," I replied.

We jumped on the #3 train and after a few transfers we took the A train to the last stop at Rockaway Beach Park. The train felt like it was going in slow motion. My depressing thoughts seemed to run faster than the train I was in. I whipped out a Nutri-Grain Bar to calm my nerves. Eating a Nutri-Grain Bar in slow motion is like chewing on sandpaper with the sound magnified in your head like a screeching, dying cat[28].

"Anthony, what have you been up to lately?" I murmured, not sure I currently cared enough to hear his answer.

"Well, let's see, as you know I dropped out of college last semester because it simply was not for me," Anthony replied.

"So if you are not in college, what have you been doing lately besides taxi driving in the evenings?" I asked.

"I'm glad you asked. For the last four months, I have been involved in an incredible network marketing company. Their products and compensation plan really rock. At the rate we are growing, our company should be at $500,000,000 in sales this year." He folded his arms across his chest and looked satisfied.

"Are you making any money?" I asked.

"Well, I reached the first executive position and now I have eleven new members on my team. If we all keep duplicating our efforts—as I know we will—my income will continue to grow because I generate a residual commission on all our sales. The best part is that we get to be trained by the best in the industry. On a weekly basis, I am being trained and developed in the areas of recruiting, presenting, negotiating, overcoming objections, and closing the sale, just to mention a few."

"You really sound excited." His excitement was beginning to get through to me.

"You bet I am! I'm not going to share the opportunity with you quite yet because I know you're going through a rough time. So I want to give you your space for now, but when the time is right I'll share it with you because I would love for you to consider this amazing opportunity. Network marketing is one of the few businesses out there that allows you to start with a minimal investment, and with sufficient hard work and effort you could become a millionaire. Did you know that 20% of all millionaires in the world made their fortune through network marketing?"

I nodded my head just to agree. As he said this, we arrived at the last stop. He spoke the whole way there. Despite the fact that

I was in and out of our conversation, I knew feeling depressed at home was far worse.

It was around 2 pm and the beach was lonely and deserted. It was the middle of December and the seagulls were flying everywhere looking for food. As we walked, I thanked Anthony for always being there for me. His support really meant a lot to me. He was even there for me when dad first went to jail seven years ago. He was my childhood friend.

I'd heard before that your friends from your childhood are like family. And this is how I considered Anthony. This is why I trust him so much and he is the only person I look for besides Mr. Rodriguez whenever I am sad or depressed. The love is so huge between us that just being in his presence made me feel safe and protected. I shared with him how Jennifer having cancer made me feel hopeless.

"Richie, you once told me that everything always turns out in the end. It may not turn out like you want it to, but it will turn out. So why beat yourself up if that future hasn't even arrived yet? I know I may not be the best person to give you advice because I've never been in your situation but what I do know is that, if you have made it this far, why quit now when your family needs you the most?"

As he spoke, my lungs contracted and his message came through loud and clear.

"Yeah, I guess you're right," I said half-heartedly.

"It seems to me that you are more committed to your suffering than you are to having a great life. I know it's tough, but don't let that stop you from being a champion. Last week, I attended my first regional rally with the network marketing company I'm involved with. The company's top producer gave a speech that had many in tears. He shared with us that we cannot let our sadness affect our performance, and we must not let life's tragic events stop us from taking action. He continued to say that many unforeseeable events would happen in our lives and throw us off our game. It's just called life! The truth is that the more we focus on our problems, the sadder we will become. He instructed us to not focus on our problems, but rather on our commitments and goals. He said when our commitments and goals are bigger than our problems, this alone will propel us into action again.

"Absolutely nothing replaces action. It's inside of action that leadership shows up. When you are in action it will lead you to a better place. Yes, even leaders have their share of problems, but they don't let it stop them from taking action. The coolest part is that when leadership shows up, things quickly start to turn around. Does that make sense, Richie?"

I nodded and managed a smile. "It sure does. It makes all the sense in the world. I really needed to hear that. Anthony, you are becoming a powerhouse."

"Yes, I am. So let's get a quick bite to eat and head back home so you can encourage your sister, who really needs you to be there for her. And, so you can get into massive action and become the champion salesperson you were born to be."

"Yes, yes, that is what I am going to do! Thank you bro, you're the best. Anthony, when was the last time I told you I love you?"

He laughed loudly. "Never! You never did!"

"Good, well here it is—I love you—so come here and give me a hug so we can get out of here."

We hugged and then headed to have our favorite beach sandwich: a philly cheesesteak with cheesy fries.

*****

"On the train ride back from the beach, all I kept thinking about was what Anthony shared with me. As soon as I got off the train, my pager beeped. It was my cousin, Paul. I asked myself, what could Paul possibly be paging me for? This was so unlike him. All these ugly, terrifying thoughts raced through my mind. I immediately went to the nearest pay phone and called him."

"What did he say?" Darnell asked.

"He just wanted to let me know my uncle was in town and that he wanted to see me."

"So, who was this uncle?"

"That's what I wanted to know myself. It turned out this was my dad's brother whom I had never met. I heard Dad mention him a few times, though. The main reason why I never met him was because he left to go to the Marine Corps when I was a young boy and he'd apparently never been back since. Paul told me my uncle was over at his home so I jumped back on the train to meet him."

When I arrived at Paul's home, Staff Sergeant Hernandez was sitting in the living room. He was still in uniform since he just came back from a ceremony at Fort Hamilton. Standing tall, at about 6"1', looking lean and mean, he was quite a sight to look at. He was impeccably dressed and his uniform was pristinely pressed. His biceps were trying to rip out of his sleeves. His eyes glowed with confidence. His shiny shoes reflected his heroic figure. He resembled a GI Joe figure. His ribbon rack was neatly placed and contained all the colors of the rainbow. I wondered if he used a ruler. He must have, they were too neatly arranged. It all translated into a world of accomplishments to me.

"So you must be Richie, how you been?" my uncle asked. I just stood there in awe looking at his chest full of colorful ribbons.

"Hey, soldier, what language do you dream in?" he asked.

At first I hesitated, then I said, "English, I guess! Why do you ask?"

He smiled at me. "You look a little distracted."

"Oh that... yeah, I was just looking at all of your military ribbons. How many do you have, sir?"

"Sir! Don't call me 'sir'. I work for a living," he replied in an authoritative manner before bursting out laughing.

That left me even more confused.

"Hey now, don't look so confused. In the Marine Corps, we only use 'sir' when talking to commissioned officers. I'm what you'd call 'enlisted'. We don't like to be called 'sir' because we like to think we work harder than the commissioned officers do," he winked and laughed again, but stopped when he saw I was not laughing at all.

"Look, I didn't mean to ridicule you," he continued, "my apologies. I have been in the Marine Corps for fourteen years and that's just my normal reaction every time I hear the word 'sir.' I must really be more sensitive when speaking to non-military personnel. To answer your question, I have over twenty ribbons and I'm proud of every single one. One more piece of information you should know is that us 'enlisted soldiers' like to be called by rank then our last name. But you can call me Luis just like your father does."

I did not know whether to be happy or concerned in his presence. He just had way too much power for me to handle. After we spoke some more he went to change into what he called his "civies". Later, he explained that "civies" stood for civilian clothes. I must say that all of this military jargon was getting to me.

Even when he came back into the room in jeans and a regular T-shirt, I was still nervous being around him. I guess I had a hard time grasping the fact that we were of the same blood and that this man was really my father's brother. Unlike my dad, he was a champion.

"So how is your dad, Richie?"

"He's good, I guess."

"When will he get out?" Staff Sergeant Hernandez asked.

"He still has about sixteen more years. If he behaves, he can expect to get out by 2017. What about you, sir... no... I'm sorry... I mean Staff Sergeant Hernandez?"

"Come on, please call me Luis. What is your question, exactly?" he replied with a welcoming smile.

"When will you retire from the Marine Corps?"

"As strange as it may sound, I also plan to retire in 2017. At that point, I will have thirty years in the glorious Marine Corps of the United States. So I guess your dad and I will be starting our new lives together."

I thought, how interesting that two brothers who both had so much power and potential could end up in completely different places.

During the next few hours, he really opened up to me by sharing what he did and went through in the last fourteen years. The more he shared about his military experiences, the more interested I was to hear the end of his story. After a little while, I started to see his true colors and felt like I was connecting with him on such a profound level. Luis was a real champion and I felt so honored to talk with him. What began as a boring conversation turned into an uplifting conversation.

"So, Luis, what was the toughest part you had to go through when you first joined the Marine Corps?"

"Well as you know, I joined the Marine Corps in 1987, coincidentally the same year your dad was sentenced to 30 years in prison. After passing through boot camp, they sent me to specialize in my M.O.S."

"What is that?" I asked.

"Oh, that stands for Military Occupation Specialty. I became a motor transport operator, and I didn't like it one bit. For the next four years, I did just enough to get by. Afterwards, I decided to join the infantry. I wanted to prove to myself that I could be more useful in the Marine Corps and I definitely looked forward to going to war as a grunt."

"Grunt? What's that?"

"A grunt is another word for a foot soldier. Anyways, I didn't want be known as a plain old truck driver–I could have easily became a truck driver without having to join the Marine Corps. Does that make sense?" Staff Sergeant Hernandez asked.

"Yes sir, it does...I mean Luis," I laughed. Then, he did the weirdest thing. He let out a big roar.

"*OO-RAH*".

"OO-RAH," I repeated, "what is that?"

"It's a Marine Corps thing. It's our battle cry. It also stands for charge!" he smiled triumphantly.

"Wow! That's pretty cool. You guys have your own language. So Luis, what was your greatest challenge when you became a grunt?"

"Without a doubt, it was difficult from the beginning because here I was a newbie Infantry Sergeant with no Infantry experience. They would follow my commands, but laughed behind my back."

"Luis, recently I became a real estate agent and I can certainly relate to your story because I'm going through some of the same things."

"Oh, so you know what I mean. Richie, picture this: I had five people who had to report to me and I'm pretty sure they all wondered how a leader like me with little combat experience could lead them into war."

"Oh my lord, that's exactly what is happening to me, Luis. I just took over my household expenses and responsibilities. As you already know, my sister is not doing too well."

"Yes, I know; I was at the hospital visiting her earlier today."

"Yeah. My family doubts I will make it in the real estate business. Quite frankly, I doubt myself at times, too," I admitted.

"Just remember that it is normal to doubt yourself when you are under pressure. I know, I've been there many times before. But this is what I have learned during those tough times: Leadership develops when you put yourself into a leadership role. It's the only way it will come to fruition. You know you are in a leadership role if those around you are disagreeing with you. In essence, leadership is the transition from wondering how to do something to actually putting yourself out there in the line of fire and taking a stand for what you know is right. Yes, you will make some mistakes, but eventually you will get better and better and suddenly those same people who criticized you will start to praise you."

"I never looked at it that way, Luis."

"Well you betta' start quickly," he commanded, then cracked a smile.

I smiled back at him. "Please continue with your story because it's helping me see my current situation in a different light."

"About one year after being a grunt, I got my first opportunity to show just how good of a soldier I was, when I applied to the Marine Corps Force Reconnaissance Unit. This is the special forces unit of the Marine Corps. This unit is to the Marine Corps what the Navy Seals are to the Navy. In order to be accepted into this program, you have to be in amazing physical shape and you also have to come highly recommended by your superiors. Then, you have to take a physical fitness and endurance test that lasts up to four hours. This is also known as the Marine Corps Recon Screening. It's comprised of running, swimming and hiking and it must all be accomplished within a certain time frame. This brutal test usually weeds out the weak ones—most people fail it. But once you pass it, the real training begins.

"Nearly half of those who enter the Recon initial 12-week training end up quitting at some point and don't see it through to the end. For those who make it through the entire training, they will have pushed their physical and mental limits near to their breaking points.[29]

"The 12-week program includes swimming training, endurance training, night time training, sniper training and mountain warfare training. I guess you could say I went to hell and back more than 100 times during the high intensity training. That's not to mention the advanced trainings we had to take in the mountains and the 40+ days of sniper training. By the grace of god, I passed and became what the Marine Corps calls a Recon Marine."

As this man talked, I reflected on my life and felt like a wimp. All of a sudden, my problems did not seem so bad. I will be the first to admit that the hair on my forearms, back and legs were standing up from the admiration for this valiant man. I thought my chest was going to pop from the inspiration I was receiving.

"Man, you are the real definition of a champ. That was some tough training!" I replied.

He looked at me carefully, as if waiting for me to continue talking and when he saw that I had nothing else to say, he continued, "It sure was, and it prepared me for my first combat. On the morning of Dec. 11, 1989, I performed my first combat jump into Panama for 'Operation Just Cause'. Due to the urgency of this operation, we had to do a risky jump at 1 am at only about 450 feet off the ground. Since it was pitch black, we had a hard time seeing where we were going to land. At a moment's notice, I realized I was about to run smack into the side of a building. In a flash, I turned sideways and covered my face to avoid injury to my face and head."

"Did you get hurt, Luis?" I sat up straighter, engrossed in his story.

"I sure did—my elbow smashed into the side of the building and three seconds later, I was on the ground and blood was gushing everywhere. To this day, I can't describe with clarity how it all happened and the thoughts that were going through my mind. Sparing you the visual details, let's just say that my elbow was completely mangled. They wanted to evacuate me, but I refused to leave my troops behind. I covered up my wounds enough to slow down the bleeding and stuck with my comrades.

"After the battle slowed down, I went to get my elbow treated. Three weeks later, I was back in the U.S. and earned my first combat ribbon. It's this one right here, the one that has the bronze star on my air wings. Each star represents a combat jump."

"Man, that was intense, sir. I'm sorry for calling you sir—I'm just so used to referring to Mr. Rodriguez as sir. He's my ex-boss. He's also my mentor, best friend and like a second dad to me."

"Don't worry, Richie, you can call me whatever you want. I can see you're a good kid and you do it out of respect."

"Yes sir, I do!"

Immediately, he let out another big "OO-RAH!" that cracked me up to pieces.

"Richie, when I returned to base, I instantly gained the respect of my platoon and especially my squad. There were also a few jealous soldiers who had been in my unit for much longer than me and had not logged any combat jumps, but that's life." He shrugged.

"On August 6, 1990, 'Operation Desert Storm' kicked off. The next day, my unit, the 2nd Reconnaissance Battalion, got deployed to Saudi Arabia. There I was, part of numerous nasty battles. One of the worst was the 'Battle of Fallujah'. I really improved my combat experience the hard way. Talk about long and incredibly hot days. If there's one thing I learned on the battlefield, it's that if you stand still and freeze at any moment, you will be killed. That applies to life as well. In life, if you have a tough moment and you find yourself stuck or paralyzed by your circumstances, you better figure it out and get into action fast. If you don't, you will die. I'm not talking about dying literally, but rather that your spirit will die. What remains is a healthy body, harboring a lifeless spirit.

"There is nothing worse than that feeling. How many people do we know who walk around in apparently healthy bodies but seem to be dead on the inside? Somehow they got stuck or frozen by a circumstance and, before they knew it, their passion for life disappeared."

As he said this, I realized he was talking about me. That is exactly what happened to me, I thought. These words rang loud and clear in my mind. Somehow, this woke me up from my worst nightmare.

But since the story was so good, I just nodded and said, "Yep, that makes sense, please continue."

"As you can see Richie, I went from a city kid, to a motor transport operator, and then from an Infantry soldier with no experience, to a Marine Recon leading a reconnaissance unit into war. I know for sure that if I was able to accomplish this, you surely can accomplish anything you set your mind to."

In listening to him, I saw myself more clearly than I had in a long time. Without realizing it, Staff Sergeant Hernandez became my lifeline to what's possible in life. I now understood what was possible in my life if I stopped worrying and complaining about my circumstances and instead went for it with all my heart. That's what Staff Sergeant Hernandez had done. He was relentless, persistent and there was no obstacle that could prevent him from accomplishing what he set out to do. His words really spoke to me.

*****

After this long conversation, I developed the strength to go visit Jennifer at the hospital. When I arrived, she had just gone through her first treatment and was feeling very weak. Even though she felt worn out, she was so happy to see me. I spoke to the doctor and he said the chemotherapy had a 50% chance of killing all the cancer cells. 50% was not good enough, but it was all we had for the moment.

I asked him to call me immediately if there was the slightest change in her condition. I also promised that I would support her along the entire process because that would make a huge difference in her recovery. After going over her condition, I asked him if I could take her home. He gave me permission and discharged her.

I called Anthony at the taxi base and he rushed over to take us home. On the way home, I asked her how she was doing.

"Come on, Richie you know I am a champion, this is just temporary," she sweetly replied. "Do you like my new look?" Jennifer laughed as she rubbed her hand over her shiny bald head.

"Of course, you know you've got all the family's good looks," I smirked.

I pretended everything was cool when Anthony stopped at a stoplight.

"Anthony, pull over here. I need to pick something up from the store."

I jumped out quickly so she would not see me in tears. I went into the store and went straight to the bathroom. I cried so hard at the thought of my little sister dying. Then I heard a little voice that said, "Don't you worry, Richie. Jennifer is going to be just fine. Learn to have some faith." Was it God talking to me or was it my intuition? Either way, it sure felt reassuring to be reminded of the power faith has once you claim it. What came to mind next was this biblical passage mom used to read to me when I was a boy that said, "I tell you with certainty, if you have faith like a grain of mustard seed, you can say to this mountain, 'Move from here to there,' and it will move, and nothing will be impossible for you" (Matthew 17:20).

Immediately, I collected myself, took a deep breath and washed my face. I bought some juice and chips so the store clerk would not think I was doing something funny in the bathroom. I hopped in the car and we were off. On the way home, I hugged my sister with all the love I had. I was on a love high after that revelation.

*****

After I got home and walked into the kitchen, I saw some mail on the table. As I ate my chips, I looked through the mail and saw a letter that came from the New York State Attica Correctional Facility. I opened the envelope and started to read it. I couldn't believe my eyes. Dad wanted us to go visit him. This was a really huge surprise. We had requested visiting him several times before, but each time he refused to see us. Eventually, we gave up.

In this letter, he explained that he got the courage to see us and that it was really important to him that we visit on the Christmas holidays. He asked how we were doing these days. He mentioned doing time had really changed his views on life and even mentioned that he took up some new hobbies like reading and cooking. He went on to say how he enjoyed reading history and fiction books. Some of his friends said he was the best cook they ever met. Now that was really hard to believe, nevertheless, I was happy for him.

Reading this letter made me see a different side of my dad. I decided to write him a letter telling him that we would love to visit him. I mentioned we would come on Christmas Eve. I convinced Anthony to take me. He agreed. I knew he wouldn't let me down. I asked Mom to come, but she declined. I didn't ask Jennifer because she was not feeling well, and that 350-mile trip would be too much for her to endure anyway. I didn't ask Diego because I had no way to communicate with him, so on a bright and freezing cold Saturday morning at around 4:00 am, Anthony picked me up and away we went.

On the way up there, I wondered how the experience would be. I was so nervous. I had so many questions and frustrations to let out. I even wondered if I was doing the right thing. No, of course I was doing the right thing. Just because nobody wanted to go didn't mean it wasn't right for me to go and be there for him. The complainer was on loud speaker and trying to run the show. So I shut him up by creating that it was going to be an awesome day full of family miracles.

After a long six hours, we arrived at the state prison. Anthony parked and chose to stay in the car listening to music. Walking up to the big stone building alone was intimidating, to say the least. After going through security, they guided me to the visitor waiting area. My heart was beating one hundred miles an hour. I could not believe I was about to see my father after all of these years.

When I entered the visitor building I was directed to a line for check in. It was a windowless room with approximately forty other people ahead of me in the line who were waiting to see their respective families. The check in process felt uneasy. While waiting in line people chit-chatted about their families and how long they had been in the joint. One person bragged about how much she put in weekly into her man's commissary. Another mentioned she drove eight hours to see her husband. The more I heard these conversations, the more nervous I felt. It was hard to grasp the reality of the situation for all these people.

Approximately twenty minutes into the line one of the prison officers said out loud, "Next person, step up to the line," in a serious and intimidating tone. He proceeded to drill me with a bunch of questions and asked for my ID, then checked their internal system to make sure I was on the guest list. After he finished processing me, he asked me to put into a locker alongside the beige wall all of my items except for my ID and a form he handed me. Then said "do you understand everything I have just told you"?

"Of course I do," I said, like I've been there before.

Then he said, "After you put your stuff away, go and sit down over there and wait for one of us to call your name." Then he pointed to a group of metal chairs where the other visitors were sitting. There they waited anxiously to see their brothers, fathers, boyfriends, sons, husbands and friends. I decided to stand and wait it out. Those grey metal chairs looked like they were going to hurt my skinny butt.

It would be one hour before it was my turn. That hour felt like six hours in the cold and musty room. When they announced my name over the speakers, my heart stopped. I stood up with sweaty palms and walked with a nervous twitch in my step. I was guided over to another building after going through a final security checkpoint. Once I arrived, I opened the huge metal grey doors and entered the inmate visitor area. Breathing long and profusely, I walked over to a table that was more like a counter where inmates sat on one side and the visitors sat on the other side. I later found out that this was a normal setup for maximum security in a state prison. I walked over to the section where he was sitting at a table waiting for me. As I walked closer, I saw him fidgeting in his chair. Apparently, he was more nervous than me. He looked like he had aged twenty years. My father stood up to greet me.

"Hey Richie, how's my boy doing?" He then extended his hands to shake my hands.

"I'm good, Dad." I said as I gave him a big hug. After ten seconds of hugging we sat down again to continue our chat.

"So, where's the rest of the family?"

"Do you really want to know?" I said, as I took a deep breath.

"Yes, I would," he replied in a calm, even tone.

That alone surprised me. This place must have really mellowed him out. I went on to explain why the family didn't want to come visit and he really took it hard. He shed a few tears as I poured it all out. The last time I saw my father cry was when he got arrested, so seeing him cry again really evoked all these memories from the past. This day was not going as well as I had created it after all.

"You know, not a moment goes by that I don't regret all I did. Everything that is happening today is because of me. Instead of crying and complaining all the time, I have learned to take responsibility for my actions. Now I have to learn to live with them. I live with them in my heart, my head and within the four walls of my cell that remind me daily of my mistakes," Dad smiled.

"So, Dad, how's it been going lately?"

"It's not easy, son. When I think of the past I feel pain. When I think about the future I experience anxiety because it's just something I can't have. So I've trained myself to just think in the present and live one day at a time. I constantly have negative thoughts running through my head and often doubt if I'll live to see another Christmas. It's crazy in here, Richie. Everybody is in for seven to life so they really don't care about anything anymore. Just the other day, an inmate killed another guy with a shank."

"What's a shank?" I asked.

"That's a homemade knife. You never know who has one. You're constantly looking over your shoulder and you certainly don't know who to trust. It's very depressing. Truth be told, I have not felt the wind on my skin or seen the sky now for thirteen years. It sucks. After a while, it begins to take a toll on you. Your thoughts are going so fast that you can't keep up with them. You just can't turn off your mind. Man was not made for this. We are physical in nature. We break down in here. When they walked me into my first cell, I noticed a circular pattern on the floor. You could tell the previous inmate walked in circles so often that it marked the floor. Only pacing could have made that scratched up pattern. You could tell he was going crazy. Seeing that on the first day really scared me. But enough about me."

He took a deep breath and looked me in the eyes. "What really concerns me is that, from the looks of it, Diego is following in my footsteps. I really wish he would quit, but when you think you know it all, there's no space for anybody to tell you otherwise. The main difference between him and myself is that I am physically in jail and he is mentally in jail. So you tell me Richie, which is worse?"

"That's a good question Dad, but I don't have an answer."

"You're a good kid and I'm proud of you. You're the head of the family and it's great to know you are supporting your mom and sister in these tough times. I know I'm not really the type of father to give advice, but for what it's worth, here goes: Always remember that life is a test. There will be times in life when you will get a surprise quiz. That is the unexpected occurring. All I ask is that you do whatever it takes to pass the test. Stay focused, think before you leap and don't do anything stupid."

I must say it felt really good to hear my dad give me some good advice. That alone was worth the whole trip. Even though I have heard it from Mr. Rodriguez in different versions before, it felt different because it came from my dad.

"So, you're probably wondering why I never asked you guys to come visit me," Dad said.

"I just want you to tell me the truth."

"Is that what you really want? The truth? Because I got buckets of it. I can drown you in the truth."

"You got my full attention, Dad. This is what I have been waiting for."

"Richie, the truth is I did want to see you but I didn't want you to see me under these circumstances. It was truly embarrassing for me. I felt helpless, useless, a nobody, a real piece of shit. I felt like I was a burden, but at the same time I really missed all of you. Trust me, it's a lousy feeling to walk around in."

At this moment, I felt I had to say something to genuinely cheer him up; I didn't want to come all this way to leave him more depressed than he already was, especially during the Christmas holidays.

197

"Dad, can I have a heart to heart conversation with you? I mean, can I tell you something? There's something I've wanted to get off my chest for a long time."

"Son, go ahead, I am all ears and ready to listen with an open heart."

"Please, promise to not get upset. I am going to be straight with you. Something I've never done but, I feel it needs to be said."

"Give it to me straight, Richie. I am not the same person you once knew."

"Glad to hear that. Well, here goes... on the way up, I was doing some thinking. It occurred to me that I really never saw you as a father. No, what I mean is that I never really saw you like a father figure. I say this because you were rarely there for me when I most needed you. It's strange how I talked to my friend Anthony's dad more than I talked to you, even when you were around. The worst part was that behind your back I would talk bad about you. Not because of what you did, but because I felt you were never there for me. Now that I am older, I see things differently. I want to apologize for being an ungrateful son. That was so unfair of me to think like that of you. Today I realize that you were just doing the best you could and you did it the only way you knew how. What I really want to know is whether you can forgive me for thinking all those horrible thoughts and speaking bad about you behind your back...."

"No, please forgive me," he mumbled, "I deserved it."

After I said this, my dad started weeping uncontrollably. I did as well. Except this time, it was not from pain but from joy. We both felt a sense of relief that could not be explained with words. I knew in that moment I had released him from his guilt-ridden emotional prison.

For the first time in a long time, I had allowed myself the gift of expressing gratitude and love towards my dad. He stood up and hugged me as much as he could—even with the long counter in between us. As we hugged, I whispered into his ear and said for the first time in my life, "I love you Dad, and I always will." The guards quickly told us to sit down after five seconds or so. They were the best five seconds of my life. Talk about a Christmas present. We couldn't have wished for more. Showing up today impacted us in ways we never imagined possible.

After this emotional moment, he opened up and shared his past with me. I didn't realize just how little I knew about my own Dad. Somehow, my kind words had cracked though his hard ego. For the first time ever I was able to receive his genuine love.

In that moment, I got that if I could be powerful with my father, I could be powerful with any man. I also got that there is no bigger authority on earth than my father. If I could deal with that authority, then anything and everything was possible. I felt like nothing could stop me and surely no man on earth could intimidate me. It was such a freeing feeling and a very powerful one.

*****

"Darnell, are you getting anything from this conversation?"

"Richie, you must be a mind reader. I was thinking of how much of an ungrateful son I am with my dad. My dad is really a great person and I am always giving him a hard time. Now I can't wait to get back to Brooklyn and tell him how much I love him," Darnell smiled.

"That's so great!"

"So Richie, what happened after that?"

"We spoke some more then we left back to New York. On the way back, I shared with Anthony all of what I had learned. He noticed how happy I was and how much freedom I had around the conversation. I thanked him for really supporting me and then I told him that I didn't see him as a friend but as the brother I never had and he replied, 'Ditto, bro.'"

"When I went to work the next day, I was so fired up and felt so free. Getting love and support from Anthony, Staff Sergeant Hernandez, and Dad made a huge difference in my attitude, especially since all their love and support came in a moment in my life when I needed it the most. My conversation with my dad and just letting him open up to me was an experience I will never forget.

For the next several months I went on a selling rampage. I broke the company's amateur sales record by selling ten homes in seven weeks. I was the same person on the outside but a very different person on the inside. Something inside me shifted. I was no longer the same person. I became unrecognizable and unstoppable. Everyone noticed the change.

One day, Erick, a salesperson at my office, saw the sales

manager write up my new sale on the sales board. Right around that time I was coming in the office, he yelled out, "Here comes the Champ."

I laughed and asked, "Why are you saying that?"

He told me he really looked up to me because I chose to press forward in spite of all of my adversities. Since then, everyone in the office called me 'Champ'. Up until that point, only my close friends and family called me 'Champ'. Now my colleagues were doing the same. I liked the nickname so much I decided to call everyone in my life Champ as well. That included clients, lawyers, colleagues, and even the lady behind the cash register. Just about anybody I ran into anywhere. Pretty soon, I would hear my nickname everywhere. Those I had called Champ were now calling me Champ as well. It kinda took off from there."

"That's so cool, Champ. Basically, you changed how other people perceive you."

"I could not have said it better if I tried. You're learning real quick."

"Of course, I am hanging out with the champion," Darnell said as we both laughed.

As we stopped to get some gas, Darnell asked, "Richie, what happened to Jennifer after she finished her first treatment?"

"Her cancer cells were dying quickly. This was good news, but came with a huge price. The treatment was so strong that she was vomiting more often as a result of the drugs being pumped through her veins. One of the doctors recommended that I speak to a local organization in Astoria, Queens that runs blood drives for the National Registry. He said that their mission was to save lives by recruiting bone marrow donors and providing support services to children and adults with leukemia and other diseases treatable by bone marrow transplants. After he gave me their name and address, I went to visit the Icla da Silva Foundation the next day."

Eight months had passed and we still had no donor. The clock was ticking. The Icla da Silva Foundation performed blood drive after blood drive and still no luck. Mom and sis were really starting to lose hope. Jennifer's future looked bleak. On one of her off days she confessed to me that she was sad and could not help but to worry about her future. I took the opportunity to tell her that in the Bible, every miracle that ever occurred happened because it resulted from a gigantic problem. I explained that miracles are born from disasters. Without a disaster, there would be no miracles.

"Jennifer, as you can see, God created all of those miracles and he will do the same for you. You are his little angel." As I said this she smiled from ear to ear. "Jennifer Myla Hernandez, do you know what your middle name stands for?"

"I never knew it stood for something," she replied.

"Of course it does. It stands for <u>My</u> <u>L</u>ittle <u>A</u>ngel, so hang in there, sweetie."

"Oh, thank you Richie, I love you so much. You're the best thing that has ever happened to me." She threw her arms around me and hugged me tight.

*****

I was unrecognizable even to myself. Somehow, I became so powerful that no problem was too big for me. It all happened because I chose to confront, instead of run. I chose to create instead of doubt. I chose to lead, instead of follow. I chose to be of service, instead of complain. What I had realized is that in life, shit happens or a shift happens; either way, you choose. I chose the latter.

I was also present to the fact that if you don't relate to yourself as a champion or as a person who can turn things around, then they will never turn around. But, when you relate to yourself as someone who can turn things around then the impossible becomes possible. This is what I call "Championing Yourself". You have championed yourself when you recognize that you are the source. The old saying "If it's got to be, it's up to me," backs up this statement. When you recognize you are the source, your inner champion is unleashed. When the champion is let loose, you become someone who can achieve the unimaginable.

This perspective helped me handle my sister's situation with ease. I was able to study and maintain a GPA of 3.5. I was also able to sell between three to five homes per month. I even bought my first car and paid in cash. Paul knew someone who was selling a 1994 Toyota Corolla that was in great condition and low mileage. Sure, it was a few years old, but I didn't care. After some negotiation, I bought the car at a steal, paid him in full the same day and he handed me the title.

The Corolla was navy blue with a beige leather interior. I was a happy camper. The best news was that I didn't have any monthly payments since I bought it cash. Last, but not least, I finally was able to buy the three family home I so badly wanted since I was sixteen. I even did it before I turned twenty-two. It felt great to complete many of the goals I set for myself. I could not have achieved so much without all the support from my power circle.

*****

The best news of the month was that I found out mom and I were going to graduate the same week. Talk about an amazing month! I will never forget it. I can remember mom and sis coming with me to buy my graduation suit. Mom picked out my suit and shirt. Jennifer picked out a pink tie.

"Pink! Are you crazy?" I gasped.

"Oh, come on, you know it's my favorite color," Jennifer smiled ever so sweetly.

"But Jennifer, people will think I'm a weirdo," I protested.

"Richie, do it for me, I'm your only sister," she said, batting her long eyelashes.

"Okay, okay. But only if Mom promises to wear a pink dress, too," I smirked. I knew Mom didn't like pink but if it would make Jennifer happy then we'd graduate in pink.

My graduation was on a Thursday and Mom's was the following day. When we arrived at my college auditorium, Anthony, Paul, Augustine and Mr. Rodriguez were there waiting for me. I felt overwhelmed with joy. The ceremony really inspired me and represented completion. I realized that I had broken a pattern in our family. I felt a sense of pride knowing that I was able to break through difficult circumstances despite negative patterns that existed for many years.

Today, I would be the first one in my family to graduate from college. Most of all, I was ecstatic to experience this significant event with my mother and sister. Mom wore a beautiful black blouse with a beige skirt and pretty black shoes that was adorned with a delicate navy blue ribbon. Jennifer wore a gorgeous white dress. She certainly looked like an angel. She decided to come to the ceremony without a wig.

At the time, she was still bald. She didn't care what others

202

thought about her. She was just so happy that you couldn't help but to fall in love with her. The ceremony was beautiful. Celebrating my achievements with my family and closest friends made my graduation unforgettable. After the ceremony was over we all took a lot of pictures then left to my favorite restaurant. The graduation was a day to remember forever.

*****

The next day was Mom's graduation. She looked so stunning in her pink dress. Anthony and Paul tagged along for her ceremony. The school had a pre-war charm to it. I loved how these older buildings preserve their character over the years and how the owners keep the integrity of the structure by not changing the original design. We could not have asked for a better place to have Mom's ceremony.

There was a moment during the ceremony when Mom said, "I will be back in a few." After about fifteen minutes, Paul nudged my arm and said, "Yo bro, look your mom is on stage. She's the one sitting to the right of the school principal."

"Oh my lord, you're right." I told Jennifer and some people behind us asked us to shush because we were making too much noise. We all wondered what she was doing up there. Then it dawned on me that just maybe she was going to get an award. Yeah, that must have been it.

Then, the college President went on stage to present the Valedictorian. When he called out my mom's name I almost fainted. This was her surprise for us. Talk about a champion. Somehow in the middle of all of this chaos she managed to get excellent grades. As she stood up, Jennifer and I held hands with tears in our eyes. Talk about a defining moment.

"What was her speech like?" Darnell asked, his eyes lighting up in excitement.

"Gee, it seems like it was just yesterday, Darnell. I am going to try to recall the same speech to you she delivered that day. Here goes:

It is truly an honor to address you today. I would like to give a special thanks to the members of the faculty, the school administration, staff, all the families present today, friends, and to my fellow graduates. Can you believe it? The moment we have looked forward to has finally arrived. I'm sure many of you feel that today is a bittersweet day. I know many of you are excited about embarking on your new journey, yet many of you are sad about leaving the school that has become your family for the last four years. I, for one, am very honored to sit among the future lawyers, teachers, politicians, accountants, businessmen and women, business executives and future leaders of this great nation. The best part of this whole experience of making it this far is that you get to know yourself as someone who completes projects and goals.

When you know yourself as someone who is a "completer" you experience the gift of knowing yourself as a person who can confidently start any project and even better finish any project. Through this experience you get to own that, and that, my fellow graduates, is priceless. It becomes who you are and how others see you. They get to relate to you as someone who gets things done, because in their eyes you are a "completer". Not only that, it also builds a reference or a file that is embedded in your memory. A file that you can refer to whenever you feel like quitting. Someday down the road, you will want to quit a project or dream you started and in an instant you will be able to reference all the projects you completed and just thinking about this will propel you forward into action again. My request is that from today on you take on huge projects in life; projects or goals that you are passionate about. And once you start them, don't stop until you complete them. True champions are not measured by the projects they start, they are measured by the projects they finish.

Now, just because you have completed the goal of graduating today, it does not mean you have arrived. The word arrived is an unconscious trap for many. Unconsciously, thinking you have arrived starts to shut down your creativity. Just know that your graduation today was not a place for you to arrive because there is nowhere to get to. It is just a place for you to acknowledge yourself for what you have accomplished.

Another way of looking at it is to consider that reaching the top of this mountain is really great, but now you are left at the bottom of another mountain. A new mountain of the unknown for you to conquer. The only difference this time is that the bottom of this new mountain is above the top of the old mountain. Looking at this notion from this premise leaves you empowered to push through, just when you thought you have arrived.

Now that you know you are a completer and that arriving only leaves you at the bottom of the next mountain, be aware that the greatest gift was not completing or arriving. Although they are great, really great, the true gift is the person you become in the process. Who you become is the gift. You are the gift because during the journey there were days when you did not feel like studying but you did. There were days when you wanted to sleep late while working on a school paper or studying for a test, but you didn't. There were days when you felt like quitting because you had some difficult circumstances but you didn't. There were days when you had no money to pay for your books, lunch or school transportation but somehow you found a way. Somehow you still came. Who you became is the true gift.

I want to leave you with the words of the great philosopher, Jim Rohn, who said, "Success is not to be pursued, but attracted by the person you become." As you embark on new journeys in your life, I invite you to become the person your inner self is telling you to become. And when you become what you want, you will get what you want. Stop searching for the magic pill and just start being the person you want to become and then take actions consistent with who you chose to be.

In closing, I would like to give a special thank you to three people who are my heroes. To my son, Richard Hernandez, who is a trooper and a fighter. When he found out that his younger sister was diagnosed with leukemia he told me to quit my job so I could focus on her health and my school. If it were not for his support I would not be here on this stage today. It's because of you, Richie, that our family is a better family.

My second hero is my youngest daughter, Jennifer. Since the day you were born I knew you would grow up to be someone special and special you are. I want to let you know that you are the wind beneath my wings. You are my inspiration and a role model to follow. I thank God everyday because he put the both of you in my life. I also want to acknowledge my son, Diego, who could not be here. I love you more than you could imagine. Lastly, I want to thank all of you. You have become my family. Today, I tremble in awe because I am present to your greatness and your love for your family and humanity. As we depart to embark on fulfilling our personal destinies my request is that you go forth and multiply the love that God has bestowed on us. Thank you!

When Mom finished her speech the audience gave her a long well-deserved, standing ovation. It was wild in there. The walls trembled with energy. Female students and even the mothers were screaming, "You go girl, we are so proud of you!" When she came over to our section, we all hugged her and I told her how proud we were of her; especially considering all the circumstances she had to face as a single mother from the ghetto. We all cried as we celebrated this joyous moment.

*****

On our way home that evening, Mom asked me to lower the radio, then said, "Richie and Jennifer, I want you to know that whenever I was going through my tough times all I thought about was you guys. I wanted to show you that it doesn't matter what age you are, or what problems you have, it's never too late to go after your dreams. I wanted to lead by example. I hope you will always remember that whenever you encounter tough times on your journey to success, to never quit—no matter what you are going through." We stood quiet just letting her message sink in.

Paul was the first to break the silence. "Auntie, I must say that I'm so moved by your accomplishment and especially of that speech you gave today. The truth is that I have always wanted to become a doctor–"

"You did? You never told me Mr. Paul, or should I call you Dr. Paul?" Jennifer interrupts.

"Oh, that sounds good. Can I continue?" he demanded.

"Yes Dr., please go on," she giggled.

"I've always wanted to become a doctor, but I was too embarrassed to tell anyone. After a while I just forgot about my dreams until today. Seeing Richie's accomplishments and yours as well has really inspired me to pursue my dreams. Someday down the road I will invite you all to my graduation. I hope you know that witnessing your achievements this week really inspired me to go for it!"

"Wow, Paul that is so awesome that you're taking the first step in pursuing your dreams. Before you know it, you'll be standing there waiting to get your diploma and Mom, me and Jennifer will be right there in the front row," I smiled.

Chapter Nine

HOW TO MAKE GANGSTA MONEY WITH THE WEALTH BUCKET SYSTEM

"There is a big difference between personal growth & financial wealth growth. Both are important for long-term success."

— Edward R. Muñoz

"Smart entrepreneurs follow proven formulas."

— Edward R. Muñoz

I was truly living the best times of my life. I was a selling machine. It got to the point where I was cashing anywhere from $2,500 to $5,000 checks on a weekly basis. On a regular month, I would average four of these commission checks, and on a good month I would get five to eight of these bad boys. It was very exciting but also overwhelming. It really hit me when the bank teller started calling me 'Mr. Hernandez'. Then I knew I had leaped to the other side. I realized it was time to sit down with my mentor, Mr. Rodriguez, to discuss potential investment strategies.

When I left the bank, I called Mr. Rodriguez from my cell phone and invited him to a nice dinner. He gladly agreed and I took him to our favorite seafood restaurant in City Island at the Lobster Box. It's pretty weird how just two and a half years ago we were here celebrating my 19th birthday. Back then, I was barely getting by from day to day. Now, I was on the fast track to success. It's pretty amazing what can happen when you have a champion mentoring you. And let's not forget how drastically your life can change when you keep yourself coachable, even on the days when you don't feel like being coached at all.

When we arrived at the restaurant, I told Mr. Rodriguez, "It's on me today, so don't be shy; order whatever you want."

"Are you sure?" he laughed. You see, this was our ritual.

Whenever we came to this restaurant, he would tell me to order whatever I wanted, only now I got the chance to return the favor. It felt great. We ordered our usual: their famous broiled lobster tail, a baked potato and a side of King Crab legs with lots of butter. I washed it all down with a glass of ginger ale.

After we had a nice dinner, I talked about what was happening in my life. I also shared with him my new concerns. All he did was laugh. This wasn't exactly the reaction I was expecting to receive from my wise mentor. I must admit, I felt a bit confused.

So I asked, "Mr. Rodriguez, why are you laughing?"

"It's just that this is the first time you've ever needed my help on how to manage your money. You usually come and ask me to teach you how to make money," he chuckled again.

"Come on Mr. Rodriguez, I'm very serious about this. I'm really concerned." I was a little hurt by his laughter.

"I get that you're concerned, so let's get to it. First thing's first. The main reason to make money is for the purpose of investing, because if you don't, you will spend the rest of your life working for money instead of having money work for you. Secondly, before I can provide you with some possible investment strategies, I have to let you know some of the problems you may run into." Mr. Rodriguez leaned back and looked at me. "So Richie what do you do with your checks when you receive them?"

"I deposit them in my checking account. What else would I do with them?" I answered.

"Yes. That's my point, everybody does that. The only problem is that when you need money, how do you access that money?"

"I usually use my debit card." I wondered where he was going with this.

"Exactly; and on average, how many times do you use your debit card on a weekly basis?"

"I usually use it about five to ten times, I guess. What's your point?"

"Richie, that's the problem! Most people deposit all their money into one location. Then they can access the money with such ease, and by the end of the month guess how much money they have left?"

"None?" I uttered quietly.

"Yes, none. And usually the money runs out before the next paycheck comes. If you want to build real wealth, you should consider canceling your debit card. This is the exact reason why I personally don't use debit cards. I once read somewhere that about 70% of Americans withdraw over half of their weekly income via the ATM. The ATM is a beautiful advancement in technology. This system gives you 24/7 access to your money, but if not used wisely, it also has negative consequences. For example, let's say you're out getting gas for your car and you head inside to pay. At the counter, you then see all these tempting snacks staring right at you. Tell the truth, does temptation usually win?"

I nodded, beginning to understand. "Yep. You're right. Often temptation wins, and I pull out my debit card and swipe it to pay for the gas and snacks."

"Now, what would happen if you didn't have that debit card?"

"I wouldn't buy the snacks."

"Exactly. You would not buy them. You'd probably be ten to twenty bucks richer each week. But given the American way, you want everything available to you. The system is set up for you to spend to your heart's content. The system encourages us to get a credit card so you can have access to funds—money that does not belong to you. Because you have a debit card, you can spend your money anytime, and because it's your money, you spend it guilt-free. I personally never had that problem because I never had a debit card when I was young. When they became widely available to consumers, I decided not to get one. I knew it would be too difficult to avoid the temptation of using it. Some of my friends back then called me old-fashioned. But I'd rather be old-fashioned and rich, than in-fashion and broke."

Mr. Rodriguez continued, "What would happen if you didn't have your debit card, but you did have your credit card in your wallet and you wanted to treat yourself to a nice dinner? In most cases, what do you think you would do?"

"I would go out and have that dinner." I admitted.

"Yep, and you would do it guilt-free. After all, what's $25 bucks? A few dollars here, a few dollars there, and suddenly the month has gone by and you have no money to show for it. Then you look at your bank statement and you have anywhere from ten to upwards of thirty additional expenses that add up to a large amount of non-planned spending activities. I will be the first to admit that a debit card is a great convenience, but one that many people tend to overuse by spending more than they should.

"This never-ending cycle limits the consumer's mindset in developing any future financial progress. They keep depositing their checks into their checking account, then they're spending all their money via debit cards. Once they run out of money, they start using their credit cards and end up getting into even more debt. If they only knew that buying on credit is merely stripping their future to enhance their present. They justify their spending by saying, 'I'm going to take out $100 from my $750 check with my debit card because I worked really hard this week and I deserve a break.' So when the $100 is gone, guess where they turn to next, Richie?"

"The rest of their money?"

"Exactly. So whenever they need it, they get it. Pretty soon, their checking account is depleted. And all this because of their undisciplined obsession with their non-planned spending activities. After observing many of my friends and colleagues falling into massive debt by following these bad habits, I decided to create a system which is known today as 'The Wealth Buckets'."

"The Wealth Buckets! What is that?" I asked enthusiastically.

The Wealth Bucket System is a Proven and Simple Method for Saving Money and Creating Wealth. It is a system that has a short-term, mid-term and a long term-plan for your financial success all in one. It's something I created by accident. Without this strategy, I would not have been nearly as successful as I am today."

"I knew there had to be some formula to your success. Now you're finally going to share it with me. I'm so excited that I can hardly contain myself. Hold on a second, though. I just want to get my notebook out from my briefcase. I need to take notes so I can refer to it from time to time." Again, Mr. Rodriguez just laughed when he noticed my sincere ambition. "Okay," I said, "I got everything. Fire away!"

"The first thing I did was to take inventory of my bank statements and calculate how much money I was spending on non-planned spending activities in the last three months. After calculating, I noticed I spent anywhere from $200 to $300 extra each month on non-planned activities. I multiplied that by 12 months, and realized I was spending about $2,500 to $3,000 each year on non-planned activities. I was so disgusted when I saw this because I had nothing to show for this lost money. At the same time, these numbers represented about 15% of my income. The sad truth was that I didn't know what I used the money for during that time. All I know is that the money was gone and I had nothing to show for it.

"After pondering for a minute, I thought, 'What if I took my weekly check and dumped it into my checking account that would be used only for my monthly expenses?' I named this account 'Bucket #1'. My monthly expenses included my rent, utilities, shopping, car insurance, etc."

Bucket #1
Monthy Expenses

"So what did you do when you needed money for your everyday expenses?" I asked.

"Now that's a good question, my young champion. After running the numbers, I realized that I needed $35 to carry me through the week for food and traveling expenses."

"That doesn't sound like a lot of money for your weekly expenses, Mr. Rodriguez."

"Keep in mind, I am talking about the days when I was young," Mr. Rodriguez laughed to himself.

"Oh yeah, I forgot you were born in the dinosaur age." I grinned at him.

"Looks like you have a few of your own jokes now," Mr. Rodriguez chuckled. "No more jokes, Richie. This is some serious stuff we're talking about and I need you to stay focused."

"Okay, okay. I got it. Please continue," I said with a hint of impatience.

"As I was about to say, that $35 had to carry me through the rest of the week. No ifs, ands, or buts. To make sure I stuck to my budget, I used a bank that was fifteen minutes away from my house, instead of one that was around the corner. I did this intentionally--I needed to make it as tough as possible for me to have access to my money.

"After Bucket #1 (monthly expenses) had reached two months of savings to cover my living expenses, I decided to open up a new account. This became Bucket #2, and represented my savings bucket. All of the money I used to spend on non-planned activities would now go into this bucket. Suddenly Bucket #1 started flowing into Bucket #2 (savings bucket)."

Bucket #2
Savings Bucket

"To help explain this, let's say that Michael the plumber makes a weekly salary of $700. That equals about $2,800 a month, and after cutting back on his cable plan, daily coffee and other money wasters, he finally brought down his monthly expenses to $2,000 to cover his personal expenses. Next, he withdraws $100 each week to cover gas, transportation and food. He's now left with an extra $300 from his monthly salary to pour into Bucket #2—the savings bucket. If you took that same $300 and multiplied it by 12 months, that would be an extra $3,600 smackaroos at the end of the year that is now in Bucket #2. Not bad for a person who thought he could not save an extra $3,600 bucks.

"Now let me stop for one moment, Richie. I would only advise people to put this money into Bucket #2 if they have no debt. If they do have debt, my advice is to pay off or pay down their debt every month with this extra money. You should not build wealth while still in debt. It's too risky. I would suggest you send extra payments with this money to your smallest debts first and pay the minimum on other revolving debts. This allows you to pay off the small ones fast. As soon as they're out of the way, you can focus on paying off the next smallest one.

"I would even consider calling the creditors and negotiating with them so they can drop your interest payments temporarily or permanently. A little here and a little there all adds up. My philosophy, Richie, is that in order to build wealth you must first 'Get to Zero'. If you are in debt, you are below zero. It's much harder to build wealth if you are in debt up to your neck. Now, once you get to 'Zero', you can build anything you want because you have nothing holding you back. You are now free like a bird and can fly as fast and as high as you want. Richie, I have helped many people get out of debt just by sharing this part of my Wealth Bucket System."

I was in shock at the revelation. "Wow, Mr. Rodriguez! Now I understand why there are some people who never get out of debt and why they never get ahead. It makes all the sense in the world."

"Now, when your debt is cleared you can really start seeing your money grow in Bucket #2 because Bucket #1 will overflow into Bucket #2. Having this money here serves various purposes. First, it serves as an emergency bucket should the unexpected occur. This bucket becomes your back-up. Most people don't have a backup plan when the unexpected occurs, so they turn to a credit card, which drives them further in debt. In the event they don't have a credit card, they are left having to borrow money from someone. Your goal should be to have six months of your monthly expenses in Bucket #2.

"Let's return to Michael the plumber. If his monthly expenses were $2,000 a month, his goal should be $12,000 in Bucket #2, and not a penny more. Now once you accumulate that $12,000, this is where the fun starts. Now you're ready for Bucket #3: the frozen money bucket.

Bucket #3
Frozen Money Bucket

"I created Bucket #3 because I found I needed no more than six months of reserves. But I also did not want my money just sitting around. So I decided to dump all my extra income into Bucket #3. This bucket would serve as my extra money because I felt I still was not ready to start investing in real estate. Instead, my plan was to build a war chest so that I could take advantage of any good real estate deals the moment they hit the market. Not just any deal, but the best deals in the marketplace. I chose real estate because studies have shown that the wealthiest people on the planet either made their fortunes from real estate or have their money invested in real estate[30].

"So what did I end up doing with the money that overflowed from Bucket #2, you ask? Well, I'll tell you what I did. I invested the money in Certificate of Deposits—otherwise known as CD's—because they're not as easily accessible as cash and also have a higher interest rate than a traditional savings account.

"Another good thing about CDs is they come with maturity dates. Right around this time, I was doing pretty good in my sales career, so I decided to start by buying one six-month CD with the extra money that was in Bucket #2. At first, each CD was in the hundreds range, then quickly increased into the thousands range. Then I got to the point where I had up to three CDs at one time.

"Eventually, Bucket #3 (frozen money bucket) accumulated into one year's worth of my expenses. The best part was that my CDs were paying a higher yield than Bucket #2 (savings bucket). Even better, Bucket #3 was not as easily accessible as Bucket

#2. Freezing money into Bucket #3 ensured that I wouldn't be tempted to dip into it.

"Richie, remember that keeping all your money in your savings account is very tempting. One day you might say, 'Hey, since I have all this extra money, let me go buy those new sofas that are on sale...' Or, 'let's use the money to go on vacation to Disney this summer—besides, we deserve it. I'll put it back soon...' And before you know it, you'll be back at square one. To avoid this from ever happening to me—I froze my money by purchasing CD's. When I felt comfortable about the savings I had accumulated in Bucket #3, I decided I was ready to create Bucket #4: short-term real estate holdings."

Here's my disclaimer*: Bucket #4 [Short-Term Real Estate Holdings] is only for the more aggressive investor and for those who want to retire earlier than most people. If you consider yourself to be the more conservative investor, you will want to skip this bucket and move on to Bucket #5 [Long-Term Real Estate Holdings Bucket]. However, the choice is yours.*

Bucket #1
Monthly Expenses

Bucket #2
Savings Bucket

Bucket #3
Frozen Money Bucket

Bucket #4
Short-Term Real Estate Holdings

"Basically, I figured I could the money from Bucket #3 (frozen money bucket) to buy great real estate deals I could flip because I felt I was in a good position to take some smart risks. I chose flipping properties because flipping allows you the opportunity to create some quick equity rather than waiting for market appreciation.

"Let me explain what flipping properties means, in case you don't know. House flipping essentially is buying a house or property with the intent to sell it quickly for a profit.[31] I also chose flipping and investing in real estate because I had no interest in making banks rich at my expense. Richie, I once read in the 'Upside Up of Real Estate Investing' by Bob Zachmeier that...

> 'When you travel to most major cities in the world, you'll notice that the tallest buildings are usually owned by banks or other financial institutions. The reason that banks are able to afford the tallest buildings in the world is because of the huge profits they make 'serving' us! The banks pay us interest when we deposit our money with them and they charge us interest when we borrow from them. The difference between what they pay and what they charge is commonly referred to as 'the spread.' Usually, the difference, or spread, is five percentage points or more. For example, if a bank pays you 2% interest on the money in your checking account, but charges you 7% on an automobile loan, the spread is the difference of 5%. This is a great return for the bank because the money they lend isn't even theirs! They use, or "leverage" other people's money (OPM) to create an unbelievably high profit.[32]'

"I decided to invest in real estate so I could create my own bank of wealth. Instead of letting banks earn 5% interest or more on my money, I would generate the wealth myself through my own investments. By now, I was in a position where I could put a big down payment on a property and finance the rest. This system was really working great for me. Since I was not in a rush, I could literally sit back and just cherry pick the best deals. I would only look for the properties that had the most upside. Through trial and error, I quickly learned to not make an offer on a property unless it met my two primary rules:"

Rule #1: I make my profit at the purchase, not when I sold it.

"The deal had to be so good that the profit was already built into the purchase price. For example, I once bought a single-family residence for $150,000 that was easily worth $195,000. I could literally have sold it the next day and would have made a healthy $40,000 profit, even after expenses. One thing is for sure: you can never get hurt making a profit."

Rule #2: <u>I needed to make sure I was low-balling my offers.</u>

"Let me set some context on what a low-ball is before explain this concept. A low-ball offer is when someone makes an unrealistically low offer in hopes that the other party will take it. Basically, you make this low offer to see just how low potential buyers are willing to go. Often, I would get these great deals because I would make low-ball offers that made the sellers very uncomfortable when they heard them. If I made an offer and did not feel uncomfortable or embarrassed after I presented it, then I knew it was not a good offer. In my experience, most investors do not make low-ball offers because they worry that the owners will not accept them. Just remember that you have a good down payment in your back pocket and this puts you in the driver's seat. You have what they want, and you need to have the mindset that they need you more than you need them.

"Now, if they feel confident that you do have the funds and means to purchase their property, they'll think twice about scaring you away. In my experience, there have been times when sellers have said 'no', but there were plenty of times when they said 'yes'. My profit came from all those 'yeses', not from the 'nos'.

"After I purchased these great deals, I would then do the necessary repairs and quickly put the house back on the market at a price I knew would sell quickly. I was not interested in being greedy. I just wanted a quick sale so I could make a solid profit and pay back the amount I borrowed from Bucket #3 (Frozen Money Bucket)

"Any remaining profits would then go into Bucket #4 (Short-Term Real Estate Holdings) so I could keep the machine moving. Pretty soon, my real estate portfolio started growing and I made a ton of money from my flips. Then I was faced with a couple of choices: 1) I could either invest my money into an income-producing property, or 2) I could invest my money into an income-producing business."

"Since I was doing well from my flips, I decided to do both. My first business was a small *bodega* (grocery store) in East New York. As a matter of fact, Richie, it's the exact bodega in which you used to work in."

"Oh my God, that's amazing!" I blurted out in sheer surprise.

Mr. Rodriguez nodded. "Yes. I bought it because I love buying products and then marking up the price for a profit. I also bought some buildings and, after paying some heavy capital gain taxes from my flips, I found out I could roll over my proceeds and do what's known as a 1031 tax deferred exchange into another long-term property to avoid paying capital gains taxes.

"In a nutshell, these transactions allow the investor to continue his investment in another property without losing investment equity due to taxes. Richie, to this day I still own some of those very properties I bought through a 1031 tax exchange."

Bucket #5
Long-Term Real Estate Holding

"These long-term properties fell into Bucket #5: Long-Term Real Estate Holding. My income-producing businesses also fell into Bucket #5. This bucket was full of good debt and good profits."

"How do you mean?" I asked.

220

Mr. Rodriguez smiled and shook his head at me. "You know what, I think I'm going to start charging you a fee from now on for all of this good advice, Champ."

"Come on, you've never charged me before, why start now Mr. Rodriguez? C'mon, keep going! You've got me on the edge of my seat; stop playing around and let's get back to business."

"My, oh my, you went from a boy to a business man right before my very eyes. I'm proud of you, so let me get to it before you beat me up," Mr. Rodriguez chuckled.

*****

"Debt is usually perceived as a dirty word. But knowing the difference between good debt and bad debt can be the difference between being wealthy or financially broke for the rest of your life. Good debt is investment debt that creates value and generates a cash flow. Some examples of good debt are student loans, real estate loans, and business loans. Basically, you should use good debt to finance purchases that will either increase in value over time or will generate an immediate cash flow. Bad debt includes debt you've taken on for things you don't need and couldn't afford at the time—a trip to Punta Cana or Fiji, for instance. The worst form of bad debt is credit card debt, since it usually carries the highest interest rates.

"Another way to look at bad debt is when you invest in something that goes down in value immediately. That's bad debt. Now that you know the difference between the two, I want you to realize that most people have a lot of bad debt and relatively few people have good debt. Your ultimate goal in life is to be up to your neck in good debt because that is what builds wealth. However, most people are up to their neck in bad debt and are broke as a consequence.

"So Richie, if you're going to buy an income-producing property make sure the income your investment produces covers the monthly mortgage payment. And not just the monthly mortgage payment, but all the expenses—property management fees, taxes and insurance, to name a few—plus gives you a return. An investment is not an investment unless it yields a return; a profit. The only reason to invest is to make a profit.

"Don't make the mistake some people do when they justify not making profits for the sake of owning their first property. I once had a friend who told me, 'Oh, I have a property and even though it doesn't generate a profit, it's okay. At least I own a property. I know I'm not making any money, but at least my money is invested in a real estate property.' You should never do that. This kind of mindset is a big real estate no-no. You should only invest to make a profit. The profit should cover all of your expenses and then you should return the profits back to Bucket #3 to buy more properties or other investments. This type of investment makes sense, Richie."

I was nodding along with the explanation. "You're right, Mr. Rodriguez, this all makes a lot of sense to me. Can you give me an example of a recent investment you've made so I can see how you calculated the numbers?"

"Sure thing, champ." Mr. Rodriguez reached for a napkin to break down his formula for buying properties.

"Recently I purchased a 4-family quadruplex in Cypress Hills by Highland Park. The seller was asking $379,000 and I made an offer of $325,000. After much back and forth, they countered with $350,000. I then came back with $335,000 because after running the numbers, it would generate an 18.94% ROI—Return On Investment—and I never buy a property unless it generates at least a 15% ROI."

"So, why do you want a minimum of a 15% return?" I asked.

"If there's one thing I learned the hard way—15% never turns out to be 15%. You always have to factor in for unexpected costs for things like repairs. That is why I try to get the best return I can for my money to leave some space for the unexpected. For instance, your boiler might go under on a cold winter day, a tenant leaves or stops paying rent, or your water main might bust on a hot summer day; this leaves a safeguard for the unexpected. Some new investors will go for as little as a 10% ROI, but I think that's way too risky. Look at this napkin that outlines my calculations and how I calculated my ROI."

Purchase Price: $335,000

Down payment: x 14% (10% Down Payment + 4% for Closing Costs)

$ 46,900 My Total Investment

Gross Monthly Income: $3,600 (4 Apartments @ $900 ea.)

x 12

$43,200 Yearly Income

Monthly Expenses: $800 (Property Insurance and Utilities)

Monthly Taxes: $300

Monthly Mortgage Payment: +$1,759.47

$2,859.47 x 12 = $34,313.64 Yearly Expenses

(Profit Formula):

Yearly Income: $43,200

Yearly Expenses: +$34,313.64

$8,886.36 Yearly Profit

How to Calculate your Rate on Investment (ROI):

Net Profit (divided by) Your Equity Investment $8,886.36 / $46,900 = 18.94% R.O.I

Equity Investment (Down Payment + Closing Cost)	$46,900
Total Return	
Gross Income	$3,600
- Expenses	$800
= Net Operating Income	$2,800
- Mortgage Payments	$1,759.47
= Monthly Return	$1,040.53
- Income Taxes	$300
= **Monthly Positive Cash Flow**	**$740**
Calculate Return On Investment (ROI)	
Equity Investment /	$46,900
Yearly Cash Flow (Monthly Cash Flow x 12)	$8,886.36
% Return On Investment	**18.94%**

"Now tell me Richie, where can I get a return like that? It's not going to happen by letting my money sit in a checking or savings account at my local bank. I also have more interesting news for you."

"More than you have already shared with me, Mr. Rodriguez? Wait, please don't throw away that napkin, I want to save it as a memory of today so when I become wealthy like you someday, I will be able to remember that today was the turning point."

Mr. Rodriguez laughed. "Richie, you always say that everytime I share something new with you."

"Yeah, I know but today you are showing me your money making strategies by teaching me your most guarded treasure: 'The Wealth Bucket System' and for that, I will always be in debt to you."

"Oh, stop being so dramatic, young man, and let me continue; I have more to share." He cleared his throat and continued. "Richie, that 18.9% ROI is just the beginning. Have you ever heard of 'Rule of 72?' "

"Can't say I have. Everything you've shared is new to me."

"That's because I'm sharing with you the vocabulary of the rich. The poor do not know these words or terms and that's why they will remain financially poor unless they learn the vocabulary of the rich. To become rich financially you must first be financially literate. The Rule of 72 is a basic principle of the financially literate.

"The Rule of 72 is a math formula that tells you how long it will take to double the value of money you invest into a property. Dividing 72 by your ROI gives you the number of years it will take for the initial investment to double. Let me write this out on a the napkin again:"

$$72 / 18.9\% = 3.8$$

"You see Richie, this calculation translates into 3 years and 8 months. By using the Rule of 72, you can double your money in 3 years and 8 months because the interest is compounding and every day that passes your money is growing as well."

I stared at the napkin with the math on it. "Compounding? You've lost me, Mr. Rodriguez; could you explain a little more exactly what you mean here?"

"Yeah, basically compound interest is interest on interest. Compounding is the result of reinvesting interest, rather than cashing it out so that the interest in the next go around is earned on the principal sum plus previously accumulated interest[33]. Is this making more sense, Richie?"

"It's a bit more clear now, Mr. Rodriguez, but I still don't fully get your example. If you multiply the yearly income of $8,886.36 by 3 years and 8 months, it only gives you $39,099.98 not the $46,900 I originally invested. I don't see how I doubled my investment. I think your formula is off."

"Richie, let me explain it another way. If you took a penny and it doubled in one day, how much would you have the next day?"

"Two pennies?"

"Exactly, and if those two pennies kept doubling every day for thirty days, do you know how much you would have at the end of those thirty days?"

"Can't say I do," I said.

"Pull out your calculator and let's see what happens," Mr. Rodriguez said as he started writing on another napkin and generated the following numbers:

Day 1: $0.01	Day 11: $10.24	Day 21: $10,485.76
Day 2: $0.02	Day 12: $20.48	Day 22: $20,971.52
Day 3: $0.04	Day 13: $40.96	Day 23: $41,943.04
Day 4: $0.08	Day 14: $81.92	Day 24: $83,886.08
Day 5: $0.16	Day 15: $163.84	Day 25: $167,772.16
Day 6: $0.32	Day 16: $327.68	Day 26: $335,544.32
Day 7: $0.64	Day 17: $655.36	Day 27: $671,088.64
Day 8: $1.28	Day 18: $1,310.72	Day 28: $1,342,177.28
Day 9: $2.56	Day 19: $2,621.44	Day 29: $2,684,354.56
Day 10: $5.12	Day 20: $5,242.88	Day 30: $5,368,709.12

"Richie, as you can see, by day 30, you would have a whopping $5,368,709.12! That's the power of compounding. Compounding is a magical force; this is why I love the Rule of 72. The point I'm trying to make here is that any dollar duplicated with the right return could turn into huge profits, so don't try to understand it, just know this is how it works. In 3 years and 8 months, I would have doubled my investment of $46,900 to equal $93,800. And that doesn't count any money I paid down on the mortgage and any appreciation on the property received."

"Well, Mr. Rodriguez, I sure would appreciate more than doubling my investment, but I don't think this is what you're getting at. Can you explain this concept of 'appreciation' a little more?"

"Sure, Richie. Basically, appreciation is the increase in value of an asset over time. To help explain this, let me share an example. The other day, I was reading in the newspaper that the average appreciation rate from the early 1900's to present day is 4.6%. Through all of the ups and downs of the different economies this country has faced, it has somehow maintained an average of 4.6%. During the worst recessions, the rate has gone down to about 1%, and in the good times it got all the way up to 10%.

"For this example, let's be conservative and look at the appreciation rate over the next four years. Pass me that napkin over there, Richie."

I did so and he wrote:

You factor Appreciation Rate (New Equity) + You are Paying Down the Mortgage Every Month When You Make Your Payment + 4 years of Cash Flow + Your R.O.I. From Your Initial Investment + Tax Benefit = Mucho Dinero!!! $$$

He tapped the napkin with his pen and looked at me. "So what do you think of that formula, Richie?"

"That is an amazing formula. Becoming financially literate is the answer to anyone looking to get out the ghetto. Now I know why the rich get richer and poor get poorer. They just don't take the time to learn these concepts, as you say."

"Now you're getting it, Richie. Oh, one more thing, I never bank on appreciation; that's an added bonus. However, I always bank on positive cash flow."

"Ok. I'll definitely keep that in mind when I buy my first investment property," I replied enthusiastically.

"Yeah, and you better not forget it," Mr. Rodriguez chuckled, "following this formula allowed me to grow Bucket #5 the Long-Term Real Estate Holdings. Am I confusing you with all these numbers and formulas?"

"Nope, it's all making perfect sense. Just give me that napkin before the waiter picks it up by mistake." Mr. Rodriguez now laughed profusely. "I promise you that not only will I use this formula, but I'll also share this information with as many people who want to learn how to be wealthy. Did you use the profits of your properties to buy more properties?"

"Yep. As I saw Bucket #5 grow over the years, I started to see each property build different amounts of equity. I would leverage the equity I had from properties I bought some years earlier to buy even more properties.

"For example, when a property's value increased 30% or more over the purchase price, I would then refinance the loan to recover some of our investment capital. This money is then invested in other properties. Richie, to determine the value of a property, the bank hires a real estate appraiser. The appraiser evaluates market data from similar properties in the area and establishes an estimate of the property's value. After the value has been established, I typically obtain a new loan for 80% of the appraised value and retain a 20% ownership stake in the property. The new loan I obtain is usually for a higher amount than is required to pay off the old loan, so the bank pays me the difference. With the difference, I would then use it to buy another property. This type of loan is called a cash-out refinance. The best part is that the check I receive from the refinance is often more than I initially invested in the property. At this point, we no longer have any of our own money invested in the property, but we still own 20% equity stake, receive monthly revenue from the rents, have money to buy another property and receive income tax deductions! The best part is that the money we receive from the refinance is not tax deductible because refinancing is not a taxable event, but selling is![34]

"Now, the key factor was that I would only refinance these properties if they had appreciated by at least 30%, or put another way, if it had a minimum of 30% equity. This is why buying it at the right price makes a real difference. Pretty soon, Bucket #5 became its own animal, and each Wealth Bucket began feeding into another. It was really cool watching everything I had planned come into fruition. Looking back, what started this engine to take off was my ability to spend less on my non-planned spending activities and save the rest."

(Disclaimer: If you consider yourself an aggressive investor,

you will want to take the profits from your investment properties (i.e. monthly cash flow) and put it back into Bucket #3 so you can buy more investment properties, instead of waiting for the equity to build up. Once you have all the investment properties you want, then and only then should you advance to Bucket #6 [The Retirement Bucket].)

| Bucket #1 Monthy Expenses | Bucket #2 Savings Bucket | Bucket #3 Frozen Money Bucket | Bucket #4 Short-Term Real Estate Holdings | Bucket #5 Long-Term Real Estate Holdings | **Bucket #6 The Retirement Bucket** |

"At one point, I realized that I needed to set up some retirement plans apart from what I already had, so I decided it was time to create Bucket #6: The Retirement Bucket. The first thing I did was to sit down with my financial advisor. He went over different retirement options with me. This was the first time I'd ever heard about a whole life insurance policy and defined pension funds. He also spoke to me about a handicap insurance should the unexpected happen, and encouraged me to upgrade my health insurance.

"He even suggested I buy long-term blue chip stocks so I could diversify my portfolio while still playing safe. I did this by taking a portion of my profits from Bucket #5. My financial advisor said that I was at a point where I needed to create a safety net by diversifying my assets. So, that's exactly what I did. Doing so created peace of mind knowing that, should the unexpected happen, I would be covered.

"Richie, you may be asking yourself, 'where does the fun come in?' So I figured out that I was going to be making a lot of money along the way and I wanted to really enjoy my life. So, I thought I needed to create space to have some fun, and along came Bucket #7: The Fun Bucket. Before I tell you more about this, let me draw it all out for you so you have a visual:"

Bucket # 1 — Monthy Expenses | Bucket #2 — Savings Bucket | Bucket #3 — Frozen Money Bucket | Bucket #4 — Short-Term Real Estate Holdings | Bucket #5 — Long-Term Real Estate Holdings | Bucket #6 — The Retirement Bucket | Bucket #7 — The Fun Bucket

"So you see, Richie, it was the perfect time to create Bucket #7 since I had so much feeding in from Buckets #5 and #6. I decided to take anywhere from 5-10% of the net profits from each of Bucket #4 and #5 and use these proceeds to invest in the pure enjoyment for my future.

"In this bucket, you will be saving for what makes your heart content. It could be that 5-star vacation to Dubai, a trip around the world, your dream car, a sailboat, an RV, or just whatever you consider fun. The best part is that you will enjoy spending your money guilt-free because there's no greater feeling than having fun with your profits.

"Here's my golden rule when it comes to having fun: I use profits to enjoy myself and I use capital to build investments. For example, let's say you want to buy a Rolex. As long as you let your investments pay for it, then you might as well say it was free. It's free because you didn't have to pay for it, but your investments actually paid for it, if you catch my drift.

"Now Richie, there were times when some opportunities came my way. For example, once I got the chance to buy a home and flip it immediately. So, to complete the deal, I borrowed the money from Bucket #7. After I did the flip, I would return what I borrowed from Bucket #7 along with the 10% in net profits it generated. At this point, Bucket #7 needed its own security guard because the bucket was getting way too fat."

Mr. Rodriguez paused and silently waited a few seconds for my response, and then said, "Richie, why didn't you laugh at my joke?"

"This ain't no time for jokes. I'm too inspired right now."

"Okay. I got it. I see you're in business mode," Mr. Rodriguez chuckled, "so let me share with you the last bucket of my Wealth Bucket System."

"The final bucket was Bucket #8: Contribution Bucket. In this bucket, I would also take anywhere from 5-10% from Buckets #4 and #5 and dump a percentage of profits into this bucket. In this bucket, I now had money to donate to my church or favorite cause. There's no better feeling in the world than knowing that you made a real difference, whether it's sponsoring a child and paying his college tuition or building a well in a small village in Africa to bring water and electricity there. Contributing to society puts me in a position to help others and feel good about my prosperity as well. It's good to know that when I leave this earth I will leave it better than it was when I arrived. The best part was that the money I used to contribute was coming from my money machine—The Wealth Bucket System. You can't beat that!" Mr. Rodriguez said with a grin of satisfaction.

"Richie, this is why sometimes you see successful people and you wonder how they have such a great lifestyle and so many toys. We see their lifestyle and successes but we don't see their sacrifices. Let me now share with you the #1 pitfall you could ever make with respect to your money. I wanted to share this with you in the beginning but you would have never understood it had I not explained the Wealth Bucket System first."

I leaned forward more. "Now you've got me curious, Mr. Rodriguez."

"Often, when people get ahold of a little bit of money in their hands, they tend to go from Bucket #1 (monthly expenses) straight to Bucket #7 (The Fun Bucket). They totally skip the entire Wealth Bucket process because they let money control their emotions. They go out and buy nice cars, clothes and a house that exceed their real budget and take one vacation too many. They become the 'All flash, No Cash' group. The worst part is that everything they buy in Bucket #7 (the fun bucket) are all depreciating assets. Yes, they are fun, but they tend to lose value very quickly.

"On the other hand, there are people who set up their money to work for them like I did and, as a result, have anywhere from $20,000 to $100,000 in their Fun Bucket. Others who were even more successful have over $1,000,000 in their Fun Bucket, and start to wonder if it will ever run out. If their money is working for them, it never will run out because they took the time to set up a system that feeds itself." Mr. Rodriguez put his hand on top of mine and looked steadily into my eyes. "In this system, Riche, the fun never stops. Additionally, the power to contribute on a large level never stops. Their new problem becomes finding new ways to have fun and discovering more organizations to contribute their money so they can build a better world for now and future generations. Please, keep this in mind the next time temptation kicks in."

"Don't worry, Mr. Rodriguez, I will never belong to the 'All Flash, No Cash' Group. To the contrary, I will follow your system to the 'T' and build a machine that fills my Fun and Contribution Buckets to insanely high numbers," I said.

Mr. Rodriguez smiled and relaxed. "Now you got it. I just wanted to make sure I covered that important point."

"Thank you for doing that."

Go here to download "The Wealth Buckets"
infographic with full color:
http://www.theunderdogcode.com/bookresources

*****

"So there you have it, Richie. I just broke down my Wealth Bucket System. What do you think?"

"It all sounds way too simple." I shook my head and looked down at my notes.

"It may seem simple for you now that you know my system, but it also requires a lot of hard work and dedication. Now, I can promise you one thing: If you follow my system and stick to it, you will reap great rewards."

"Wow, I must say that you always impress me with your strategies for personal and financial success but you definitely knocked it out of the park this time."

Mr. Rodriguez jumped in and said, "I'll leave you with one more thing, Richie. Why do you think most people don't succeed in becoming wealthy?"

"There are many reasons why this is the case," I replied, "but the one thing that comes to mind is the story you told me when I first started working for you. You said that there are two main reasons why people never achieve their dreams: First, people are never clear on what they want to achieve in life and secondly, they are not willing to pay the price to get it."

"I am so glad you remembered. You have a great memory, Champ. You saved me the time of repeating it for you. But there is a third one Richie. The third one is having a strategy for building wealth, and that is exactly what I just shared with you today. Does that make sense?"

"That certainly makes a lot of sense!"

"Now I also have a few final questions for you, Richie, then we have to go before they kick us out of this restaurant," Mr. Rodriguez said with a smirk. "Are you clear on what you want to accomplish in life? Are you willing to pay the price? And lastly, are you going to follow the 'Wealth Bucket System' to the 'T'?"

"Come on Mr. Rodriguez, you know the answer is a big yes! Not only will I follow all of your strategies for building wealth, but I will also share it with the world with your permission. I just know that deep down in my heart there are a lot of people who can benefit from your success and wealth building formulas. So what do you think? Can I share these strategies with other people?"

"If it's going to better the greater good, I am all for it," Mr. Rodriguez replied.

"Now, let's go home, I have a lot of work to do," I smiled.

On the way home, all I could think about was the conversation we had in City Island. My whole view of money had shifted 180 degrees. I was so present to the fact that 'your net worth will always be directly related to the people you network with[35].' I felt so grateful and alive. I was truly blessed to have Mr. Rodriguez in my life.

Chapter Ten

THE POWER OF CHOICE

"You can't live a rich life making poor choices."
— Brad Lea — CEO of LightSpeed VT

"Poor choices, difficult life. Powerful choices, great life."
— Edward R. Muñoz

B usiness-wise, I was on an emotional high, but when it came to Jennifer, things were not looking too good. Her young life was slipping away as each day passed without a donor match. This was no soap opera; it was real life happening right before our eyes. But everything changed the day we received the call that there was a match. We had waited for this call for so many months. Finally, there was a glimmer of hope. One match out of 40,000 people was a dream come true. The donor passed the entire battery of tests and everything was a go.

However, at some point during the overly long approval process, the donor got cold feet and mysteriously decided to back out. Our family was devastated. There were no solid answers as to why she changed her mind. But since the donor's information was confidential, we had to just accept the fact that we were back to the drawing board.

The chances of finding another donor seemed dismal. Jennifer grew increasingly impatient, and so did mom. Every day that passed offered less hope. The once cheerful, vibrant young lady was now growing sadder by the day. My sister got to the point where she stopped smiling and didn't want to go out anymore. She ate less and didn't even want to come out of her room. We were getting desperate. Boy, did we need a miracle—and fast.

Cancer patients rarely find donors on more than one occasion—you'd have a better chance at winning the lottery. However, luck was on her side, and within two months the hospital found another donor. This time, the donor did not back out and the operation was scheduled for September 10th, 1997. We couldn't help but feel nervous and excited at the same time. Would it work? Would it backfire again? There were so many questions and fears in our heads. Well, there was only one way to find out.

As the week of the operation approached, a nurse from the hospital called us. She wanted to give further details about the donor's surgery. It looked like Jennifer was really going to get her transplant after all. The moment of truth was finally here. Mom just stood by, looking at me with her big brown eyes, waiting to see what she said.

"So, what did they say, Richie?" Mom asked impatiently.

I held up a finger to quiet her. "Shush, Mom, I'm still talking!"

After I hung up the phone, I told her that the donor's operation was a success. Finally, God answered our prayers. Jennifer's operation was scheduled to take place on Wednesday. On Tuesday evening, we all got together with our fellow church members and prayed for her operation to be a success. Right before the operation was about to take place, Mom looked Jennifer right in the eye and told her, "Sweetie, I just want you to know that I will be right here waiting for you. Please promise me, young lady, that you will return."

"Of course, Mom, God would not have it any other way," Jennifer replied with confidence.

I remembered then that one of the nurses asked me to hand Jennifer a note before she went into surgery. After giving Jennifer the letter, she decided to read it out loud for all of us to hear.

Dear Jennifer,

It's me, Jamela. I am your donor. I am still recovering from this operation, but I just wanted you to read this and know that when I was called upon to be your donor, I did not think twice about it. I read your profile and it moved me to tears. I lost my daughter to cancer nearly five years ago and though I was not a match for her, I promised myself that I would someday save someone's life. I prayed to God constantly so that he could find me a match. As of today, you are, as your middle name says, "My Little Angel". Today, I contribute a piece of me in memory of my sweet daughter Angelica, who I will always remember and cherish. I love you so much, and I don't even know you. May God bless you with a successful operation and I can't wait to meet you one day soon.

Love, Jamela King

We all cried as she read the letter. We were so moved by the kindness of a stranger. Life can be so sweet when we live for others and so bitter when we only live for ourselves.

Just as the orderlies began to wheel Jennifer to surgery, she slowly released my hands and said, "See you soon, Richie."

My eyes quickly filled with tears. Trying to keep my voice level and calm for Jennifer's sake, I murmured, "Yeah, see you soon, Myla."

We were instructed to wait for her in the waiting area. I tried to rest, but my sleep was constantly interrupted by nightmares. I woke up in a cold sweat. Since sleep wasn't working out, I walked around and tried to start conversations with the security guards, but that just made things worse. They told me horror stories of patients who came in with similar cases and died within weeks of their operations. Time became my worst enemy.

Four hours later, the doctors notified us that the operation was a success. Talk about a relief. Only time would tell if the good news would last. She stayed in the hospital for an additional six weeks, as the doctor wanted to keep her under close observation since the first 100 days would determine the long-term outcome of the transplant. After that time passed, she was allowed to go home, but had to visit the doctor regularly. He noted that if the disease remained in remission for one year, the chances of it returning would be very slim. At first, we treated her delicately, but in no time flat, Jennifer Myla Rodriguez was back to normal. Her life-threatening disease was fading into history.

*****

Meanwhile, I realized that I needed to get back to my investments and money-management strategies. I guess I had neglected things for a while so I could dedicate my time to helping my sister, but by a combination of a little luck and solid planning, bucket #3 (Frozen Money Bucket) was starting to grow by the day.

The money was flowing like water, mostly because I knew

what I wanted and was willing to pay the price to get it. I also had a proven system I was following step by step. My goal was to build up my residual income to over $500,000 per year. I told myself I would not stop until I achieved my goal. During the next few years, I continued to watch my buckets increase. Seeing all this progress was incredibly exciting, and I must say that there were many times when I was tempted to go and spend a chunk of my money on a fancy car or an exotic vacation. The need to go straight to Bucket #7 (The Fun Bucket) was extremely tempting.

Whenever I felt the need to have a little fun, I would hear Mr. Rodriguez's voice saying, "Richie, if you get too cocky with your money, you will end up becoming one of the 'All Flash, No Cash, Really Cool looking Guys'." The very thought of this happening made me sick to my stomach. Instead, I found ways to have fun without being lavish. Besides, fun is all in how I interpreted it. I could literally choose to go camping with my friends and have an awesome weekend or go and spend a lot of cash at a tropical resort and come back with thousands less in my pocket. As strong as the temptation was, I decided to stick to my original plan.

I noticed at a young age that most people like to spend lots of money just to stand out and look good among their peers. Cars, clothes, jewelry, and vacations are all a way of looking good so that they could feel like they were accepted in their social groups. People started to wonder why I was driving an older car and wearing average-looking clothes since I was doing so well financially. I started to realize that those who made those comments were of the "Spender Mentality" type. But the few people who agreed with me clearly were "Investor Mentality Champions". After a while, I decided to only spend my time with the "Investor Mentality Champions" as opposed to the complaining, don't want to be nothing, settle for less, talk all the time, gossiping spenders. They were lost in the world of looking good, while I was in the world of looking to build wealth.

*****

"At the young age of 26, I bought my first investment property. I was finally on a roll. Life was sweet and all my hard work was beginning to pay off. It was a small duplex in Brooklyn. When I went to withdraw some money to put a down payment from bucket

#3 (Frozen Money Bucket), I realized I had more than I thought. I called the other realtor and told him that instead of closing in 60 days, I was going to close in 20 days and make an offer that was not contingent on a mortgage. In other words, Darnell, I was changing it to a cash offer."

"Richie, did he really believe you?" Darnell asked.

"The truth was that the realtor was skeptical. He could not believe I was buying a $175,000 property with my own cash. To calm his nerves and gain his confidence, I decided to put $25,000 down on the contract to secure the transaction. To sweeten the pot even more, I said that the money was non-refundable should I not close within the time I had specified. He was so impressed with my business attitude that, every time he had a good deal, I was one of the first people he'd call up. He was definitely good for a few flips a year."

"Richie, what kept you going?"

"I'll admit, Darnell, the bucket system was a bit challenging in the beginning because I had to overcome my own fears and doubts and give it some time to really work for me. But after it started running, my confidence began to soar. Somewhere along the process, I realized that I could literally have a net worth of one million dollars by the ripe age of thirty years old. The more I thought about it, the more it seemed attainable."

"Net worth—what do you mean by that, Richie?"

"Your net worth is calculated by subtracting your total liabilities from total assets. For example, if all of my properties are worth $1,980,000 in the open market and I only owe the bank $980,000 in mortgages, the remaining balance amounts to $1,000,000. And that million dollars, Darnell, is my net worth."

"That sounds like a lot of money for a kid who came from the projects," Darnell said, gesturing to some tall projects as we were driving down the Bruckner Expressway in the Bronx.

"Yes, it is, but as I said before, your net worth will always be proportional to your network of friends. I guess I was lucky to meet Mr. Rodriguez, but I also made it a point to listen to him and follow his advice by being coachable and taking massive action. Does any of this hit home for you, Darnell?"

"It sure does, Richie. I really do look forward to making some changes, and I definitely see the importance of choosing my peers wisely. I also hope that you can be there for me just like Mr. Rodriguez was there for you."

"Come on, bro, you know I got your back." At that, we both started laughing.

"Richie, do you mind pulling over in McDonald's to get a quick bite to eat? I'm starving!"

"Sure thing, let's get a quick bite, but it has to be quick so we can get home before it gets dark."

We ordered, brought our food to a table and sat down to eat. Then Darnell asked, "So, whatever happened to Diego?"

"Well, we only saw each other whenever he came to visit Jennifer. He would bring her jewelry, clothes, and flowers during her recovery period. Diego became the neighborhood drug lord. He often referred to himself as 'Tony Montana' from the classic movie 'Scarface'."

"Why did he call himself that?"

"He said he liked Tony's attitude and the way he ran his empire. But to be honest, I personally thought he was even worse off than Tony."

"Why would you say that, Richie?"

I lowered my voice and leaned closer to Darnell, "I once heard that one of his workers took off with some of his merchandise, so Diego tracked the guy down, took him to an abandoned building over on Mother Gaston Blvd. and Pacific Ave., tied his hands together, and hung him from a pipe. Word has it that he taped his mouth, stripped him naked, and then covered his entire body with peanut butter."

"Why would he do that?" Darnell asked as he gobbled down his Big Mac.

"He did it because..." I sighed and shook my head, "Please don't talk with food in your mouth—it really annoys me."

"Sorry. Okay. Just keep talking," Darnell said, as he took a sip of his Pepsi.

"They did it because rats love peanut butter. With a good imagination; you can probably guess the rest of the story."

Darnell's mouth gaped open. "That's brutal! Did they ever find the poor guy?"

"They sure did, a few weeks later after they noticed he was missing. Some boys who were playing hide and seek in that building noticed something stunk really bad, and when they peeked inside the room they could not believe what they saw. The atrocious odor blinded their sight a bit, but under the foggy odor, they saw white and slimy maggots slivering over what appeared to be a person. He was unrecognizable. Dental records would later reveal it was him."

"C'mon, dude. Quit it already! You are totally grossing me out with all these nasty details."

"Consider that payback for talking with your mouth open, my friend." At which we both chuckled.

As we finished laughing, we got back in my car and sped off. It was getting late and I wanted to drop Darnell off before the sun set.

*****

As we drove through the remaining streets, I continued my story. "At the age of 33, I hit my net worth goal of $1,000,000. I will be the first to admit that I did not hit my goal at 30 as originally intended, but I'm glad I set a goal and strategy to accomplish it, for it stretched me to find ways to make things happen.

"Ironically, the same year I hit my goal, Diego was sentenced twenty years to life. It's crazy how two brothers took different paths, made different decisions, and ended up at different destinations.

"Life is definitely full of choices. Yep, yep. So, what happened? How'd he get caught?" Darnell mumbled, chewing on some fries at the same time, obviously not having learned his lesson the first time.

"During these times, Diego was rolling in some seriously dirty cash. Word has it that he had at least twenty people working under him. Every once in awhile, one of his street soldiers would get caught and go in for a few years. When they would go in, they were quickly replaced. They all knew the golden street rule: 'never rat on the boss, because if they did, they would put their families in danger.' Diego had built a system he thought was unbreakable.

"Before any informants, cops or detectives could get to him, they first had to go through his street soldiers—the guys who sold on the corners or in well hidden basements—and then the next layer were the guys who delivered to those guys. These were his captains. They were real tough, and could easily get rid of a soldier at will. Last in the chain of command was him, 'King Tut' Diego! He was real smart. He never carried drugs and he certainly never delivered them.

"Unfortunately, every thug—I mean, dog—has its day. Eventually the King was overthrown."

"So, how did he get caught?" Darnell repeated impatiently, this time with no food in his mouth.

"If it wasn't for his greediness, he would still be around today, doing his thing. You see, Darnell, he wanted to expand his territory, but he ended up getting heat from the East New York drug lords. It all started when one of his street soldiers, who also happened to be a local gang member, got into a fight when he was selling at a corner that he wanted to claim. That argument led to a gunfight and it took his life. Next thing you know, there were gang fights almost every week. Diego's advantage was that he had a lot of money and a lot of guns. But the other guys had something he did not: They had connections with the local NYPD. They paid to have the NYPD shut Diego down, and the NYPD wanted him out because he represented a huge threat."

One afternoon, Diego received a call from one of his guys that one of their customers was complaining about the merchandise. He said it tasted weird and asked for his money back. Diego immediately jumped in his black-on-black Land Rover beast and drove there. Little did he know it was a setup. Yep, the cops bribed one of his guys. If he did not follow their plan to the 'T', he would go to jail for a very long time.

When Diego arrived, he immediately started arguing; all along, he was being recorded. Somehow, he thought one of his own guys added baking soda to the cocaine so it would double in size and they could make more money. This thought really pissed him off, since he prided himself on selling the best quality product for the best price the market could bear.

Then, out of nowhere, the cops rolled in and there was an exchange of fire. It sounded like a Fourth of July fireworks show. As you can see, history repeated itself. Diego shot one of the cops as he ran into the boiler room to seek cover. The cops tried to penetrate through the steel doors and fired several magazines of bullets with no luck. It wasn't until they tossed some tear-gas under the door that he began coughing and screamed at the top of his lungs, "Stop, stop, stop you fuckin' bastards—I give up yo!"

The cops advised him to throw his gun out and walk out backwards with both hands on his head. He threw the gun to the ground and limped out, covered in blood. The One-Time Brownsville Drug King was no more. Just like our dad, Diego was down for the count.

*****

"Coincidentally, the same day Diego went down was the day I was about to closing on my first 12-unit building. It was a corner property with two commercial units. One of them was a grocery store and the other was a laundromat. This was by far my biggest purchase since I started investing in real estate, and was an even bigger deal because I got the property at a really good price. At the time, the owner of both stores only had two years left on his lease, and said he would consider selling his businesses if I renewed the lease for ten more years. This provided me with an opportunity to buy the building at a cheaper price. Also, I had the opportunity of raising the rent when I renewed the lease or if I could buy the business owner out and run the two businesses myself. Either way, the deal was a slam dunk.

"It's so ironic how you and Diego came from the same neighborhood, same projects, same dysfunctional family, similar friends, same circumstances but somehow both ended up in different places. Why exactly is that, Richie?" Darnell asked.

THE CHOICE...

"Darnell, it all starts with choice. We, and only we, are responsible for our own choices. Each day, life presents us with an opportunity to choose:

- You can choose between good or bad
- You can choose to do the right thing or the wrong thing
- You can choose to complain or contribute
- You can choose to take action or be at the mercy of your problems
- You can choose to be proactive or reactive
- You can choose to accept people as they are or try to change them

- You can choose to read, learn, and grow or sit back and watch life pass you by
- You can choose to go after your dreams or watch others achieve their dreams
- You can choose to chase success or learn how to attract success
- You can choose to be a failure or learn from your failures

"As you can see Darnell, today's choices will create the future you will have tomorrow. At the end of the day, you are the only one who can make the choice to move forward in your life. Whenever you make a choice to move forward, your world will change. These choices—whether big or small—could have a profound impact on your future."

"It helps to know that I am in control of my future. But what happens if I make the wrong choice?" Darnell cut in.

"Unfortunately, one bad choice could set you back a few months or a few years. But a series of bad choices could make you lose sight of your future. That future may not turn out so well if you make a series of bad choices today. You need to fight for your future and it begins with one good choice at a time. This is why it is important to take the time to choose wisely. It's that simple."

"That sounds easy, but what do you do when you are faced with a really tough choice?"

"Darnell, life will consistently present you with challenging circumstances and new problems on a daily basis. But it will be up to you how you choose to react to those circumstances. Let me share with you what Mr. Rodriguez once showed me about choosing powerfully—no matter what the circumstances. I've got a notebook in the glovebox. Go ahead and pull it out. One of the pages in the back has a diagram. I sketched it out a couple days ago."

Darnel flipped to the back and found the diagram.

THE CHOICE MAKING SUCCESS MODEL

"Darnell, every choice you've ever made came from one of these ten drivers. You will notice that the drivers on the left side take you on a downward spiral and leave you feeling powerless when confronted with an important choice. However, the drivers on the right side help you create massive momentum in everything you do and put you in a powerful mindset when making a powerful choice."

"As a matter of fact, every choice I made also came from these ten drivers. The only difference is that back then, I did not realize this, and now I do."

"Richie, before you continue with this topic, can you please tell me what you mean by 'driver'?"

"Oh yeah, I almost forget to explain what a driver is. Drivers are thought pattern generators--you could also call them motivators. They influence and trigger certain behaviors and, ultimately, the choices we make."

I took a moment to look at Darnell's face, which looked puzzled. "Is any of this making sense, Darnell?"

"It's starting to make a little sense. I'm sure I'll understand it a bit more once you explain the ten drivers in your choice making formula." Darnell said, but the confused expression on his face hadn't changed.

"It's called 'The choice making success model', not the choice making formula," I said in a serious, but slightly sarcastic tone.

"Darnell, I really want you to understand the importance of how a driver impacts the choices we make in life, so let me explain it in a simpler way. Let's assume you get behind a steering wheel of a car. Once you press on the accelerator and put your hands on the steering wheel, you become the driver of that vehicle. Well, the same happens to us on the inside, metaphorically speaking. Something is driving you internally to behave in a certain way whenever you have a problem, challenge, or need to make a difficult choice."

"So if you want to make better choices, all you have to do is change the driver behind the wheel. For example, if you have a bad driver behind the wheel that is 'you', you will keep crashing and get nowhere. But if you have a good driver behind the wheel that is 'you', you will get very far. In a few minutes, you will see exactly how these 10 drivers are..."

Darnell jumped in before I could continue elaborating and said, "It's definitely making more sense now. There's no need to explain it further. I get it now. The way I see it, most people my age concentrate on what they want to drive instead of learning what drives them. Once we learn what drives us, we will have the power to make better choices. And these are the choices that will change our lives for the better."

As Darnell uttered these words, I felt my chest expanding. It was hard to contain my excitement. He was finally reading my message loud and clear. All that came out of my mouth was, "Glad to see you are finally getting it."

"Go ahead now and let it rip. I am anxious to learn what drives people to do what they do," Darnell replied enthusiastically.

Level 1: Fear Driven

Fear is a natural phenomenon that has been around since the evolution of mankind. It is an instinct that is there to protect you. Let me share a quick story to prove my point. Imagine for a moment that you are out hunting and suddenly you see a bear 50 yards away from you. Suddenly, this bear starts running toward you. The first thing that will happen is your body will activate a fear mechanism in you. It is activated to protect you and help you survive the problem at hand. This activation is what psychologists call an "action urge". It is an urge to take immediate action. Said another way, you are now being driven by your fears.

As you can tell from this example, fear was activated to protect you from an imminent threat. This is known as an "authentic fear" because it relates to something that is happening in real time. However, there are also "inauthentic fears" that we conjure up in our minds about things we think will happen but never actually do. An example of an inauthentic fear is worrying about bombing a presentation you have to give in front of 100 people or failing in a business venture that you haven't even started. Now, here's the kicker: your body does not know how to distinguish an authentic fear from an inauthentic fear. All your body wants to do is protect you, so when it feels threatened in any way, it is activated and starts to drive you.

When you let your fears drive your actions and choices, you miss out on so many opportunities and end up making a bunch of mistakes in the process. Just think about it for a moment. How can you make good choices if fear is your driving force? When fear controls you, it pins you to the ground and paralyzes you. At least that is what it feels like in the moment. It clouds your judgement and puts you in a position to make horrible choices. This is why we should never make new choices or decisions when we are driven by fear.

Level 2: Past Driven

In the Disney movie *The Lion King*, there's a line where Rafiki says, "It doesn't matter, it's in the past." As the movie progresses, we find out that what happened in the past indeed matters, as it affects both our present and our future. In fact, we all live with the ghosts of our past.

Have you ever recollected your mom's voice telling you to "finish everything on your plate or you can't have dessert?" Even though she may be thousands of miles away or may have passed away, her voice still sounds the same in your head as it did when you were six years old and didn't want to finish your broccoli.

Everything that happened in your past can have a bearing on

your current lifestyle and thought processes. This can be both good and bad. If you had encouraging parents and teachers, their positive belief in you can still be a source of encouragement for you today. But the negative things you were told or that you experienced in the past can also influence you and keep you from realizing your full potential in the present[36].

This happens because the decisions you made in the past may continue to affect you in the present. Each decision you've made, from the people who helped you along in your youth and the projects you started to the simple choices you made about what to eat or where to live, has played a part in getting you to your present moment right now.

If you haven't already noticed, the impact the past has on you is actually bigger than you think. The worst part is that the past holds you prisoner because we keep living there every time we bring up negative events from the past. This is why it is very important to not make decisions in the present if you're in a place in your life where all you do is talk and live from the past. It's simply not the right place to make decisions from.

On another note, constantly thinking about the past is a form of victim-based thinking. As you continue to focus on things that happened a long time ago, you are giving more of power away, thus leaving you virtually powerless in the present.

Level 3 - Reaction Driven

It is impossible to make good decisions when you are constantly reacting to all your circumstances. People who often find themselves in reaction mode become the drama queens and reaction kings of society. On a more serious note, did you know that when you react to a negative situation, your brain actually shuts down? It also creates an enormous amount of anger on both sides.

When you are reacting to a problem or situation, you fail to see the negative consequences that may come about as a result of your negative attitude. Reacting in this manner also creates distance between you and the other person you are arguing with. The worst part is, the more you keep reacting in a negative fashion to that person, the more you will lose credibility in their eyes.

People who are constantly reacting are in victim mode,

whether they realize it or not. You see, when you react poorly to a person's comment or throw a fit every time someone gives you bad news or says something you disagree with, in that moment you are essentially giving your power to the person or event that caused that negative reaction in you. This may be why you are left feeling powerless. Now you tell me: how can you possibly choose powerfully when in this negative emotional state?

Level 4: Desperation Driven

When the brain is flooded with desperation, we are driven to take certain actions that lead to bad choices. Often when in this state we seek solutions to a problem in a fast or desparate manner. When in desperation, we are driven by an urge to win at all costs, often creating huge negative consequences should we fail.

Being desperate is a tough state to be in. It is such a limited way to live because desperation only fosters more desperation. Nothing good evers comes from desperation. There are a bunch of people in prison who made choices out of desperation. There are many broken marriages because partners made choices out of desperation. There are millions of people with high debt because they made financial choices out of desperation.

The list goes on and on. When you're in that state of mind, your judgment is clouded and your personality is thrown off. It's hard to think clearly when you are being driven by desperation. Without even realizing it, you may start to come across as aloof, standoffish, or extremely anxious, and that can be disconcerting to some people.

Another reason why people make desperate moves is because they think they have no choices. And by choices I mean options. They have no other options. So they take the path of least resistance. If they only took the time to brainstorm possibilities and create more options, they could put themselves in a position to choose.

Your ability to choose implies that there is more than one path you can take. This creates ease. When ease is present, desperation begins to dissipate and disappears. It doesn't matter if you are broke, have very little resources or time to move ahead, there are always options. If you are committed, you will always find other options. But you will never discover other options if you are being driven by desperation. This is why you should avoid at all costs making any type of decision or choice when in a state of desperation.

Level 5: Instant Gratification Driven

When faced with a decision, some people may decide to take the path of least resistance. It's the driving force behind their outlook and perspective. They have no patience when going after a goal or intended outcome. Simply put, they demand instant gratification. It all started at the beginning of mankind.

In the caveman days, you had to hunt for your food if you wanted to eat. Your first challenge was finding anything you could to turn into a weapon. This task alone could take weeks, and sometimes months. Then you had to figure out how you were going to catch these wild animals. It took creativity and patience; otherwise you would never bring food back to your family. While you were away hunting, your wife had to look after the youngins, gather wood, and search for fruit to feed the family. She also had to wash all the clothes by the river while being careful not to become the prey of a nearby wild animal. Those sure were the good old days.

Over time, human beings discovered easier and faster ways to perform these ordinary tasks. As daily activities became easier, people grew lazier and more comfortable in this setting. Now you tell me, who lights fires these days? Even when you're camping, people bring all their gadgets to make a quick, hassle-free meal. It's genius. People rarely use wood to heat their houses anymore-- it takes too long to heat up a house and requires too much patience. They want comfort now, not thirty minutes from now.

Another example is the Internet. In the past, if you wanted to do research for school you had to either own an encyclopedia set or head to your local library. Today, all you have to do is google any words and in 1.1 seconds—bang!—you have at your fingertips nearly everything you need in order to complete your school paper. Oh, and let's not forget the days when we had to mail a letter just to communicate with someone.

I remember when my dad would watch a boring program just so he wouldn't have to stand up to change the channel. Once he sank into his favorite recliner, not even a crane could lift him.

Then the dream invention came out: the remote control. This new device allowed us to fly through channels at the speed of light. Thanks to the remote control, we could flip through channels faster than Muhammad Ali could strike a jab.

All of these facts prove the point that we are so used to wanting immediate results because we are driven to want things right now. The urge to accomplish things right away may put us in harm's way for making the wrong choices every time we allow this driver to control us.

*****

"Darnell, as you can see, the last five drivers I just shared are not good places to be in, particularly when making bold moves and powerful choices in our lives."

Darnell nodded. "I know what you mean. Especially with level three in being reaction driven. I have to admit, I can see how I've been doing that in my own life. But not anymore! This conversation has really helped me see how I can change my thinking when it comes to making choices."

"That's great, Darnell! Now, these first five drivers are often our automatic ways of thinking. I call this set the 'survival drivers'. I decided to call them that because these drivers limit you in every way possible. When driven by these drivers, you will just coast in life instead of producing greatness. They are meant to have you survive at whatever you are dealing with. They don't push, motivate, or empower you to go beyond what you are capable of. What these five drivers have in common is that they all operate at an unconscious level--in the background on automatic unless interrupted.

"If you want to make much better choices in your life, you need to intentionally access the following five drivers that will empower you to create a much more fulfilling life."

Darnell held up a hand to stop me. "Richie, before you share these drivers with me, can you tell me how I'm supposed to activate them? I mean, if they are as powerful as you say, I would like to know what is the process to—"

I interrupted Darnell in my rush to properly explain, "You activate them by committing to them. When you make a commitment to these drivers, and I mean a real commitment, your mental focus shifts. With this new focus, you start to think differently. If you commit to thinking about them on a consistent basis, eventually these drivers will start to use you. They will take over your thoughts and drive your behavior and the choices you make. The more you do this, the faster they will become your automatic drivers to be used by you."

"Okay, got it," Darnell said enthusiastically. "So what do you call these other drivers?"

"I call them the 'fulfillment drivers' because when you focus on these drivers, they fulfill you at your deepest levels."

"So, I've heard the word 'fulfillment' before, but what does it really mean?" Darnell asked.

"Darnell, to me fulfillment represents your highest desires achieved. Fulfillment is the thing that you want most, and the pursuit and accomplishment of it fills your entire body and mind with elation. You feel full of life, happiness, and joy all at the same time.

"Basically, you fulfill yourself in ways that it just can't get any better. At least, that is what you are experiencing. When focusing on these drivers, they will provide an experience quite the opposite of the survival drivers.

"Here's a short list of people who were fulfilled because they activated these drivers:"

- Martin Luther King
- Mother Teresa
- Michelangelo
- Selena Quintanilla
- Albert Einstein
- Jim Carrey
- Carlos Slim
- Richard Branson
- Cristina Saralegui
- Stephen King
- Oprah Winfield
- Celia Cruz
- Kris Carr
- Rosa Parks
- Vincent van Gogh
- Simon Cowell

"Darnell, now that I have shared with you this list of champions who all activated their fulfillment drivers, I want to remind you that a driver is often triggered internally when it's time to make a choice. In some cases, the survival drivers are triggered, but we must learn to activate the fulfillment drivers to put ourselves in the best position to win, make better choices, and be fulfilled in the process. With that said, let me share the five fulfillment drivers."

THE CHOICE MAKING SUCCESS MODEL

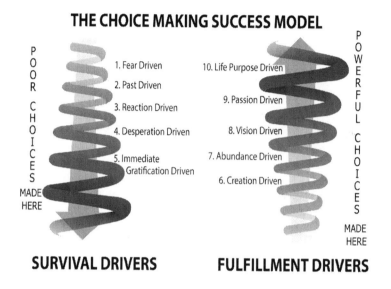

SURVIVAL DRIVERS

FULFILLMENT DRIVERS

Level 6: Creation Driven

Abraham Lincoln once said, "The best way to predict your future is to create it." President Lincoln clearly knew that the importance of allowing oneself to be driven by creativity. Creation driven means that it's up to you to be proactive in creating the life of your dreams. You do this by intentionally creating what you envision your life to look like, regardless of your current situation. You know you are creation driven when you are:

- continually reinventing yourself
- brainstorming possible alternatives to your current challenges

- seeking new perspectives from those you admire
- taking ownership of your mistakes
- focusing on solutions instead of your problems
- constantly asking yourself "Who do I need to become to turn this situation around?"
- constantly in "curiosity mode"
- asking better questions
- being open to new things
- allowing yourself to be a kid again when entering into a creative state
- going to sleep with your best ideas in mind

As you can see from this list, there is no secret to unlocking your creative genius. It all starts with the desire to proactively create. By putting yourself in creative situations, your inner champion creates a world full of amazing choices.

Level 7: Abundance Driven

This type of thinking implies there is way more available to you than what is before your very eyes. But in order for you to see beyond what's right in front of you, you must first step into this type of mindset. Once this mindset becomes your new way of looking at life, then and only then will it start to drive you. Once driven by abundance, you start to notice that there is more than enough out there for everyone.

An abundance mindset believes that there is enough fruit out there for all. It tells you that there are so many chances and opportunities to be explored in the world. The abundance mindset believes that you are just one step away from meeting the person of your dreams. It believes that where there is a will, there's a way. The abundance mindset frees you from your fears and allows you the opportunity to go for it because you know your heart's desires are within your grasp—no matter how big they are. Suddenly, the impossible becomes possible. This is why it is imperative to allow abundance to drive you into greatness.

People with an abundance mindset believe the following:

- "If I need money, I'll find the money." They don't go the easy route or look for shortcuts.
- "If I need people, I'll find the people." They don't lock themselves in front of the TV for long hours when looking for people to join their business opportunity.
- "If I need ideas, the ideas will come." They don't sit back and complain about their current circumstances.
- "If I want to meet the person of my dreams, the person of my dreams will appear." They don't sit back and cry about it, they just be about it.
- "If I need a great opportunity, the great opportunity will come." They don't sit back with their arms crossed, they create a future so inspiring that it literally pulls them into action.
- "If I need _____, _____ will come." You fill in the rest; remember, you are the author and creator of your life. Now that's having an abundance mindset!

An abundance mindset also allows you to see life in a more long-term perspective. Thinking with an abundance mindset allows people to experience high levels of happiness and productivity, because they let go of all of that unnecessary fear, anxiety, and desperation that comes with chasing instant gratification.

The abundance mindset provides certainty that what you so dearly want is just around the corner. It's not like you're just going to sit back and wait for things to happen. Instead, this mindset drives you to take action coming from certainty and not fear, and from faith and not doubt.

Level 8: Vision Driven

One of the best ways to ensure you choose powerfully is by making choices that affect positively your vision of the future. Said another way, the best choices are made when you decide to put your focus out in the future on something you want to accomplish instead of in the past.

When you choose to focus on the vision you want to realize, it will affect the present in a purely positive way. When you put your attention on the vision you created, you instinctively think about where you want to go and what you want to accomplish along the way. It will drive you to come up with creative ways to realize that vision you set for yourself out in the future. For example, when you focus on growing your sales team, purchase a commercial space to expand your business, or begin planning a new project, you are inspired to think differently and make better choices in the present.

Let's say you are presented with a promising business opportunity. Don't make the mistake of letting your decisions come from your past failures. That would be a perfect example of "living in the past". To have the greatest chance of success in your endeavors, your choices should be aligned with your present and future goals, with the vision you created for yourself and not from your past mistakes and failures. If you did that, then you would be "living in your vision". Doing so will bring you that much closer to accomplishing your goals.

The moment you stop thinking about the past, and put all of your attention and focus on the vision of the future you have created in your mind, you will notice your future will start to look a lot brighter. When it seems like that goal you want to achieve is far away and out of your reach, it's probably because you started focusing on your past again.

This is why it is important to constantly think on a daily basis about your vision. When you constantly think about this vision it will consume your thoughts and drive you into taking new actions. It will drive you to be unreasonable and do the unthinkable. It will unleash your highest and best performance.

Level 9: Passion Driven

Passion is something you do with all of your heart. It could be defined as an activity, an idea, an ideal, or even an occupation that you pursue without regard to time or difficulty. It's simply following the path your heart's desires. Following the path of your heart's desires is the path of the highest self. In this moment, your wish for yourself and God's wish for you are in total alignment.

Did you know that making decisions out of passion could lead you to fulfill your destiny? A destiny that is full of endless happiness, fulfillment, and one that leaves behind a legacy for others to follow. When you follow your passion, everyone benefits from your decisions and actions. Your passion has the potential to create inspiration in others--not to mention all the love and contributions that you deliver abundantly throughout the world because you made the decision to follow your dream. The world would be a better place if more people pursued their passion. As a matter of fact, the world would be a better place if everybody was driven by their passion.

The reality is that many people simply don't feel energized and connected to their lives. If you've ever felt this way or know of others around you who might, here are a few indicators that they may not be following their passion:

- If they feel down at work, they're not following their passion.
- If they hope for a better job or a better life, then they're not following their passion.
- If they're always complaining about their boring job or life, they're not following their passion.

Passion is what breathes oxygen into your soul. Knowing what you're passionate about allows you to live with purpose. It allows you to make a difference in your life and the lives of others. You can discover your passion by asking yourself the following:

- What would you like to do if money was not an issue?
- What are you constantly dreaming about that sparks excitement every time you think about it?
- What makes you come alive?
- Who would you like to help?
- What message would you share with the world?
- What mark can you leave on humanity?

The answer to these questions will tell you what you are passionate about. Discovering and pursuing your passion will open a completely new world for you, filled with freedom, abundance and excitement. All you need to do is give your inner champion the go-ahead to move toward it. You know you have passion when your soul is smiling, you have peace of mind, and you wake up each morning fired up! Passion keeps you up late at night working on some projects while others easily get bored, restless, tired, and sleep all night. Your drive will provide a surge of confidence that others will envy. It will cause a shift in you so drastic that you will become unrecognizable to others. Things that historically have never moved will start moving because you started moving.

When you choose to follow your passion, you achieve more. You're more efficient, effective, productive, happier, and more likely to reach peak performance levels in all your endeavors. Your decision brings out the best in you. Simply put, it unleashes the champion within. So if you want to live a life of happiness, fulfillment, and mastery, I invite you to act from your passion rather than your fears. Let passion be your driving force behind all your decisions and choices going forward.

Level 10: Life Purpose Driven

I will start this section by quoting Jack Canfield in his book, *The Success Principles*: "I believe each of us is born with a life purpose. Identifying, acknowledging, and honoring this purpose are perhaps the most important actions successful people take. They take the time to understand what they're here to do--and then they pursue that with a passion and enthusiasm."[37]

They say the two most important days in a person's life is the day you are born and the day you discover your life's purpose. Having said that, let me start out by asking you: Are you just living your life going through your day to day activities, or do you have something driving you that is deeper? Or maybe there's something you want to accomplish in your life--a sort of impact that will fulfill you to your core. And being driven by that. Discovering your life purpose is important to know because it grounds you in what you are doing. Without it, you are like a sailboat lost at sea without a compass or modern GPS to guide you. Your life purpose connects what you enjoy doing to your innermost and deepest values.

If it creates fulfillment at your deepest level, why don't people take the time to discover their life purpose? The thing is that most people do not know how to discover their life purpose. Others think it takes too much work to find it or discover it. The truth is that once you choose to discover your life purpose, it will take time, but it will be worth it.[38]

Finding your life's purpose is the single greatest thing you'll ever experience about yourself. It's meeting and working with the "you" that you were born to be. This is why it is worth doing the introspection to discover it. Before you connect to your life purpose, you'll question most of the things in your life. Everything you do will be up for debate within yourself, from making agreements and managing your time to your choice of a spouse or from what type of job to take. All of that lack of clarity is constantly swirling around your head, causing you to choose from scratch over and over again. That doesn't happen when you discover your life's purpose. Suddenly, you eliminate most of the questions in your head because they get replaced with only one: Is this going to help me fulfill my life purpose?

To discover your life purpose, you will have to do some real soul searching to learn what is really important to you. It will require all of, or at least a combination of, the following:

- Meditating on things you've enjoyed doing in the past.
- Praying to your god or asking the universe for guidance in discovering what you were brought to this earth to fulfill.
- Constantly asking yourself a series of questions to inquire what it is that is at the root of who you are and what really matters to you.

This process of continuous exploration is a transformative process. "People who achieve greatness have followed their life purpose with vigilance and tenacity. They operate at a high level of performance because they are driven at their core by their life purpose. They are driven by heart. They live on the edge and play full out."[39]

*****

After I finished talking, I looked over to Darnell and noticed how attentive he was to what I was sharing. I decided to ask him if he had any questions on what I just shared because I wanted to see if he had processed and understood the last driver—*the life purpose driver*. "Hey champ, do you have any questions on what I just shared so far?"

"Richie, what you just shared is mind blowing. You rocked my world with these last five drivers. But can you tell me the difference between passion and life purpose? I only ask because they kinda sound like the same thing," Darnell asked with a look of curiosity.

"I'm glad you asked because they may sound similar, but trust me they are not at all. The best way I can explain it is this way: People get passionate about what they like to do but they don't necessarily realize why they do it. They'll get trapped up in their skill set to cook, box, or sing, but they don't realize those abilities--or let's call it their passions--are just a skill set at the end of the day. It's obviously a skill set they fell in love with and are passionate about, but unfortunately what they are passionate about is not fulfilling them on anything."

"Why is that?" Darnell asked.

"Look at it this way. Your passion certainly makes you happy and fills a void, but what I want you to understand is that your skill set is your delivery tool and your vehicle for fulfilling your purpose. Unless you understand that, you will think your passion and life purpose are one in the same."

"Richie, please repeat that one more time and say it slowly this time so I can let it sink in to my thick head," Darnell tapped on this head.

"Okay, got it. Here goes. Your skill set is your delivery tool and your vehicle for fulfilling on your purpose. Is that computing in your thick skull?" I said with a little grin.

"Yes, it's starting to. Go ahead and continue," Darnell grinned back at me.

"For example, if you are passionate about DJing, then all you are doing is DJing. It will make you happy and the world will certainly benefit from your art of music, but there is a higher level for you to experience--a level of happiness and fulfillment very few people on this planet get to experience.

"Continuing with my DJing example, let's say you discover your life purpose, and you've determined it's to spread love on the planet and be a source of inspiration for those who lack the courage to pursue their dreams. Then, everything you do from that point on will come from your purpose. It wouldn't matter if people booed you off the stage--you would still come across as a loving and inspiring person. So in this case, DJing would be your vehicle for delivering your life purpose."

Darnell interrupted again. "Ah, now I got it. Man this is

powerful! You had me confused for a moment. Based on what you just shared with me, I now see that passion is what you love to do, but your life purpose is what you were designed to do."

"You are dead on, Champ. I couldn't have said it any better," I said with a smile from ear to ear. "I'm glad it's all coming together for you. So, when you are clear with your life purpose you organize your life around it.[40] Everything you do becomes an expression of it. And I do mean everything. At this point, it will be easy to say 'no' to any opportunity which you cannot fulfill or express your life purpose with. Now you can see why 'life purpose' is the last driver on the list. When you discover your life purpose, it automatically impacts the previous four drivers I just shared with you."

17 Inspiring Quotes to Help You Live a Life of Purpose[41]

1. *"It's not enough to have lived. We should be <u>determined to live for something</u>." —Winston S. Churchill*
2. *"The path to our destination is not always a straight one. We go down the wrong road, we get lost, we turn back. Maybe it doesn't matter which road we embark on. Maybe what matters is that we embark." —Barbara Hall*
3. *"People take different roads seeking fulfillment and happiness. Just because they're not on your road doesn't mean they've gotten lost." —Dalai Lama*
4. *"The heart of human excellence often begins to beat when you <u>discover a pursuit that absorbs you</u>, frees you, challenges you, or gives you a sense of meaning, joy, or passion." —Terry Orlick*
5. *"Definiteness of purpose is the starting point of all achievement." —W. Clement Stone*
6. *"To begin to think with purpose, is to enter the ranks of those strong ones who only recognize failure as one of the pathways to attainment." —James Allen*
7. *"The mystery of human existence lies not in just staying alive, but in finding something to live for." —Fyodor Dostoyevsky*

8. *"The soul which has no fixed purpose in life is lost; to be everywhere, is to be nowhere."* —*Michel de Montaigne*

9. *"If you can tune into your purpose and really align with it, <u>setting goals</u> so that your vision is an expression of that purpose, then life flows much more easily."* —*Jack Canfield*

10. *"The person without a purpose is like a ship without a rudder."* —*Thomas Carlyle*

11. *"Efforts and courage are not enough without purpose and direction."* —*John F. Kennedy*

12. *"<u>True happiness</u>... is not attained through self-gratification, but through fidelity to a worthy purpose."* —*Helen Keller*

13. *"The best way to lengthen out our days is to walk steadily and with a purpose."* —*Charles Dickens*

14. *"Singleness of purpose is one of <u>the chief essentials for success in life</u>, no matter what may be one's aim."* —*John D. Rockefeller*

15. *"Musicians must make music, artists must paint, poets must write if they are ultimately to be at peace with themselves. What humans can be, they must be."* — *Abraham Maslow*

16. *"Everyone has been made for some particular work and the desire for that work has been put in every heart."* — *Jalaluddin Rumi*

17. *"<u>You must first be who you really are</u>, then do what you need to do, in order to have what you want."* —*Margaret Young*

And here is one of my favorite quotes on finding your life purpose:

> *Figure out what you love to do as young as you can, and then organize your life around figuring out how to make a living at it.* — Pat Williams[39]

*****

When I finished sharing the life purpose driver, Darnell jumped in, "This is by far the most powerful concept I have heard all day. Whoof, let me take a breath and let it all sink in now."

Darnell leaned back in his seat and pondered for a few minutes while looking at the sky.

I could tell by the serious look in his eyes that something inside of him was awakening, and I let him sit in silence so he could figure out what it was. He glanced over and made eye contact with me. Darnell opened his mouth as if to say something, then stopped and shook his head. Finally, he spoke. "Richie, I can now see why you are where you are in your life. I can tell that you live and die by this 'Choice Success Model'. Am I right, Richie?"

"You are 100% right, Darnell, and for the record it's called 'The Choice *Making* Success Model'. Indeed, this simple formula has helped me make better choices, especially when I had to make difficult decisions."

"Since you mentioned the word decision, can you explain the difference between a choice and a decision. Aren't they the same?"

"I am glad you asked. There is a big difference between a choice and a decision. The line between what constitutes a decision versus a choice may be slight. Let's look at the definition of each in Dictionary.com:

Decision: the act of or need for making up one's mind[41a].

Choice: the right, power, or opportunity to choose[41b].

"When you dive in deeper, the origins of the two words are interesting. The word decision comes from 'cutting off', while choice comes from 'to perceive'. Taking the origins and definitions together, we may gain some clarity.

"With decision, it is more of a process orientation, meaning we are going through analysis and steps to eliminate (or, *cut off*) options.

"With choice, it is more of an internal approach, meaning something internally is driving us to perceive what the right or wrong choice may be.[42]

"As you can see, choice is a perception and your perception ultimately is driven by the driver that is present when presented with a difficult choice."

"Richie, I will be the first to admit that before this conversation I thought decision and choice were the same, but now I can see that they are very different," Darnell said.

"Glad you now see the difference between the two." I replied.

"Richie, everything you have shared about 'The Choice Making Success Model' is phenomenal. I now see how activating the fulfillment drivers can put me in a position to win at life and feel fulfilled in the process. I guess the only thing that I would like to know is what should one do when dealing with a very difficult choice? I mean it all sounds cool in theory but, in reality, *could I really make the switch and choose a different driver when I have to make a difficult choice?*"

I thought for a long second then said, "Darnell, since I am driving now and I can not write on a piece of paper for you, please pull out your notepad and write down the 5 C's for powerful choice making."

"Okay, let me write them down," Darnell said as he pulled out his notepad. "Okay, shoot."

"Go ahead and write down these five words in this exact order:

Circumstance ——> Context ——> Commitment ——> Connection ——> Choose

Circumstance: When dealing with a problem or circumstance, first take a step back and inhale a few deep breaths. Doing so resets your nervous system and allows you to think again on the best way to approach your situation. Secondly, do your best to not give it a negative meaning. If you continue to harp on why this happened, you will not gain the mental clarity to move past your problems.

Context: The next thing to do after you have gained your composure is to change the context. Context is another word for perception. Choose to interpret or perceive this situation in a positive light, regardless of what it is. Doing so will empower you to see the present situation in a whole new way. It will guide you to see the good in everything you are dealing with.

Commitment: Now that you have changed the context, the next step is to get present to your commitment. Getting present to what you are really committed to will empower you to regain your focus and power. You accomplish this by asking yourself, "What am I committed to right now?" This question will help you address the commitments that are most important to you right now in your life.

Connection: The next crucial step is to connect to some or all of the fulfillment drivers and never give up on them. I want you to attach yourself to them no matter how scary the circumstances are. What most people do is run from their circumstances when the tough gets going. What they are doing in essence is letting the circumstance dictate them instead of sticking to the principles within the fulfillment drivers category (creation, abundance, vision/goals, passion and life purpose). What you need to get is that you can not change your circumstances, but what you can do is stay connected to the principles within those drivers. When you do this, this becomes the context from which you live your life from. So now regardless of what is happening in your life, this new view (context) allows you to see your circumstances differently.

Choose: Now choose a driver to focus on, and then voice your new choice. Declare it. Be it. Choose it. Choosing powerfully involves choosing over and over again. It must become a lifelong practice. Over time. the fulfillment drivers will become your new default. They will override your survival drivers, thus resulting in making more powerful choices on a consistent basis.

THE CHOICE MAKING SUCCESS MODEL

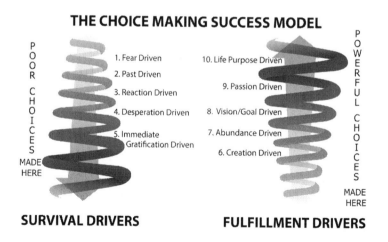

SURVIVAL DRIVERS   FULFILLMENT DRIVERS

To download this infographic with full color, check out:
http://www.theunderdogcode.com/bookresources

*****

"So there you have it young man. Do you now see how you can switch to a different driver when having to make a difficult choice?" I said as I thumped my index figure on the diagram on the notebook he had on his lap.

"Richie, I like this simple formula for staying connected to the fulfillment drivers, no matter what problem I am facing. I wrote them down on a separate page in your notebook as you were explaining them. I promise I will refer to them the next time I have a difficult choice to make," Darnell said as he ripped out the page he was referring to.

"Hey, I have one final question for the day since we're so close to reaching my home," Darnell said as I approached the tollbooth at the Triborough bridge.

"Shoot. No time to waste, Champ,"

"Do you know your life purpose?"

"I sure do."

"Do you remember when you discovered your life purpose?"

"Yes. It was after the last success principle Mr. Rodriguez shared with me before he passed."

"Do you mean to say that he died?!" Darnell exclaimed.

"Yeah, he did, but I am so grateful for the last success principle he shared with me, for I know without a shadow of doubt that it was the most powerful one out of all the success principles he had shared. Getting my life purpose has brought so much meaning, happiness, and direction to my life. Let me share quickly how I discovered it before we arrive to your home."

Chapter Eleven

DISCOVERING YOUR
LIFE PURPOSE

"You have to know what sparks the light in you so that you in your own way can illuminate the world."
— Oprah Winfrey

When purpose leads, fulfillment follows.
— Edward R. Munoz

Ten years had passed since I hit my net worth goal of $1,000,000 and my net worth had tripled. Within those ten years, I had purchased, rehabbed, or flipped over 150 properties. I now owned 9 six- and eight-family buildings in Brooklyn in the Bushwick area and saw a nice equity increase over those years. I also purchased a nice one-family residence for Mom and my sis Jennifer in Valley Stream, just 30 minutes from the drug infested hood area we used to live in. It felt great to accomplish many of the things I had once set out to accomplish. All of those years applying the success principles Mr. Rodriguez had so relentlessly shared paid off big time. Yet something was missing and it was hard to pinpoint it. Let me share with you when I first started to notice this unusual feeling.

On a hot sunny summer day, I was laying on a beach lounge chair by the pool in my backyard when I peered out of my sunglasses and heard the all too familiar click clacks. It was Maria, our maid, walking toward me. I leaned up in my chair and saw her navigating carefully around the pool's corner so as to not fall in. Once she got close she said, *"Richie, tienes una llamada."* Richie, you have a call. She handed me the cordless phone.

"Who is it?" I murmured in a low, disinterested tone.

"Es el señor Rodríguez, el quiere hablar contigo." Mr. Rodriguez wants to speak with you, she said, as she covered

the phone with her palm so the other listener could not hear our secretive conversation.

When I heard those words, I felt a knot in my stomach and decided to dodge his conversation. "Tell him I am not here," I demanded softly.

She took a deep breath then said, *"Pero señor Richie, esta es la tercera vez que el llama hoy."* But Richie, this is the third time he called today.

The truth was, I felt like shit. This wasn't like me to avoid my mentor, but something bigger than me forced me to say, "I know that--just tell him I am not here." My voice raised louder with each passing second.

Maria shrugged her shoulders in confusion, raised her eyebrows, then politely said, *"Esta bien señor Richie. Como usted diga."* Okay, as you command, Mr. Richie.

It was hard to explain what I was feeling, but as successful as I was, I felt depressed. It made no sense to me. I mean, I mastered the success principles Mr. Rodriguez had shared with me, but somehow I was still depressed. The worst part was that I was too embarrassed to let Mr. Rodriguez know what I was feeling, and this insane behavior drove me to avoid him, as strange as it sounded. Deep down in my gut, I knew that I would not be able to hide much longer.

*****

On the following day, I was working in my home office and heard a knock on my custom mahogany doors. I assumed it was Maria, so I hollered, "Come inside!" To my surprise, it was Mr. Rodriguez. I nearly passed out when I saw his powerful figure enter the room. His demeanor and presence told me I was in for it.

"How are you doing, Champ?" Mr. Rodriguez said seriously, but with a sarcastic bite to his words.

"I'm good, sir." But I didn't really believe the crap that was coming out of my mouth.

Mr. Rodriguez then started to catch me up on everything he was doing. He shared the details of his last trip to Punta Cana and when he planned to return. He talked about why he officially handed over the reigns of his supermarket business to his oldest son Henry, and about a children's book he had just finished writing.

When he finished talking, he looked over toward my direction and said, "So what's new?"

"Nuthin' much," I said half-heartedly.

"Come on Richie, be truthful. You have not been your normal self lately." It wasn't a question, but rather an observation.

I knew there was no point hiding the truth from him anymore. He'd come to visit me and was clearly concerned. "Man, I have been feeling weird lately. Somehow I feel I've lost my drive. It's hard to pinpoint what I am feeling."

"Are you sick? Have you been to the doctor?"

I shook my head, dejected. "No, I have not. I'm not sick. I just don't look forward to life and business the way I used to."

It was at this point that Mr. Rodriguez started to explain the Choice Making Success Model in more detail. He explained how the survival and fulfillment drivers influence our behavior and choices. But I was really taken when he talked more about the last driver: the *life purpose driver*. Up until this point in my life, I had done a pretty good job with the first four fulfillment drivers—*creation driven, abundance driven, vision driven, and passion driven*—but the last driver was something I only vaguely recalled. For the first time in my life, I felt a strong desire from within to discover my life purpose. I saw it as the missing piece in the puzzle of my life.

The more he spoke about about it, the more this driver intrigued me. I think it intrigued me because up until this point in my life, I had only been driven by success. Every action came from the desire to be more, do more, and have more. I mean who can blame me considering where I came from? Ultimate success became my goal and that is why I was always inspired by the success principles, for they guaranteed a path to reach my goals without having to compromise my integrity. But once I became successful, I felt something was missing and did not know how to describe it. At times, I just thought I was complaining so I never brought it up to Mr. Rodriguez.

As Mr. Rodriguez continued to speak about the importance of discovering your life purpose, I felt life being zapped into my being. It was exactly what was missing. It made me realize why I had lost meaning for what I was doing.

At one point in the conversation, Mr. Rodriguez asked, "Richie, how is this information landing. Is it making sense? Is it helping you see life through a new pair of lenses?"

"It sure is, Mr. Rodriguez. The reason why I am not talking much is because I am still processing everything."

"Do you have any thoughts so far?"

"It really resonated when you said that your life purpose keeps you grounded in your heart. That really spoke to me because I have noticed that everytime I come from my heart, I feel so much joy."

Mr. Rodriguez enthusiastically jumped in and said, "That's because your heart is where your life purpose lives. Once you discover it, you find a permanent home for yourself.[43] I say this because your life purpose wants to use you for something that is greater than yourself and it needs your heart to accomplish that mission and purpose. It can not come from your head. Only your heart can fulfill on this mission."

As he spoke, I caught myself taking deep breaths. These ideas were more than words. They represented my life. Mr. Rodriguez kept speaking when he saw the message was driving home.

"I know 100% for sure that every human being comes to this earth called to fulfill a purpose. And today my intention is to help you discover your calling," Mr. Rodriguez said cheerfully.

I felt dismayed. "But I thought I had discovered my purpose! My purpose was to be a great businessman, a master negotiator, and a millionaire."

"Now I see where you got mixed up. Most people that want to succeed from a braggadocious standpoint rather than purpose. When this is the central focus, people may end up becoming rich, yet at the same time, unfulfilled. This is because there is an assumption that when you are rich you will automatically be happy on the inside. When money and success stop being the main motivators, there is a void. These people constantly fall into boredom and continually ask themselves, 'Is this it? Is this all there there is?'"

At this point he stopped talking, leaned closer to look into my eyes and put his right hand on my shoulder, then said, "Am I right?"

I felt a knot in the pit of my stomach. It felt like I'd swallowed a golf ball. He hit the nail on the head, but I wouldn't dare admit it. Not out loud at least. I nodded in agreement so Mr. Rodriguez could continue.

"I also see that the becoming a good businessman became a passion of yours, much like painting becomes a passion for an artist. But I will be the first to tell you that type of success is not necessarily what I was referring to. Your passion definitely inspires you to be your best, but your life purpose is the driving force behind everything you do.

"Let me put it another way," Mr. Rodriguez continued, "On the outside, it may have looked like your contribution to the planet was to do real estate be a successful entrepreneur, but your real contribution on this planet is to fulfill on your life purpose through everything you do. At this point, real estate or being an entrepreneur is just a vehicle to fulfill your life purpose. Now take a moment to let this sink in."

I was processing it all slowly, savoring this information like a kid savors a lollipop that he was longing for.

"So now your real job is to figure out who you are at your core, and then spend the rest of your life in alignment with that.[44]"

"This process sounds scary to me, Mr. Rodriguez. Frankly speaking, I am afraid to discover who I really am," I said.

"It's even worse to get to your deathbed and suddenly realize you never knew who you really were," Mr. Rodriguez said in a serious tone before flashing his champion smile.

"Okay, you got me," I said, taking a deep breath, "you always know how to convince me. Now that you have my full attention, what is my first step to discovering my life purpose?"

"In most cases, I first encourage people to discover their passions before helping them discover their life purpose. But in your case, let's get right to it since you already know what you are passionate about. I need you to take this very serious, Richie. Before I continue, I have some good news and some bad news. Which do you want first?"

"I'll let you choose, sir," I replied.

"Okay, let me start with bad news. This may come as a surprise, but please try not to give it a lot of meaning. Can you promise me that?" Mr. Rodriguez said.

"I'll try," I said, a bit nervously.

"Okay, here goes. I was at the doctor's office today and my doctor shared the results of my blood work he took a few weeks ago. Turns out I have cancer in my colon. It's at stage three." Mr. Rodriguez paused for a moment, not looking directly at me. "It's pretty advanced at this point."

*****

What? Tears rushed down my face before I had fully comprehended his words. I was shocked into silence, watching Mr. Rodriguez for any hint that he was lying to me. I kept asking myself if all this could have been a dream. However, the look on his sad and distraught face confirmed the new reality.

"Yes, I know it's a shocker, young man. It certainly was very disturbing news," Mr. Rodriguez said.

I managed to regain my composure and stutter out, "Disturbing news? It's more than disturbing news, it's actually devastating news." My hands were shaking almost as much as my voice.

"Yes, you are right, but I see it as a transition to a better place--at least that is the meaning I chose to give it," Mr. Rodriguez said calmly.

"How much time did the doctor say you have before your 'transition'?" I asked desperately.

"They gave me six months at most, but it could be sooner. From the looks of it, God wants me to visit him before my 76th birthday. I know it's not the greatest news, and this is why I came to see you in person. I am counting on you to continue my legacy. As you can see, my clock is running low on time and who's to say when it will stop ticking. There's no time to waste, my Champ. That is why I am committed to help you discover your life purpose before I depart and transition to the next life." He said this with a big grin, but tears were welling up in his eyes.

We spoke for a few more moments, and then he stood up as if he was leaving. "Hey, don't leave yet." My voice came out in a whisper.

"I am not feeling well. I am going to leave now," Mr. Rodriguez said.

"Wait, what about discovering the purpose for my life? When are we going to talk more about it?" I said.

Mr. Rodriguez smiled sadly and shook his head. "I have nothing more to say. Now it's your turn to start looking inward to see what is truly important and what matters most in your life.

Do some research on the topic by reading books in this area, or go ahead and Google 'discover my life purpose' and see what pops up. We can discuss this further when we see each other next. I'll talk to you again when I return from a short trip to Miami. I want to spend some time with my son, Rodolfo." Then he stood up, gave me a quick hug, and left before I could break down and start crying again. He knew me all too well.

*****

During the following weeks, I researched everything I could on the topic of discovering your life purpose. I purchased several books and read hundreds of articles on the internet. I really didn't want to disturb Mr. Rodriguez because I knew his health was waning and I wanted him to see that I was willing to do the work to discover it on my own. Somehow, this conversation awoke something profound in me. It made so much sense. More than ever, I wanted to discover the purpose of my existence. Finally, my heart was open to receive and discover the question of my life that had been dormant for so many years. About three weeks into my research, I received a call from Mr. Rodriguez.

"How you doing, kiddo?" Mr. Rodriguez said by way of greeting.

"Man, I'm pumped," I said enthusiastically, "but forget about me--how's your health?"

"Fine, I guess, given the circumstances. Yesterday I had my third round of chemo. Anyways, let's not focus on me. What's new with you?"

I proceeded to tell him everything I have learned about the topic of discovering your life purpose and how anxious I was to finally discover it for myself. I finished up with, "Mr. Rodriguez, there are so many methods on the internet on how to discover your life purpose and I don't know where to start. Any suggestions?"

"Hey, Champ, go ahead and pull out a piece of paper and write this down," Mr. Rodriguez said. "I call it the five stages to discovering your life purpose. It..."

I interrupted, "But why didn't you share this with me three weeks ago when I first asked for your support in this area?"

"I think by now you know how I operate, young man. You know I only divulge information when I feel the student is ready for it. I first needed to see that you were willing to take on this assignment before I gave you the next one. Additionally, I did not want you to get too heavily influenced by the information I was giving you, because then you would continue to use me as a reference to learn more about this life purpose topic instead of discovering it for yourself. Unlike the other principles I have shared with you throughout your life, this principle is not something you need to learn to grow and become more; rather, it is a principle you need to get on your own with limited guidance from other people. Okay, enough said on this topic," Mr Rodriguez declared, "here are the five stages to discovering your life purpose--make sure to write them down in this order:

1- Discovery 2- Disruption 3- Darkness 4- Divine 5- Deliver

"Richie, did you write them down in the exact order?"

"I sure did, boss. What's next?" I asked impatiently.

"Good, let's start out with the first stage: *Discovery*. To help you discover who you are at your core, I need you to do the following. Write down these 11 questions I am about to dictate to you. I will tell you what to do with them after you write them down."

Mr. Rodriguez then said each statement out loud very slowly, making sure I would not miss a word:

- What is trying to emerge?[46]
- What is trying to unfold?[47]
- What is my purpose for living?
- What are your deepest values?
- What is my unique role in this life?
- What do people typically ask you for help in?
- What activities make you lose track of time?
- What makes you feel great about yourself?
- What would you regret not fully doing, being, or having in your life?
- Given your talents, passions, and values, how could you use these resources to serve, help, and contribute to people, beings, causes, organizations, the environment, or the planet?[48]
- You are now 90 years old, sitting on a rocking chair outside your porch; you can feel the spring breeze gently brushing against your face. You are blissful and happy, and are pleased with the wonderful life you've been blessed with. Looking back at your life and all that you've achieved and acquired, as well as all the relationships you've developed, what matters to you most?

"Richie, did you get all of these down in the exact order as I said them?"

"Yes, sir," I said, matter of factly.

"Good, now I want you to write them on five index cards before you go to bed and carry them everywhere you go for the next two weeks. Take these five index cards and put them in places throughout your house where you can see them daily. Your only job is to review these questions on a daily basis. Asking these questions is the first stage to discovering your life purpose. It's called the discovery stage because it's where you start to do the work to see what's important to you. It will help declutter who you aren't and get to the truth of who you really are."

"Sounds like a lot of work, sir. I thought it was going to be easier than this," I admitted.

"Up until now, I have shared many success principles with you where all you had to do was put them into practice. However, this life altering success principle requires you to do some intense work. I can't do it for you. I want you to consider that the universe and your creator are constantly pushing you toward your life purpose. And as soon as you give up the resistance and do the work, the universe and your creator will start to pull you toward it."

"It's starting to make sense now. I guess I just have to trust the process and stop overthinking it."

"Correctomundo, Champ. Asking yourself these questions on a continual basis will unleash higher levels of potential and new desires will come about in the form of signs, people, hints, and nudges. This is how you activate the universe to help you with the unfolding of your essence and your truths. Slowly but surely, this process will start to build momentum in the direction of clarifying your life purpose.49"

I took a deep breath and said to myself, man, here is a person who has just a few months before he dies. If he is taking his time to spend it with me on this topic, I am going to do exactly as he says.

"Do you have any questions so far?" he asked, after I'd been silent for a minute.

"No, not at the moment," I said.

"Good, I have to go now. I'm going to take a nap. These medications have me feeling a bit drowsy. Goodbye, Champ. Talk soon." Then he hung up.

*****

As soon as we got off the phone, I went to my local office supply store to buy index cards and also decided to buy a journal. I thought it would be a good idea to carry one around so I could jot down any ideas or thoughts that came to me as a result of these questions.

Later on that night, I decided to plaster these 11 questions on the ceiling of my bedroom and fell asleep asking myself these questions. I kept repeating them and went off into a tangent of dreams. I slept like a baby that night.

I carried the questions with me everywhere I went. I wanted so desperately to discover my life purpose before Mr. Rodriguez passed. This added pressure made it worse. Two weeks into the exercise, Mr. Rodriguez gave me a call to see how it was going. His timing was perfect because I had just completed a closing on a real estate property.

Mr. Rodriguez greeted me with, "How's it going, Champ?"

"Man, I just had a closing and it went well, but I must say this exercise has me frustrated," I said.

"Why is that?" Mr. Rodriguez asked.

"I feel like it's not coming to me. If it's one thing I can assure you, it's that I am really trying hard to get this. I'm afraid..." I paused, unsure of how to finish the sentence.

Mr. Rodriguez jumped in. "I know--you're afraid you won't get your life purpose before I pass. It's all good Richie. It will happen when it happens. Try not to force it. I think you are resisting listening to the signs or the answers."

"Sir, with all due respect, I am not resisting anything."

"Maybe you aren't, but just consider for a moment that you are resisting. Don't try so hard to discover who you are. Minister Dr. Michael Bernard Beckwith says that when you are in this space, all you have to do is ask this question: What quality needs to emerge for me to get through this moment?"

I responded immediately. "The first things that came to mind were patience and curiosity."

"Yes, those are definitely two good qualities to stand in during this discovery process. Standing there will certainly release the pressure to get it in an instant. I once heard Dr. Beckwith say this about the discovery process: 'This process of asking questions is very important because it allows your life purpose to naturally and organically and awesomely unfold. These questions are designed to help unfold the unfolding of your life purpose. They help unfold what is already there yet it is blind from your eyesight. The beauty is that once this unfolding starts, it will never end. It will become the journey of the unfolding. For evolution never stops evolving and so will you.'50 So keep at it, Champ, and trust the process," Mr. Rodriguez stated, his energy waning and his voice softening.

"Okay, will do, sir. Stay well and take of yourself," I said in a loving and caring voice, "and don't forget, I love you with all my heart."

"I know you do, my Champ. Talk soon," He said, then hung up the call.

*****

Two weeks had passed since I had that conversation with Mr. Rodriguez, and because I had a lot to share with Anthony I decided to accept his invitation for lunch at his new restaurant. In the past three years he opened three restaurants and this one was number 4. When I arrived, he already had my favorite appetizer on the table, *camarones con tostones y unas cuantas rodajas de aguacate*—yummy! I can never say no to fried plantains with shrimp drenched in a red tomato sauce, accompanied with avocado.

"Come on over here, bro," Anthony said, walking me over to the back of the restaurant. "Look what I have for you," he pointed to the lavish meal he had, all ready to eat.

"Thanks, man. You really shouldn't have," I said.

"Wait till you see the lobster we have in the oven. Promise to leave a little space in your stomach for it," Anthony said, with a big latino grin that spread along his face like a *platano* (plantain) going sideways.

As we ate, I caught him up on Mr. Rodriguez's health and the inner work I was doing to discover my life purpose. After eating his delicious lobster meal, I pulled out my journal to share what I learned about purpose, and I then shared the list of questions I was reading every day. He glanced at my list and asked why I hadn't filled in my answers next to the questions.

"The truth is that I am scared to write it down, because if I do then it will shatter my beliefs about who I thought I was," I admitted.

"Do you mean your identity?" Anthony asked.

"Yes, you hit the nail on the head. I'm afraid I will stop being that person, and that is all I have known up until now," I said.

"Richie, what you are going through now is called disruption. This is the 2nd 'D' in discovering your life purpose. That's why it was important that you do the exercise exactly as Mr. Rodriguez said. Doing so will start to disrupt your identity. Without disrupting your identity, you can never discover your life purpose. So instead of looking at the exercise as a threat, you need to look at it as a necessary step in order to get closer to discovering the greatest gift any human being could ever give themself."

The more Anthony spoke, the more it started to calm my negative feelings about what seemed to be a very stressful exercise.

Anthony continued, "Just know that it's very normal to feel confronted in the process of discovering your life purpose. This exercise is designed to extract who you really are and while it excites many people, it also scares the living crap out of many. Truthfully, most people are scared to find out who they really are, because if they do, they will have to be that person for the rest of their life. As exciting as all of this sounds, some people would prefer to live their entire lives out of their identity -- which is what they do for a living -- rather than the highest expression of who they are at their core in their heart."

"Anthony, what you are saying makes perfect sense. Who knew that this process would be so scary. How do you know this topic so well?" I asked.

Anthony grinned at me, "It just so happens that I decided to become a certified life coach and this is one of my areas of expertise."

"Anthony, you are a ball of surprises. I had no idea you were a life coach. What inspired you to be a life coach?" I asked in sheer surprise.

"As you know, I am the #7 earner in my networking company out of 400,000 representatives, and I felt the need to become the leader they aspire to be. After all, network marketing companies are nothing more than a self improvement course that is attached to a compensation plan. I knew that the more I learned how to help others get their life in shape and become successful in the process, the more it would help my business grow. I also wanted to not only walk the talk but be a model for my team. Not to mention that it was an easy decision to make because it aligned with my life purpose, which is to be a force of motivation on the planet and make an impactful difference with everyone I come in contact with."

"Man, you never fail to surprise me, Champ. You've come a long ways, bro. Going back to your point on why I feel so scared to let go of who I currently know myself to be, I now see why it's so scary. I realize it's just part of the process to discover my life purpose and instead of freaking out, I need to understand that I am in what you call the Disruption stage and it's normal to feel this way. I now see that all these exercises were there to help me disrupt who I thought I was and clear the path for me to see who I really am."

"You are spot on Richie--when in the in-between of letting go of your past and discovering your life purpose, it will feel dark and scary. It's scary because you're releasing what you thought your identity was and you are afraid to discover who you really are.[51]"

As Anthony spoke, I listened in admiration. My lord, he went from a street kid to a millionaire entrepreneur and now a life coach who was living out his life purpose. He was hitting all my emotional buttons and I let him ramble on in hopes that he could help me see what I couldn't in regard to discovering my life purpose.

*****

The 5 D's to Discover your Life Purpose

Discovery · Disruption · Darkness · Divine · Deliver

Anthony knew I was very close to discovering my life purpose, and he also knew that if I did not completely understand what I was actually going through, I could easily slip back into my old ways where I thought what I did for a living was who I was.

Anthony continued, "This scary place is what is commonly referred to the Darkness stage when it comes to discovering your life purpose. It's the space in-between your identity and your life purpose. Trust me, it's a good place to be, but it can be scary as hell. It's important to understand that we need to detach ourselves from what we do to discover who we really are because if we don't, we are just setting ourselves up for pain."

"Why is that?" I asked defensively.

"Well, it's the reason you were in depression just a few weeks ago. You fell in depression because you were trying to find joy in your material accomplishments, but found out the joy was short-lived. And after repeating that process for a while thinking it would produce more joy, you found yourself in a vicious circle that never ended. That happened because you were constantly chasing joy instead of generating joy from your deepest self expression. The self expression that creates eternal joy is also called fulfillment."

"Man, how did you learn this stuff?" I asked in amazement.

"That's a story for another day. Let's just say that I too have been putting into practice the success principles you've shared with me throughout the years. So, let me ask you one of the questions I see here on this list," he said, tapping his index finger on the jornal. But before I ask you this question, I would like to know: are you ready to leave the darkness stage and enter the Divine stage to discovering your life purpose?"

I faced him with a look of gratitude and said, "Heck yeah. Shoot, I'm all ears."

"Richie, the divine stage is where you finally connect to your life purpose. It's called 'divine' for a reason. It's where you and your creator connect not head to head, but rather heart to heart and soul to soul. It's divine because you finally arrive at home. With that in mind, here is the first question I have to help guide you there:"

"You are now 90 years old, sitting on a rocking chair outside your porch; you can feel the spring breeze gently brushing against your face. You are blissful and happy, and are pleased with the wonderful life you've been blessed with. Looking back at your life and all that you've achieved and acquired, as well as all the relationships you've developed, what matters to you most?"

I thought for a long moment, then, in a moment of bliss, the words just starting falling out of my mouth. "What matters most to me is that:

- I made a difference in the lives of those who are important to me.
- I guided others in unleashing and exploiting their God-given talents.
- I left people better off than when I first encountered them.
- I inspired my children to be the best version of themselves.
- I inspired my children to be leaders in their chosen fields.
- I motivated people who quit on their dreams to continue believing in themselves and the dreams they once believed was possible.
- My immediate family was known for their character and values rather than their financial riches.
- People respect us not for our wealth, but rather our principles and morals.
- I empowered people to be powerful leaders for their businesses and communities.
- 100 years from now, people are still benefiting because of what I created and the lives I directly and indirectly impacted.
- My teachings far surpass the impact of my death.

"Whoof! Wow, that felt really good to get all of that off my chest. I think that pretty much sums it up," I said.

"Consider that you did not get that off your chest; rather, your soul finally released it. You are finally getting in touch with the side of you you have been avoiding. This is why it feels so right. Let's continue with another question: What are you deepest values? Name the first ones that come to mind," Anthony said, while his index finger touched his head pointing to his mind.

"I would say my deepest values are being considerate, dependable, reliable, friendly, truthful, creative, reasonable, inspiring, strict, and disciplined," I said.

"Good, here is the next question. You are doing really good. Stay with me, Champ. We are getting real close. What do people typically ask you for help in?"

"That one is easy. People are always asking me to give them life advice. My friends also ask me for business advice, especially how to put deals together and help with the negotiation process," I said out loud, looking up at the ceiling and pondering for a moment.

"Here's the next question: What activities make you lose track of time?" Anthony asked.

"When I am helping people out with their problems and offering motivational and business advice, time just flies," I stated.

"Okay, here's the next one. Given your talents, passions, and values, how could you use these resources to serve, help, and contribute to people, causes, organizations, the environment, or the planet?" Anthony asked.

I thought hard for a second, then blurted out, "Man, I would write motivational and business books to empower aspiring entrepreneurs to create a life and start a business that not only thrive, but also fulfill their incredible potential.". I would also host seminars to teach topics such as entrepreneurship, personal growth, wealth creation, and empowerment, just to mention a few." I inhaled a really long breath, then leaned back into my chair.

Anthony could tell I was getting closer to finally discovering my life purpose, so he came in with the final question: "Richie, what is the sacred promise you made to yourself before you were born but have never kept?"

"Well, how would I know what that promise is if it was supposedly made before I was born?" I started with a look of concern on my face.

Anthony shook his head, "You see, that answer came from your head. Stop being so logical. I need you to answer this question from your heart. Let your soul answer it for once. Close your eyes and let it guide you."

He paused and looked at my face, "Hey, follow me to my office--it's much quieter there." Anthony stood up and led me to his office. Once there he pointed me to a comfortable leather chair. He closed the door and I asked him to ask me one more time, promising myself I would let my soul answer it.

*****

To help reveal my life purpose, Anthony knew it would require me to dig real deep into my soul to pull out and give birth to my

DISCOVERING YOUR LIFE PURPOSE

ultimate purpose for living. As I sat down, closed my eyes, and took a deep breath, he could tell I was now in the right mental space to really hear this question. He asked one more time:

"What is the sacred promise you made to yourself before you were born but have never kept?"

I leaned back in his comfortable brown leather chair and dug deep to search for the answer. I kept repeating the question in my mind and started daydreaming. At a distance I could hear Anthony talking but no words computed. I was somewhere on the other side, a place I had never been before.

Suddenly what came to mind was the promise I made to Mr. Rodriguez when he visited me at Rikers Island. I remember telling him how thankful I was for the positive influence he had on my life. I remember promising him that when I succeeded, I would share with the world everything he taught me. I also told him that this was how I was going to repay him. All these thoughts came from somewhere, but then I rationalized and said to myself, wait, Anthony asked me to mention the sacred promise I made to myself *before* I was born. Could this be it?

At this moment, I noticed that I went back to my head instead of my heart. Once I got back in touch with my heart, it started speaking to me again. Suddenly, I came to the conclusion that Anthony was referring to the old me before I transformed my mindset, habits, and beliefs. Yeah, that must be it. The answer came from within and it felt real. This was the promise I made to myself before I was reborn into my newly transformed self.

I proceeded to tell Anthony precisely what I had unraveled. He heard me out then said,"Richie, if that answer feels right, then that is it. There is no right or wrong answer, only what that lies in your heart and what is truest to you. Now that you are clear on the promise you made but never kept, come up with a statement that includes some of your core values, including what you are good at, what matters most to you, and how you can benefit the greater good. This is commonly referred to as 'The Life Purpose Statement'. Again, let the answer come from within, for it will guide you. Trust your soul, for it wants you to get it. Your soul actually wants to partner with you to fulfill its purpose. It can't do it without you. Go ahead now and meditate on that now."

"I want you to know that I am ready to honor this request,

but I need you to repeat what you are asking of me. Please say it slowly."

"Sure thing. Now that you are clear on the promise you made but never kept, you need to come up with a statement that includes some of your core values, what you are good at, what matters to you, and how it can all benefit the greater good."

I thought long and hard. I went in and out of conversations in my head, then decided to get in touch with my heart and started to write on the notepad that was directly in front of me on Anthony's desk. I wrote what was already present in my soul. It came out freely and naturally. From time to time I glanced at the notes Anthony took when I answered his previous questions.

When I was finished writing, I looked Anthony dead in the eyes, smiled, and then handed him my notepad so he could see what I wrote. After reading it, he returned it to me and asked me to read my statement out loud. But before the first words came out of my mouth, tears started to stream down my face, faster than a canoe flying uncontrollably down Niagara Falls. It was an emotional moment. After a few minutes passed, I took a deep breath and stood up to center myself and get grounded. Then, I generated the words that would govern me for the rest of my life.

"My life purpose is to use my inspiration and creativity to empower others to freely exploit their God-given talents in ways that align with their core values and their highest and truest self expression."

After Anthony heard my life purpose statement, he leaned back in his chair, nodded his head, and smiled triumphantly. "Man, I'm speechless," was all that he could say. "Okay, now let's go to the final stage, which is to Deliver your life purpose to the world.

To download this infographic with full color, check out:
www.EdwardMunoz.com/The5D
(No Email Is Required - Immediate Download)

"Now that you are 100% clear on why you were brought to this planet, it's your obligation to deliver your life purpose to the world. And when you do, you become the very source of fulfillment for others. You get to save people from themselves. Consider that people were born to receive exactly what you were born to deliver. That's why it's your life purpose. When you are connected to your life purpose and you are fulfilling it, you become eternal. Your work will live past your life. For example, we are still benefiting from Martin Luther King and Ghandi and it's because they delivered and fulfilled their life purpose. When you deliver your life purpose to the world, it's like you are doing God's work but using your hands. That's what you call greatness--you're channelling God's vision of for a better humanity through you. In essence, when you're delivering your life purpose, you become a conduit for greatness to flow through you into others. So there you have it, my friend. Are you ready to deliver your life purpose to the world? Are you game?"

Upon hearing these words, I stood up so fast I threw the chair back, shouting, "Of course I am. Look man, I gotta go now. I can't wait to share my life purpose with Mr. Rodriguez. Come over here, bro, so I can give you a love hug."

After we hugged, I was out the door. I couldn't wait to tell Mr. Rodriguez what I discovered about myself.

CLAIM YOUR FREE GIFT

I am so glad you made it this far. By now, you probably feel inspired to take over the world and conquer all your dreams.

I want to gift you a productivity course called "Unleash a Performance Explosion" for **FREE**. All I ask is that you take part in the #PhotoChallenge

Take a photo of your The Underdog's C.O.D.E. to Riches book cover in your favorite place:

- In your office
- By the pool or beach
- At a local Starbucks
- In front of a cool car Or
- anywhere you desire

Post it after you've taken your picture

In your Instagram Caption, tag @EdwardRMunoz and include #TheUnderdogCode #BookReview #Bookstagram #AwesomeBook
My Instagram handle is @EdwardRMunoz

In your facebook caption, tag @EdwardRafaelMunoz and include #TheUnderdogCode #BookReview #Bookstagram #AwesomeBook
My Facebook handle is @EdwardRafaelMunoz

TAG ME

Once you tag me, I'll send you a link to download the "Unleash a Performance Explosion" course for FREE.

Photo Credit: Fotolia_124074717

287

Chapter Twelve

UNLOCK YOUR INNER RICHES

"Inside every human being there are treasures to unlock."
— Mike Huckabee — American Politician and Author

After leaving Anthony's restaurant, I felt like I was floating on air. It was surreal. I could hardly contain myself. It felt so right. The first thing I did was call Mr. Rodriguez. When I dialed his number on my cell phone, it went straight to voicemail. I tried again and again and after the 4th try, I decided to call his wife's number. She did not pick up at first, but I finally got through to her on the 3rd try about 15 minutes later. When she answered the phone, I sensed a heaviness. She wasn't her normal self.

"Richie, is everything okay? I see you called a few times," Mrs. Rodriguez said stiffly.

"Yes, everything is fabulous. I am trying to reach Mr. Rodriguez but he is not picking up his phone," I said enthusiastically.

"Yes, unfortunately his health has relapsed and—"

I interrupted, "Is he ok?" My voice was heavy with concern.

Mrs. Rodriguez sighed, "Richie, I don't know a pleasant way to say this but the doctors have sent him to hospice. His cancer has overtaken him to the point where he could leave us any day now. They said there is nothing they can do for him at this moment."

"Hospice. What is that?" My heart beating faster by now. I tried to contain my emotions for her sake.

"Hospice is a section in the hospital where they send patients to die. Are you coming to say goodbye?" Mrs. Rodriguez said. I could hear the tears in her voice.

Oh my lord. I can't believe what I am hearing, I thought to myself. "What hospital is he in?"

"He is at the St. Frances Hospital in Roslyn. Hey, Richie, I have to go now, someone is calling my name. See you here, okay?"

After she hung up, I pulled over on the Grand Central Parkway and I leaned forward and placed my forehead and hands on the steering wheel and cried profusely. I kept banging my forehead into the steering wheel and repeating out loud, "Why is this happening to Mr. Rodriguez?" He was like a dad to me and this news was devastating to say the least. After a few minutes passed by, I took a deep breath and gathered my composure.

Watching the traffic zip by, I had a sudden image in my head of Mr. Rodriguez lying still and quiet in a hospital bed. Something he had told me years ago echoed in my mind. I had been in a bad mental state at the time and was thinking of giving up on my venture. I mentioned how I was feeling and he said, "Gather yourself and head over to my house so we can talk in person. The world needs champions like you, so don't give up on yourself."

After hearing those words in my head, I calmed down, gained my composure, and headed over to the hospital.

*****

When I arrived at the hospital, I asked someone to guide me to hospice. Once I got there, I saw Mrs. Rodriguez walking into a room, so I assumed this was where Mr. Rodriguez was. At the door to his room were his two sons and daughter. Henry was the first to approach me and hugged me so hard it was like he was trying to suck the life out of me. Henry considered me a brother and every sigh he released made me see the reality of this depressing moment. While still hugging, I looked around and noticed how tired and sad everyone appeared. The remaining two siblings of Mr. Rodriguez were also present, plus a few family members I had met in the past during family events. After we finished hugging, I gave my condolences to the other family members who were in the family room at the end of the passageway. Most of them did not say a word; they just nodded their heads to acknowledge they heard me.

Then, I heard a silent and soft voice echo from twenty feet away, "Richie, please come in," Mrs. Rodriguez said as she waved her hands.

I started to head in her direction when a phone call interrupted my thoughts. I looked down to see who it was and noticed it was a real estate agent calling to update me on a closing. Without a second thought, I turned the phone off and walked into the room.

To my surprise, Mr. Rodriguez greeted me with a smile. In a weak voice, he said, "What's up, kiddo?"

"I'm awesome," I answered, but as I said it I lost energy in my knees and fell in the kneeling position right before him. My emotions overtook me and I wept like a baby desperately crying for milk. He tried to comfort me by patting my head with his hands. At one point, I took his hand into mine and kissed it, saying, "I'm going to miss you, Champ."

When I continued crying, he said, "Come on, Champ, stop crying. The truth is that I have lived a complete life. A fulfilling life. I have no regrets. Especially when I discovered my life purpose at the age of 35. So please stop crying. I request you honor my life by celebrating my departure with joy. That is what I have requested from my family, but no one seems to get me. What do you say Champ? Are you game?" He then attempted to punch my shoulders like he used to do, but failed at stretching his arms that far.

After I composed myself, I stood up. "Game on, sir."

Around this time a nurse came into the room and said, "Mr. Rodriguez are you ready for your medication?"

"Can you please come back in 30 minutes? That medicine make me drowsy."

Her voice got stern. "The kind of medicine I have for you is not only going to make you drowsy, but it will also put you to sleep. And no, I can not come back in 30 minutes. We need to do it, so can everybody please leave the room?"

"Look Miss, I really need to discuss something of importance with my son Richie," he said while glancing over at me, "and I need to do it now in case I do not wake up again. So, can we sign some papers authorizing you to come back in 30 minutes?" Mr. Rodriguez said softly.

She took a deep breath and put her index fingers on her glasses to push them up. "Okay, I'll do it just this once. Who's going to sign this document?"

Mrs. Rodriguez then stood up and told her husband, "*Papi deja que te den la medicina,*" but whatever she said did not work. He whispered one more time for her to sign the agreement, allowing us 30 minutes before coming back.

Mrs. Rodriguez stood up and signed the paperwork. After the nurse left the room, Mr. Rodriguez requested she leave us alone. She clearly did not want to leave, but decided to honor his request.

*****

291

"Mr. Rodriguez, that was the first time I ever heard you call me 'son'," I said happily.

"Come on, you always knew I looked at you like a son, Champ. Hey, we don't have too much time, young man. Time's running out, if you know what I mean. So let's get right to it," Mr. Rodriguez said, glancing at the ominously ticking clock.

"I agree." I said. Wow this man was not going to waste even one second. He was always demanding and negotiating, even while on his deathbed.

"So Richie, I have a feeling you've discovered your life purpose?"

"Yes sir, I did. How did you know?" I said.

"I just had a hunch. That's all," Mr. Rodriguez said with a little smile.

"Yes, Anthony helped guided me through the process when we met for lunch earlier today. It—"

Mr. Rodriguez interrupted me, "And who do you think helped him discover his life purpose?"

"Come on man, don't tell me it was you. That's not fair. You met Anthony through me. It would have only been fair that I'd learn it first," I said.

Mr. Rodriguez made a gasping noise, so I handed him a cup of water on the table beside him. After he caught his breath, he said slowly, "I only walked him through the process first because he was ready for it and I felt you weren't. By now you know how I work, young man."

"Okay, I got it. I am not going to argue that. Well, he was a big help and it was very freeing to finally get why I was brought to this earth."

"So tell me--what is your life purpose, champ?" Mr. Rodriguez said.

I sat back in my chair, took a deep breath, planted my feet firmly on the ground, dug deep into my soul, and belted out, "*My life purpose is to use my inspiration and creativity to empower others to freely exploit their God-given talents in ways that align with their core values and their highest and truest self expression.* Yep that's it. That's who I am at my core. From today on, I will make sure to express that purpose through everything I do, and be that purpose everywhere I am. It will guide me, keep me centered and living in the now, and most important of all, this purpose will serve to make a difference for the greater good. Just the thought of that fuels me up."

After I said this statement, I leaned back into my chair and smiled at Mr. Rodriguez. It was at this moment that I saw his eyes welling up with tears. "Are you okay, sir?" I asked.

"Of course I am. I'm just moved to tears with your discovery. It feels so good to hear you talk like this. Come over here and give me a big hug," Mr. Rodriguez said.

I leaned over and gave him a gentle hug. When my head pressed upon his chest, I felt the thin oxygen cables press on my face. But I didn't care. He extended his fragile arms around me and hugged me lightly but with lots of love. Discovery my life purpose before he passed was a monumental moment for me. Not just for me, but for us.

After standing up, I leaned over and wiped his tears away with a napkin, and then said, "Mr. Rodriguez, we have 15 minutes left before the nurse returns--I have one last question before this...ends." I paused because I did not know how to start this conversation I wanted to have with him.

Mr. Rodriguez jumped in, "I know what you want to ask me, son."

"You do?"

"Of course I do. You want to know what the code is. Am I right?" Mr. Rodriguez asked.

"You've always been good at reading my mind."

"Richie, help me sit up so we can have this conversation," Mr. Rodriguez said.

I leaned over to help him, feeling so much excitement I accidentally knocked over a pitcher of water on the nearby bedside table. After soaking it up with a pile of napkins and helping him sit up, Mr. Rodriguez said, "Richie, listen to me very carefully. I am not going to tell you exactly what it is, but I will help you discover it."

"But sir, we don't have much time," I said with a look of concern.

"Don't you think I know that? You have to trust me. If you follow my every command you will get it in less than five minutes. Are you game?" Mr. Rodriguez said.

"Yes. Shoot. I am ready."

"Go ahead and repeat this phrase five times out loud. The code is the code."

"Okay will do. The code is the code. The code is the code. The code is the code. The code is the code. The code is the code."

"Did you get it?" Mr Rodriguez said.

"Nope. Sure didn't," I said, shaking my head.

"Okay, take a deep breath and clear your mind of all your concerns over whatever you might think it is."

"Okay, let me do that now." I took a few deep breaths, cleared my mind, and said, "Okay, I am ready to start again."

"Good. This time, I want you to repeat it out loud once, then pause between each repetition. Just pretend you will get it in the next minutes. Just trust me Richie, it's going to work out fine."

"Okay, here I go. The code is the code."

I then paused and concentrated on each word. Then said it one more time, "The code is the code." Then it hit me. I shouted in excitement, "I got it, Mr. Rodriguez. I got it!"

"So, what did you get?" Mr. Rodriguez said.

"The CODE is the C.O.D.E. Each letter in the word code represents a quality we are all born with," I said with excitement.

"You are 100% right. So what do you think the first letter stands for?" Mr. Rodriguez asked.

"I think the first letter in C.O.D.E. stands for 'Choice'."

"Exactly, you chose to:

- work with a mentor
- listen to your mentor
- read positive books
- persist even when you did not feel like it
- ask for advice when you've felt lost
- get creative when pressed with problems
- commit to your dreams
- take risks
- save money
- invest in assets
- stay away from negative people
- get a college degree
- not sell drugs and take the easy path

"I could continue, but I'll stop there, Richie. The list is too long and I think you get the point. What is the second word in the C.O.D.E.?"

"I think the second word is 'Optimism'."

"You are spot on. Go ahead and open my wife's purse," Mr. Rodriguez said, pointing to her purse at the far end of the room. "Go ahead and pull out the dictionary and look up 'optimism'. Tell me, what does it say?"

I opened the worn-down dictionary and read the definition out loud: "Hopefulness and confidence about the future or the successful outcome of something."[52]

"That is exactly what you have done on a consistent basis. You chose to be optimistic in spite of your negative environment. And when you weren't optimistic, you sought out advice from me or read a positive book to stay in your optimistic state," Mr. Rodriguez coughed, then continued, "What is the third word in the C.O.D.E.?"

"I think the third word is 'Discipline'. Am I right?" I said.

"You sure are. Please look up the definition in the dictionary," Mr. Rodriguez requested.

I flipped back several pages and found it. "Mr. Rodriguez, the definition of discipline is 'orderly conduct or pattern of behavior.' [53]"

"That is correct. You've certainly had steadfast discipline. You learned quickly that motivation comes and goes, but discipline will always prevail. I saw you accomplish this by taking daily actions. Your daily actions created consistency. Your consistency created new habits. And your new habits created discipline. Now, what is the fourth word in the C.O.D.E.?"

"I think the fourth word is 'Enthusiasm'. Am I right?" I asked.

"That is certainly a good quality to possess, but enthusiasm is a byproduct of you being optimistic. The fourth word in the C.O.D.E. is 'Endurance'."

I looked up the word 'endurance' when he mentioned it. "Mr. Rodriguez, the definition of endurance is 'the fact or power of enduring an unpleasant or difficult process or situation without giving way'.[54]"

"That is exactly what you did, Champ," He said softly, his energy waning.

I jumped in to help him since I noticed he was tired and looked very weak now. "Yes, I can see how much of a persistent bastard I was. Sorry for the cursing, sir. I guess I got too excited," I said.

Mr. Rodriguez just glanced at me and smiled. I continued, "Yes, I can see how applying the other three qualities have helped me endure. Each quality builds momentum into the next. So you mean to tell me that I was applying the C.O.D.E. all along and didn't even know it?" I said.

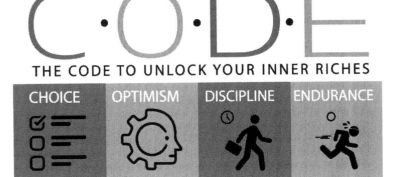

He just nodded, growing too weak to reply.

"It's all making sense now. You held me accountable to the application of the success principles and in the process of applying them, the C.O.D.E. within was unlocked," I said with excitement, "Once unlocked, it guided me to reach all my goals and create all the riches I wanted. Now I can see why you never wanted to share the C.O.D.E. with me because like you said 20 plus years ago, my mindset, habits, and beliefs first needed to change before the..."

Mr. Rodriguez grasped for air then said, "Before the C.O.D.E. was unlocked."

I continued to help him save his energy. "Man, it has all come full circle. If it's one thing I can promise you, I will spend the rest of my life empowering and guiding others in discovering the code. I can also promise you that many people are going to benefit from this message." I then looked over at Mr. Rodriguez and noticed he attempted to say thank you, but I could barely hear it. The sound was low and muffled and when I looked over at the heart monitor, I noticed a quick dip on the screen. I pushed the button by his bed requesting help. The nurse and his wife quickly rushed in and asked me to leave the room. As I exited the room, I saw the nurse injecting him with some type of medicine.

I proceeded to the waiting area and sat around for a few hours. Something told me not to leave. All I kept thinking about was how long I'd been living the C.O.D.E. without realizing it. I was literally floating on cloud nine, as strange as it felt. At one moment, I closed my eyes to take a nap and starting daydreaming about how I was going to fulfill on my life purpose. Moments later, I was awoken by a loud scream and when I opened my eyes I saw Mr. Rodriguez's family crying. My heart froze. I knew what that meant. I slowly stood up and walked toward his room. When I approached the door to his room, I stopped, closed my eyes, clenched my fists real tight, and took three deep breaths to get myself grounded before walking into the room full of cries.

When I walked in, I observed everybody desperately crying, but for some strange reason no tears rolled off my eyes. I then built up the courage and glanced over at his bed. He lay lifeless, his eyes shut. His bed was surrounded by close family members standing around him in full anguish. When I gathered my thoughts, it suddenly hit me why I wasn't crying or sad. The truth is that before me laid a man who lived a full life and died on empty. He gave everything he had to his desires and dreams. He gave every part of him to humanity. He chased his dreams and never complained about his problems. And lastly, he lived with purpose. He fulfilled his purpose during his time on earth and that made his departure a peaceful and, believe it or not, inspiring one. That is what I want others to say about me when they see me on my deathbed, I thought to myself

*****

As I wrapped up the story of Mr. Rodriguez's legacy and about to turn onto Darnell's street, I glanced over at the young man as he wept profusely. He tried to turn away so that I would not see him in this state, wiping his tears by sliding the side of his fist along his cheeks. I decided to give him another minute before asking about his current state of mind.

"So there you have it. What do ya' think, Darnell?" I asked, pulling into his driveway.

Darnel sat up in his seat, turned his head in my direction, and said, "Wow, I can't believe how much my life has transformed over the last 12 hours. That was some powerful stuff, Richie! I feel both sad and happy after that story. Man, it was so inspiring. It's hard to explain how I am feeling at the moment, but let me take a stab at it. This conversation we've had about discovering your life purpose has ignited something at the deepest level of my core. I am now looking forward to discovering my passions and life purpose. I promise I will share it with you once I discover it. Also, your simple formula for making powerful choices is phenomenal. I can now see how I can apply 'The Choice Making Success Model' to all the areas of my life. And thank you for sharing the 5 C's to making better choices, especially when dealing with a difficult moment."

I chimed in, "Man, you are on fire. Your energy right now is contagious."

"Please don't interrupt me, Mr. Mentor. I am now in my flow and I want to share all the lessons I learned today from our trip before going into my house. I know my parents are waiting for me since it's a bit late." As Darnell said this, his dad walked out of the house and patiently waited for him by the entrance so we could finish our conversation.

"Go for it, Champ. I promise I won't interrupt your flow," I smiled proudly.

"Richie, in the last 12 hours, I learned so much about what it means to live an extraordinary life. You've equipped me with tons of tools and strategies to accomplish every goal I choose to go after. Because of you, I will live a happier life, be more productive, and become a great leader. I now know the importance of honoring the champion in me instead of giving way to the complainer. I have learned that I need to take responsibility for everything that happens in my life. That if it's got to be, it's up to me. I will never forget that 'nothing works without integrity.' I will especially never forget how to turn a disempowering belief into an empowering belief. Your 'D.E.F.Y. Method' for creating new empowering beliefs was off the hook awesome!"

"I also learned so much about how the rich think when it comes to money and business. That alone was priceless. I'm blessed to have learned 'The Wealth Bucket Formula'. Oh wait! How could I forget the secret C.O.D.E. to unlock my inner riches? Thank you for teaching me so much today. I have my entire life to put everything I have learned into practice. I will live each day as if it were my last. I will always be in debt to you."

Darnell continued, "I wish you a long, happy, and healthy life, Richie. After all, I want you to see the masterpiece I will create someday! I want you to know that your impact on me has already impacted thousands, possibly even millions. All I have to say is, 'Game On!'"

As he spoke, my eyes welled up with tears of victory. A feeling of peace took over me and I felt light as a feather. Something in my heart told me he would never be the same person ever again. Once I gathered myself, I said, "Darnell, I expect nothing but amazing things from you. All I ask is that you pass on everything I have taught you to others. Never stop preaching these success and business principles. And above all, promise me you will commit to helping others discover the C.O.D.E. to unlock their inner riches. Look me in the eyes and tell me you will do this for me."

Darnell leaned over, looked me dead straight in his eyes, and said confidently, "You can count on me to do this, and don't take this the wrong way, but I am not going to do it for you. I am going to do it for me."

He then extended his arms over his shoulders and hugged me so strong you'd think he was trying to break my neck. The hug was an intense moment for Darnell, for it not only represented the freedom to be himself and take ownership of his mistakes, but the freedom to take full responsibility for how he wanted his life to be going forward.

For me, it meant victory and contribution. It meant I was finally passing on what Mr. Rodriguez had imparted to me during my life. We high fived each other before Darnell got out of the car. Upon exiting, he saw his dad waiting for him at the end of the driveway. As I drove out of the driveway, I saw Darnell running toward his dad and observed him through my rearview mirror giving him a big hug. As I turned the corner of the driveway, I could see him telling his dad something and although I could not hear it, I knew that everything that came out of his mouth was all positive. I took a victorious deep breath and drove away feeling very good about myself. I then said to myself, "Now I need to find the next person to make a difference with." As I said this, it reminded me of my life purpose: *To use my inspiration and creativity to empower*

others to freely exploit their God-given talents in a way that aligns with their core values and their highest and truest self expression.
"Now on to the next victim," I said, smiling triumphantly.

Onward my friend,
Edward R. Muñoz

CONCLUSION

Good business leaders create a vision, articulate the vision, passionately own the vision, and relentlessly drive it to completion.

—Jack Welch

Congratulations for completing this book. I commend you for sticking it out until the very end. By now you've probably made some new decisions on how to take your life to new levels. If that is your case, then I recommend you take immediate action on your decisions. Don't you dare sit on the sidelines and wait for things to get better for you. We all know that nothing motivates us more than progress. So the sooner you take action, the sooner you will start to see some type of progress, which will only fuel you to take more action.

Here are a few recommendations to take advantage of all of the principles that you learned about in this book:

1. Make a commitment to reread the book again 30 - 90 days from now. Doing so will remind you of all the lessons that were explained in this book.
2. The next time you read it, make sure to read it slowly. The first time around, you probably read it at a fast pace because you were so into it that is was a bit hard to digest all the success principles embedded in the story.
3. Reread a chapter per month for the next 12 months and choose to practice all the success principles outlined in that chapter during the month and see what becomes available in your life out of doing so.
4. They say that the best way to learn something is by teaching it. Having said that, share what you have learned in this book with a few friends or at your next company function or meeting. The more you share it, the more the principles will live inside of you.

Reach Out To Me Anytime

If at any point in this book, you read something that makes a profound difference in your life, then please do share it with me. I would love to hear how this book made a difference in your life. Who knows, I might be having a tough day and your message might serve as inspiration for me when I most need it. Remember, I am also human. I most certainly am not a robot! To send me a message, just go to my website www.EdwardMunoz.com and click on the "Contact" tab.

Here's How We Can Help Others

May I ask you a question?

Has this book made an enormous difference in your life? If it has inspired you to make new decisions, increased your confidence, given you new more peace of mind in regards to your past and motivated you to keep pressing forward in spite of your present challenges, then pass on some of the success principles in this book to someone you know who could also gain from them.

Better yet, buy them a copy from Amazon.com or buy a few copies and give them out as gifts for Christmas or birthdays. Just imagine your friends calling you after they read it and thanking you for the enormous difference it made in their lives.

MY INVITATION TO YOU

By now, you can see that I am very passionate about making a difference in the lives of the people who purchase my books and courses, as well as those who hire me to coach them or speak about reaching their peak performance and unleashing their inner champion. Truthfully speaking, mastering all these skills has not been easy. At the time of this recording, it has been a 20-year journey into learning and mastering these skills. And the best part is that I'm just getting started. I already have at least 4 more books in mind that I plan to write in the next few years and 2 seminars that I plan to unveil when the time is right.

That is why I would like to extend a personal invitation for you to follow me on my journey over the next few decades. I have a lot in store for you and that is why I am extending an invitation to follow me on my social media channels. My social media handle is @edward**R**munoz

These are the places you can frequently find me in:
www.youtube.edwardmunoz.com
www.facebook.EdwardMunoz.com
www.instagram.EdwardMunoz.com
www.Blog.EdwardMunoz.com
www.TheUnderdogCommunity.com (Our Pvt Facebook Support Group)

Feel free to send me a private message on any of my social media channels, as I try my best to reply to as many messages as I possibly can.

Lastly, I would like to offer you the opportunity to join the hottest and best weekly motivational newsletter out there. Just kidding! It may not be the best on the planet. Gosh, there are only a few million other newsletters I compete with, but many have told me my newsletters are extremely valuable, and they look forward to reading it each week.

In my newsletter, I will cover topics such as entrepreneurship, personal growth, wealth creation, and many more. More importantly, you will gain access to a wide variety of strategies to empower and inspire you to design your destiny, based on what you desire and what is uniquely important to. You can sign up directly on my site www.EdwardMunoz.com or send an email to info@edwardmunoz.com with your email address and a short message that you'd like to be added to our weekly motivational mailing list.

POWERFUL MOTIVATIONAL QUOTES BY YOURS TRULY

If you are anything like me, you value the power of a good motivational quote. I have a quote book someone gifted me 10 years ago. Whenever I have an off day I refer to it, and each time I find a quote that resonates and speaks to a specific problem I am dealing with. Quotes are more than just words on a piece of paper. They are the philosophies and beliefs behind the people who created them. A powerful quote gives you the opportunity to stand on the shoulders of giants, see life through their eyes and tap into their wisdom.

That is why I decided to include as a bonus some of my original quotes. I hope they are of value and make a difference in your life. Here they are:

Motivational Quotes by Edward R. Munoz

"Unfortunately, science has failed to create a technology to look into a human being's heart and measure their drive and passion. Especially to measure their will and desire to succeed. Consider this the next time you underestimate the tenacity of an underdog."

"Your commitments should not revolve around your life: rather, your life should revolve around your commitments."

"Realize that happiness is where you are, not out there somewhere. Learn to appreciate all that you have, and consciously make a choice to be grateful for it. Once you learn to appreciate what you have, then, and only then, should you attempt to go after other things in life."

"Creating wealth starts by just voicing out loud what

you want from the universe. It's only when you express your dreams and wishes constantly to others with conviction that the universe aligns with you for the realization and fulfillment of that request."

"There is a big difference between personal growth and financial wealth growth. Both are important for long-term success."

"Underdogs are always underestimated, undervalued, under-appreciated, and worst of all, considered underachievers. Knowing all of this gives them the extra fuel to prove the naysayers wrong."

"Debt is usually perceived as a dirty word. But knowing the difference between good debt and bad debt can mean the difference between being wealthy or financially broke for the rest of your life."

"The difference between an underdog and a loser is that an underdog gets back up stronger and faster after each failure."

"Life can be so sweet when we live for others and so bitter when we only live for ourselves."

"A loser accepts defeat. An underdog is committed to winning, even when the odds are stacked against him."

"Do your best, and I do mean your best, with the cards you're dealt. Your best effort will create the space for miracles to show up."

"There is no shortcut to success. It actually lacks integrity to take shortcuts. But if there was one shortcut, it would be mentorship. Getting a good mentor will accelerate your path to success."

"Quitting first starts in the mind, then comes out as a verbal declaration. My advice

is simple: don't think or say it out loud, because if you do, it will become so."

"Underdogs don't incarcerate themselves in a scarcity mindset. Instead, they incarcerate themselves in a possibility mindset."

"You can't put a price on your personal transformation. Investment in self will always pay the highest ROI (Return On Investment)."

"You will have everything you've ever wanted when you learn how to have a no-excuse mindset."

"Underdogs train hard in private so they can be ready in public when the time comes to prove themselves."

"When you are on fire on the inside, you have the power to extinguish all the negativity on the outside."

"The Wealth Bucket System is a Proven and Simple Method for Saving Money and Creating Wealth."

"When the will to win is bigger than your current excuses, success will kneel down at your feet and beg you to take it."

"Underdogs get excited by the possibilities they create in their head and believe in their heart."

"You can make a million dollars or you can make one million excuses of why it can't be done."

"The actions you take will always be in direct proportion to how you interpret life's events."

"A positive mental shift could be the difference between going from underdog to top dog."

"Passion is what you love to do, but your life purpose is what you were designed to do."

"Most people want to succeed from a braggadocious standpoint rather than purpose."

"Underdogs do not need alarm clocks to wake them up. Their dreams wake them up."

"Underdog mantra: I will do whatever it takes, for as long as it takes, until I succeed."

"Do you have haters in your life? Good. It means you are headed in the right direction."

"Passion, purpose, and the will to win are the biggest drivers behind every underdog."

"Underdogs don't aspire to be champions, they already see themselves as champions."

"Average people focus on excuses. Underdog's focus on execution."

"Everybody believes it cannot be done until the underdog proves them wrong."

"Your desire to succeed must be bigger than Warren Buffet's bank account."

"An underdog locks eyes with adversity and says, "you're going down, baby."

"We will always fail if we decide to make a decision coming from our fears."

"Underdogs are willing to train their entire life for their one moment of truth."

"Making money is easy when you have the right beliefs, habits and values."

"Did you know that Muhammad Ali was once considered an underdog?"

"Poor choices, difficult life. Powerful choices, great life."

"Work with what you've got and improve as you go."

"Underdog mantra: I am on fiya by personal choice!"

"Smart entrepreneurs follow proven formulas."

"Leave your past in the past way before you pass."

"You can't be a champion thinking average."

"Underdogs grind their way out of adversity."

"Underdogs turn rejection into fuel for success."

"Communicate to elevate rather than deflate."

"Success is a commitment to completion."

"An underdog who believes in himself
cannot be contained or stopped."

**"The desire to prove others wrong is the
underdog's greatest motivator."**

"Do not focus on building wealth without
first focusing on building self."

**"Declaration creates the possibility,
but action makes it a reality."**

"When purpose leads, fulfillment follows."

"Do you, and don't live to be liked."

"This shall be because I said so."

"What you resist rules you."

Would you like to download all of my original quotes?
Go to this link:
www.TheUnderdogCode.com/quoteimages

(No Email Required - Immediate Download)
Note: If you resonate with any of these quotes, feel free to share them on your social media channels or email them to friends and colleges. You can also use them as affirmations.

CITATIONS

Chapter 1

1- Lustig, Jessica. 2009. "The Fashion Thief." *NYMag.com.*
Accessed August 29, 2016.
<http://nymag.com/fashion/09/spring/54331>.

2- Pavlina, Steve. 2005. "The Power of Clarity." Accessed
August 29, 2016.
<http://www.stevepavlina.com/articles/power-of-clarity.
htm>.

Chapter 3

3- Cambridge Dictionary. 2017. "Underdog." Accessed
December 25, 2017.
<https://dictionary.cambridge.org/dictionary/english/
underdog>.

3a- Merriam-Webster Dictionary. "Success." Accessed
December 25, 2017.
<https://www.merriam-webster.com/dictionary/
success>.

4- Science Daily. 2016. "Reference Terms." Accessed
September 20, 2016.
<https://www.sciencedaily.com/terms/belief.htm>.

5- Robbins, Tony. 1992. *Awaken the Giant Within: How
to Take Immediate Control of Your Mental, Emotional,
Physical and Financial Destiny!* Free Press. Palm Beach.

6- Farlex. 2016. "The Free Dictionary." Accessed
September 20, 2016.
<http://www.thefreedictionary.com/distinguish>.

Chapter 4

7- Rodriguez, Luis J. 2005. *Always Running: La Vida Loca:
Gang Days in L.A.* Touchstone. California. pp. 170.

8- Wikipedia. 2016. "W. Edwards Deming." Accessed
October 15, 2016.
<https://en.wikipedia.org/wiki/W._Edwards_Deming>.

9- Rodriguez, Luis J. 2005. *Always Running: La Vida Loca:
Gang Days in L.A.* Touchstone. California. pp. 159.

10- Wikipedia. 2016. "Rikers Island." Accessed October 15, 2016.
<https://en.wikipedia.org/wiki/Rikers_Island>.

11- Willimon, Beau. 2013. "House of Cards". Netflix. Chapter 3: 29:00-29:49.

12- Chandler, Steve. 2012. *9 Lies That Are Holding Your Business Back and the TRUTH That Will Set It Free.* ReadHowYouWant. Florida. pp. 145.

13- Chandler, Steve. 2012. *9 Lies That Are Holding Your Business Back and the TRUTH That Will Set It Free.* ReadHowYouWant. Florida. pp. 152.

14- Goldman, Manny. 2008. The Power of Personal Growth. Personal Growth Publishing. New York. pp. 15.

15- Nuggets4Nobles. "CANI- Constant and Never-Ending Improvement." Accessed October 15, 2016. <http://nuggets4nobles.com/>.

16- Pritchett, Price. 2012. *You 2: A High Velocity Formula for Multiplying Your Personal Effectiveness in Quantum Leaps.* Pritchett and Associates. Arkansas. pp. 5.

Chapter 5

17- Chandler, Steve. 2012. *9 Lies That Are Holding Your Business Back and the TRUTH That Will Set It Free.* ReadHowYouWant. Florida. pp. 167.

18- Murdock, Mike. *Seeds of Wisdom on Habits.* Vol 6. Wisdom International. Dallas. pp. 1.

19- Murdock, Mike. May 2014. Personal e-mail communication.

20- Murdock, Mike. *Seeds of Wisdom on Habits.* Vol 6. Wisdom International. Dallas. pp. 27.

21- Murdock, Mike. June 2014. Personal e-mail communication.

Chapter 6

21a- Juicy song excerpt written by Christopher Wallace, James Mtume, Jean Claude Olivier, Sean Combs
• Copyright © Sony/ATV Music Publishing LLC, Universal Music Publishing Group, Jellybean Music Group

22 - Karrass, Chester L. 1996. *In Business As in Life, You*

Don't Get What You Deserve, You Get What You Negotiate. Stanford Street Pr.

23 - McWilliams, Stephanie. 2014. "Kiss Your Frogs." Accessed November 28, 2016. <http://www.jointheunstoppables.com/author/admin/page/5>.

24 - McWilliams, Stephanie. 2014. "Kiss Your Frogs." Accessed November 28, 2016. <http://www.jointheunstoppables.com/author/admin/page/5>.

25 - Unknown. 2016. "The Donkey and the Carrot". Accessed November 28, 2016. <https://tinlala.wordpress.com/2008/02/13/donkey-carrots/>.

Chapter 7

26 - "Sovereign." Sons of Anarchy. Writ. Paris Barclay. Dir. Kurt Sutter. FX. Linson, 2012. DVD.

27 - Papa Roach. 2015. "Face Everything and Rise." *F.E.A.R. Eleven Seven Music.*

Chapter 8

28 - Laskas, Jeanne M. 2004. "The Coward." GQ Magazine. pp. 112.

29 - Al-Khatib, Talal. 2011. "Marine Corps Recon Training: The 5 Toughest Skills to Master." Accessed October 30, 2017. <https://www.seeker.com/marine-corps-recon-training-the-5-toughest-skills-to-master-1765551752.html>

Chapter 9

30 - Zachmeier, Bob. 2008. *Upside Up Real Estate Investing.* Out of the Box Publishing. pp 16.

31 - Connors, Tiffany. 2017. "How House Flipping Works." Accessed January 18, 2017. <http://home.howstuffworks.com/real-estate/selling-home/ house-flipping.htm>

32 - Zachmeier, Bob. 2008. *Upside Up Real Estate Investing.* Out of the Box Publishing. pp. 17.

33 - Wikipedia. 2017. "Compound Interest." Accessed January 18, 2017.
<https://en.wikipedia.org/wiki/Compound_interest>.

34 - Zachmeier, Bob. 2008. *Upside Up Real Estate Investing.* Out of the Box Publishing. pp. 25-26.

35 - Gale, Porter. 2013. *Your Network Is Your Net Worth: Unlock the Hidden Power of Connections for Wealth, Success, and Happiness in the Digital Age.* Atria Books.

Chapter 10

36- Bliliuos, Eli. 2010. "How Past Life Memories and Fears Can Impact Your Current Life." Accessed February 10, 2017.
<http://EzineArticles.com/5484864>

37- Canfield, Jack. *The Success Principles: How to Get from Where You Are to Where You Want to Be.* William Morrow Books.p. 19

38- Gura, Leo. "Life Purpose" [Podcast, Episode 295]. Accessed December 25, 2017.
<https://itunes.apple.com/us/podcast/actualized-org/id998025672?mt=2>

39- Gura, Leo. "Life Purpose" [Podcast, Episode 295]. Accessed December 25, 2017.
<https://player.fm/series/actualizedorg-personal-development-self-help-psychology-consciousness-philosophy>

40- Canfield, Jack. *The Success Principles: How to Get from Where You Are to Where You Want to Be.* William Morrow Books. p. 22

41- Sweatt, Lydia. 2017. "17 Inspiring Quotes to Help You Live a Life of Purpose." Accessed December 25, 2017.
<https://www.success.com/article/ 17-inspiring-quotes-to-help-you-live-a-life-of-purpose>

41a- Dictionary.com. 2017. "Choice." Accessed January 25, 2017.
<http://www.dictionary.com/browse/choice>

41b- Dictionary.com. 2017. "Decision." Accessed January 25, 2017.
<http://www.dictionary.com/browse/decision>

42- Mertz, Jon. 2012. "Decisions vs. Choices: Is There a

Distinction?" Accessed October 31, 2017. <https://www.
thindifference.com/2012/06/ decisions-vs-choices-is-
there-a-distinction/>

Chapter 11

43- Youtube. 2016. "Watch Oprah's Uplifting Speech on
Our Empowerment Stage: 2016 ESSENCE Festival."
[Video file 25:39 - 25:43]. Accessed December 25, 2017.
<https://www.youtube.com/watch?v=wUPKMiIeGhA>

44- Youtube. 2016. "Watch Oprah's Uplifting Speech on
Our Empowerment Stage: 2016
ESSENCE Festival." [Video file 17:47 - 17:56].
Accessed December 25, 2017.
<https://www.youtube.com/watch?v=wUPKMiIeGhA>

45- Su, Tina. n.d. "Life on Purpose: 15 Questions to
Discover Your Personal Mission." Accessed
December 25, 2017.
<http://thinksimplenow.com/ happiness/life-on-purpose-
15-questions-to-discover-your-personal-mission>

46- Youtube. 2017. "Oprah's SuperSoul Conversations - Dr.
Michael Bernard Beckwith: Manifest the Life of Your
Dreams" [Video file 7:06- 7:07]. Accessed December
25, 2017.
<https://www.youtube.com/watch?v=RRUkS4pG7VQ>

47- Youtube. 2017. "Oprah's SuperSoul Conversations - Dr.
Michael Bernard Beckwith: Manifest the Life of Your
Dreams" [Video file 7:08 - 7:09]. Accessed December
25, 2017.
<https://www.youtube.com/watch?v=RRUkS4pG7VQ>

48-Youtube. 2017. "Oprah's SuperSoul Conversations - Dr.
Michael Bernard Beckwith: Manifest the Life of Your
Dreams" [Video file]. Accessed December 25, 2017.
<https://www.youtube.com/watch?v=RRUkS4pG7VQ>

49-Youtube. 2017. "Oprah's SuperSoul Conversations - Dr.
Michael Bernard Beckwith: Manifest the Life of Your
Dreams" [Video file 7:11 - 7:33]. Accessed December
25, 2017.
<https://www.youtube.com/watch?v=RRUkS4pG7VQ>

50-Youtube. 2017. "Oprah's SuperSoul Conversations - Dr. Michael Bernard Beckwith: Manifest the Life of Your Dreams" [Video file 6:08 - 6:50]. Accessed December 25, 2017.
<https://www.youtube.com/watch?v=RRUkS4pG7VQ>

51-Youtube. 2017. "Oprah's SuperSoul Conversations - Dr. Michael Bernard Beckwith: Manifest the Life of Your Dreams" [Video file 16:43 - 17:15]. Accessed December 25, 2017.
<https://www.youtube.com/watch?v=RRUkS4pG7VQ>

Chapter 12

52-Dictionary.com. 2017. "Optimism." Accessed December 25, 2017.
<http://www.dictionary.com/browse/optimism>

53- Merriam-Webster Dictionary. 2017. "Discipline." Accessed December 25, 2017.
<https://www.merriam-webster.com/dictionary/discipline>

54-Dictionary.com. 2017. "Endurance." Accessed December 25, 2017.
<http://www.dictionary.com/browse/endurance>

ACKNOWLEDGEMENTS

→ Make sure you at least read the last few words in this section (it pertains to YOU)

Here's the best part and the most challenging part of this book. This is where I get to acknowledge all the people who have in some way made an enormous difference in my life. Without them, I would not be who I am today. Some have been a shoulder to lean on during my most difficult times and others have been there to encourage me all the way through my entrepreneurial endeavors.

In the upcoming pages, I will attempt to acknowledge as many people as I possibly can. If I forget to mention your name, please do not hold it against me since there are too many to acknowledge in so few pages. If I did acknowledge everybody that has in some way contributed to my life, it would literally go into the hundreds, but just know wherever you are that I do appreciate you and everything you have done for me.

First, I would like to give thanks to the best mom ever. When I was just a little boy, you were strict with me and showed me how to always pay attention to detail. When I was left to wash the dishes, you would make sure that I didn't leave the kitchen until everything was spotless. I hated it back then, but am grateful for those lessons today. Thank you for being tough while doing it with so much love.

Secondly, I would like to publicly acknowledge my dad Virgilio R. Muñoz. I am incredibly grateful to you for so many things. You taught me hard work, persistence and consistency. You taught me through your own example to never quit, no matter how hard the challenge I was facing. I love you so much and thank you for your unconditional love.

To my three lovely children, Arlene Muñoz, Ariann Muñoz, and Edward Elias Muñoz. These three human beings are the main motivation for everything I accomplish in life. They give me 'Why

317

Power'. They inspire me to be the best version I could possibly be and more. I always strive to be the example of what's possible when you set your mind to accomplish a goal or dream.

To my siblings, Mary Muñoz, Alexander Muñoz, and David Muñoz. You guys have pulled me out of some tough spots and have never judged me during my many falls. I bet if I looked up unconditional love in the dictionary I would find your names there. I love you all very much.

To my other siblings from my extended families, Seleny Muñoz, Rocio Muñoz, Moises Virgilio Muñoz, and Juan Carlos Vargas. You guys came into my life and are a huge blessing. Each one of you has contributed to my character in ways you will never imagine. Thank you for your love and support.

To the woman of my dreams and soulmate, Yaniris Muñoz. There is so much to say about this woman. She literally met me when I was in a financial slump and she fell in love with me for who I was. Together, we have been flooded out of our home—not once, but twice. Talk about tough times. Each time, she stood by me and kept encouraging me to write more books because she knew it was not only my passion, but my god-given gift. When she felt discouraged she would pray relentlessly—and I do mean relentlessly—and would empower me daily by reading the scriptures of the Bible to keep me in faith. Now you can see why I said she was and will forever be my God-given soul mate. I love you Yani.

To my inner circle of friends. Together, we have grown closer, shared resources, cried together and influenced each other to become who we are today. I value our lifelong friendships and unconditional love and support: Chris Rosario, Elvin Rodriguez, Dee Hutchins, Erik Torres, Eddie Moquete, Armando Granados, Stephanie Horner, Omar Susana, Edward A. Rodriguez, Joy Martinez, and Juan Arias.

To my mentors. This group of people have mentored me through the good times and the bad. Each individual on this list has coached and mentored me into greatness. They saw me for who I could be instead of dwelling on my current problems and challenges. They coached me through my most desperate times. Because of them, I made different decisions and took on things that I would have never dreamed possible. I cannot say enough about the people on this list. As a group, these individuals have invested thousands of hours into my greatness: Pablo Zabala, David Fidel, MiguelAngel Burdier, MiguelAngel Lopez, Bethany Harris, Sandy Arrango, Joaquin Freddy Diaz, Nathan Hardy, Kally Bougadis, Carmen Reynal, Wilson Santos, Angel Garcia, Tony Vear, Milton Olave, Iman Khan, Ray Valle, Re Perez, Juan Guillen, Gene Flynn, Larry Raskin, Jeffrey Almanzar, Ana Pough, Manny Goldman, Craig Duncan, Alexis Aquino, Jeri Quinn, Karen Armino, Luis Fallas, Edward A. Rodriguez, Brooke Ferris, Frankie Lamumba, and Helder Molina.

I would like to honor all those who have served or are currently serving in the Army, Airforce, Navy, National Guard and the Marine Corps. Having served in the Marine Corps myself, I know firsthand that it takes a special kind of person to dedicate your life to our country. You guys embody the truest meaning of loyalty and honor. This is why I decided to add a military character in this book -- in honor of all the military veterans and current military soldiers out there.

A special thanks to the countless people I have interviewed and consulted in the process of writing this book. Too many too mention here, but you all know who you are.

A special thanks to the person who has had the biggest impact on my life outside of my family—Pablo Zabala. This gentleman took me under his wing when I was a taxi driver back in 1996. Back then, I would constantly bombard him with questions about how to get started in the entrepreneurial world. He never said no. This man stood for my greatness. He coached me out of a major depression and mentored me on how to be a motivational speaker in 1998. I am not 100% sure what he saw in me back then, but what I do know is that I am passing on everything he taught me. Pablo, I want you to know that I will forever be grateful for the stand that you were for my greatness.

A special thanks to Tony Vear. During the two months leading up to the 1st publication of the book we had daily calls where we would exchange ideas on the direction we felt would have the most impact and how we wanted to close out the story in the final chapters. He was instrumental in helping me flush out what I had in my head and get it onto paper. Several times I thought I was done with the content creation, and each time he would critique it and send me back to the drawing board as they say. Without his support, this book would not have the powerful ending that it currently has. What was created really completes the transformation Richie was so desperately seeking, and ultimately leaves you transformed and inspired by its end as well. Thank you Tony, for your unconditional support. If you are looking for someone to help you create content for a course, presentation, webinar, or book, then I highly recommend having him by your side. Feel free to reach him at pvwh1005@yahoo.com

To my writing and editing team—Mona Lisa Safai, Alexis Aquino, Aaron Cohen, and Laurel Wright. Without your relentless guidance, I would have never had such a great book. You guys took this raw product and turned it into what I consider a masterpiece. Thank you for the countless hours you so generously poured into making this classic book into the game changer that it is. Over the next few decades, I am confident your gracious contributions will touch the lives of thousands—and possibly millions—throughout the world..

Finally, to you the reader: thank you for following me on this journey of transformation. I want to acknowledge you for making it to the very end. The fact that you are reading this last section tells me that you are a person who finishes what they start. However, let's not end here. Follow me on Instagram, Snapchat, Facebook and Youtube. My social media handle is @edwardRmunoz. Shoot me a message and let me know how I can be of service. I always try my best to personally reply to each message. Never forget that "You Get Empowered When You Choose To Empower Others".

-- THE BEHIND THE SCENES STORY OF EDWARD R. MUNOZ'S LIFE --

By now you may be interested in the experiences contributing to who I am today. Some of the below is relevant, and some of which may serve as "trivia". In either case, I invite you closer into my world.

<u>Growing up</u>

I was raised in a Dominican household in Brooklyn, New York with four siblings. Even though I grew up in an environment of gang-infested streets, I relied on my parents to provide a foundation for my lessons of life. My mom, who worked two jobs to support her family, always preached to me: "Edward, responsible and powerful people always honor their word, work really hard, and never lie." My dad, who came to the United States from Dominican Republic, was known as a strict disciplinarian. He only had an eighth grade education but retired with a healthy six-figure net worth. For him, it was important to work hard, save and invest money. He taught us: "If you want something bad enough, you will find a way to make it happen."

At age 14, I took my first job. On foot, I delivered supermarket coupon newsletters to neighborhoods in Queens, New York on weekends, between 6am and 2pm. During the frigid, cold winter months, I layered my clothes with two of everything—pants, sweaters, socks—followed by a plastic covering to avoid snow getting through them. Working outdoors in the summer was not any easier, as it meant I would sweat profusely. After my route, I would go back to the supermarket and pack grocery bags for customers, an experience that paid minimum wage plus tips.

Coming of age in the Marine Corps

At age 18, I entered into the Marine Corps looking for a change and an opportunity to grow. After 6 months, the Gulf War broke out and I had no choice but to be deployed overseas. It was a bittersweet experience, as I learned another life lesson—discipline.

I was not comfortable taking orders from authority. I hated doing night watch during training exercises in the field, which meant sleep interruption in the middle of the night for 1-2 hour shifts. Every week, our rooms in the barracks needed to be 'squeaky clean'. Sometimes after several hours of cleaning, we failed the inspection and everything had to be cleaned again to meet the satisfaction of both the Sergeant and Lieutenant. Throughout my experience in the Marine Corps, I learned that discipline meant being organized, willing to take orders and exceeding the expectations of leadership.

Getting "Stuck" — a Downward Spiral

In 1994, I returned to New York, thinking I finally left the war behind me, only to find myself entering into another war—poverty. With little money, I was forced to move back in my parents' home to live in the basement. I slept in a frigid cold room during the winter months, as cold air seeped through the plastic that attempted to block the draft entering the windows. Cold showers were the norm, because of the overworked water heater. My salvation was a small electrical heater and a tried-and-true Marine Corps sleeping bag.

In the fall the following year, I registered for Communication Arts classes at NY Institute of Technology. Going to college was a better option than hanging out in the streets and getting into trouble with my friends. However, I was broke and had to hop turnstiles instead of paying the subway fare just to go to school. To make ends meet, I took different jobs. I worked as a part-time customer service representative for a television radio repair company, which ended up not paying well and left me starving. Even though I was working, sometimes I could only afford to buy a banana, a plain hot dog or a quarter juice for lunch. So, I pursued being a taxi driver and drove customers to some of the worst neighborhoods in Brooklyn (often putting my own life at risk). I was determined to finish school, so I continued studying full-time while working full-time. My future looked bleak and I felt like a slave to my circumstances. I was often tired and sleepy. I was frustrated and embarrassed with what my life had become.

Just when I thought things could not get worse, they did. My engine blew and I needed it replaced, so I took it to the auto shop. While waiting for the repairs, I walked to the local hall to play pool. I had never been there, and the place had a reputation as being a drug spot. Knowing this, I still went. As luck would have it, within 15 minutes of playing pool, cops raided the place and everyone was handcuffed, including me. Fortunately, after a lengthy interrogation, they found the guy in question and I was released. I dashed out of the scene and never returned.

Several months later I took some of my hard earned savings and I started an ice cream route. The business was promising, until I let a kid drive the truck and supervise the assistant. I drove by during busy hours to check on him, only to witness him chasing young ladies instead of focusing on work. I resisted the urge to fire him and continued to give him second chances. That summer I lost all my money and accumulated enormous debt, forcing me to sell my taxicab and pay back the person who rented the ice cream truck to me. My next mode of transportation was a "jalopy"–

one of the cheapest, oldest taxi cars on the market—which often left me stranded with passengers in the middle of highways in undesirable locations.

Breakdown after breakdown, I became lazy, depressed and overwhelmed. I slept long hours and ate several times throughout the day, only to become a more negative person. I questioned my life and my past actions. I felt like a victim and hated my life.

This period of my life was very frustrating. I felt like I was spinning my wheels all the time, and never getting anywhere. I'm sure you can relate to my story. It seemed like the harder I tried, the more debt I accumulated. I tried to go five steps forward, and ended up going 10 steps back. I knew I had hit rock bottom when the money I had borrowed from my mother to start my ice cream business was lost. The trucks were still out there, but they simply were not producing.

I had no choice but to work an 80-hour week as a taxi driver. I practically slept in my car because I had to make enough just to survive and pay my four workers. My network marketing business failed and my girlfriend even left me. To make matters worse, I had to sneak into the private house where I lived to avoid seeing the landlord because I did not have rent I owed her. I fell so far behind, it became embarrassing just to go home. She lived on the first floor and I lived in the attic, so she usually caught me even though I tried to sneak quietly past her door.

After each disappointment or roadblock, I became more depressed and overwhelmed. I slept long hours and ate several times throughout the day as a way to escape my problems. I questioned my life and my past actions. I felt like a victim and hated my life.

When I got home from work I would lie on the floor and stare at the ceiling, wondering what had happened to my life. Here I was, broke, sad, and desperate. My desire to become a millionaire dissipated with all my problems. Rather than thinking about becoming successful, I became consumed by my problems.

I was so broke, I spent the summer without an air conditioner. You can imagine how hot it was in my 400-square-foot, 2-room attic apartment. Then, when winter arrived and things cooled off, I had to go to a thrift shop to buy a used coat because I couldn't afford a new one.

Months passed by and things only got worse. I felt stuck in

my circumstances and problems, and began to feel there was no way out. Not caring about anything anymore, I didn't pay parking tickets. The consequence of ignoring the tickets was that my car was towed five times in a single year. When I went to see my father, he would say, "Are you here to ask me for more money, because I don't have any more for you." The word 'embarrassed' is certainly an understatement.

To avoid all this shame from my family, friends, and peers I decided to avoid them by working, eating, and sleeping whenever I was home. Then, one night while working the night shift at my taxi base, I ran into a woman who was a well-known drug addict. Keep in mind my taxi base was in East New York right in the heart of Brooklyn—one of New York's highest crime neighborhoods—in the late 90s during the pre-Giuliani days. This lady would come around selling things she had stolen so she could buy more crack cocaine.

Anyway "Nicky" approached me to sell a used radio. I just gave her a look that said, "You know I don't buy stolen merchandise." She hung her head and said she just wanted to see if I could give her a few bucks because she was hungry.

Well, I didn't say a word. I just turned my pockets inside out and showed her I had no money at all. It was the first time in two years as a taxi driver that I did not have a penny to my name. That's how bad things were. Maybe you can relate.

Nicky couldn't believe her eyes. "You always have money!" she said. Then she calmed down a little and asked if I was hungry.

I didn't really want to answer, but before I even could, she pulled a handful of coins out of her pocket and passed them to me. "Have some dinner on me," she said. When I started to give it back, she wouldn't take it. "How many nights did I get a meal because of you, and now I want to pay back that favor," she said.

I couldn't believe what was happening. Here was a crack lady that had come to me for help, and *I* was the one who needed *her* assistance. Wow. It hit me like a ton of bricks. That's when I knew I had hit rock bottom and started to realize how bad things really were.

Nicky proceeded to tell me that I should be more positive even though she knew things were tough at the moment. When I told her I had pretty much given up considering my circumstances, she let me have it.

"Look here, young man. I know I am not the best person to give advice, but if you want to be rich and successful it isn't going to happen by hanging around these broke taxi drivers. You need to meet and associate with successful people."

When I asked her where I was supposed to find successful people, she laughed. "You're asking me?" Then she became serious again. "Look, I don't know where you find them, but I know where you don't find them—here in your car, in this neighborhood, waiting for a call from the dispatcher."

Whether she knew it or not, Nicky had hit the nail on the head. I had somehow developed a negative mindset. It was no wonder my business choices weren't going well. I realized that I had a more negative attitude than she did, and I decided right there and then that I was going to do everything in my power to become an "Unstoppable Champion."

Getting "Un-Stuck"

In 1996, a friend invited me to a network marketing convention in New York. I was desperate, so I accepted the invitation. Within moments, a man by the name of Pablo Zabala mesmerized me. He was the speaker on stage who had a graceful, inspiring and powerful presence. His message was "the power of personal growth." It was the first time I heard this concept. He explained, "the more you grow, the happier you will be, and the more money you will make." The entire audience was captivated and engaged. For the first time in a long time, I could see a bright new future. I was anxious and excited to embark upon a new chapter in my life.

I had the courage to approach him on the break. I asked him to recommend a list of good reading books. He recommended only one book to start. It was *Think and Grow Rich*, by Napoleon Hill. I immediately bought the book and read it cover to cover, beginning my endless journey and lifetime investment in self-discovery. I read more books on leadership, marketing, motivation and sales. I attended more seminars, such as Tony Robbins Master University, Landmark Education, Zig Ziglar, Les Brown, Tom Hopkins and many others. I was on a quest to "Unleash MY Inner Champion."

Becoming Unstoppable

I read once that most successful entrepreneurs and CEOs started out by selling a product or service. This shocked me. With this as inspiration, I joined a network marketing company focused on wellness. I liked the model of network marketing because I could be in business for myself, but not by myself. With training and support, I learned how to sell. I mastered overcoming objections, conducting effective presentations, asking for referrals, and closing the sale. I also mastered empowering people, such as recruiting and building teams and developing leaders. Within a few years, my nationwide team averaged $3.5 million in annual sales.

Shortly thereafter, I was ready for a new challenge. Real Estate called me. It was something that I always wanted to do, but for some reason or another I kept procrastinating the decision to jump in 100%. After obtaining my Real Estate license, I conducted buyer workshops and attended networking events. I was so relentless that I knocked on 3,000+ doors, regardless of rain and snow, to introduce myself to potential clients in the neighborhood. Soon enough, I built a small group of loyal buyers and sellers. Through long hours of hard work and dedication, I became the agency's top salesperson within two years and was also offered a partnership position. In the following years, I built a small but powerful sales team that sold over $100 million worth of real estate.

My life turned a new direction. I had the experience of feeling 'unstoppable' in life. Regardless of my circumstances, I knew that they were just circumstances.

I started to recognize that my story of shifting from 'stuck' to 'unstoppable' would somehow inspire and influence others to do the same. Friends and family started to ask me to coach them. Universities invited me to speak to their students. Corporations asked me to deliver keynote speeches to their employees. So, in 2007, I launched my speaking and coaching business and in 2015, I decided to launch OFG: www.OxfordFundingGroup.com. OFG specializes in lending money to small to medium size businesses, and financing commercial loans.

People often ask why I am so passionate about helping them. My response is that I have a unique ability to empower people to shift from 'Stuck' to 'Unstoppable' in all areas of their life. The bottom line is that I am committed to helping people pursue their dreams, focus on their passion and create financial freedom. And that is exactly why I decided to write this book. I hope you enjoyed reading it as much as I enjoyed writing it.

Edward R. Munoz

Empowering people to "Unleash Their Inner Champion"
P.S. If you have enjoyed reading my story, make sure to sign up for your FREE GIFT of 4 full days of "Unleash Your Inner Champion" success videos and a free interview with a self made billionaire. Just text this keyword: freeaudio to 66866 or go here to register www.EdwardMunoz.com

(Join Our Pvt Facebook Support Group)
www.TheUnderdogCommunity.com

-- ABOUT THE AUTHOR --

Edward is an accomplished entrepreneur, a Marine Corps veteran, a gifted motivational speaker, author of 7 self help books, and a peak performance/business coach who believes with a passion that everyone is capable of success. He is a **leading authority** at helping people, teams and organizations unleash their inner champion.

From humble beginnings packing grocery bags on weekends and driving a taxi in Brooklyn's worst neighborhoods, to leading a $100 million real estate sales team, Edward has learned the principles that can help anyone realize their dreams. He shares his remarkable journey of inspiration with audiences in a humorous, no-nonsense style to demolish limiting beliefs and realize one's full potential.

Edward is also the Founder of the peak performance program, **Unleash Your Inner Champion.** Edward leverages two decades of **award-winning expertise** using time-tested success principles to reach your goals personally and professionally.

When Edward is not leading a seminar or keynoting a speech, you will find him leading the charge as **CEO and Co-Founder of Oxford Funding Group (OFG).** OFG was created to solve a major issue many small business owners face: access to capital. OFG understands that financing a small business can be challenging and requires knowledge of several loans programs that most small business owners do not know exist.

Unfortunately, lack of knowledge in this area can slow down business for many small business owners, and often put them out of business if they don't get working capital to keep their business afloat when times are tough or seasons are slow. Oxford Funding Group offers financing options like short and longer term loans and lines of credit to help small- to mid-size businesses grow. They also finance commercial loans and offer hard money loans for real estate flippers. For more information, visit: **www. OxfordFundingGroup.com**

Edward will be the first to tell you that his **biggest passion is writing books.** And that is why his lifelong commitment to serve the greater good has led him to create other books and best selling audio programs. Here is a list of some of the books he has authored:

1. The U-Effect
2. Overcoming The Frustration Barrier
3. Happiness Is a Habit
4. Success Through Persistence in Hopeless Situations
5. How To Create Miraculous Breakthroughs Today
6. Como Transformarte En Un Líder Imparable (Spanish Motivational Book)

You can purchase any of these books or award winning audio programs by visiting: **www.EdwardMunoz.com/Store**

Feel free to contact Edward for speaking engagements, media interviews, investment or personal coaching. One of Edward's favorite parts about what he does is sharing his knowledge with audiences in various venues, from conferences and universities to corporate meetings and summits.

You may contact Edward at **www.EdwardMunoz.com**

BOOK EDWARD TO SPEAK

When you book Edward to speak at your event, your audience will not know what hit them. Edward personally guarantees that he will deliver a transformative speech that not only energizes audiences, but gives them the tools to catalyze immediate changes in their lives.

For more than a decade, Edward R. Muñoz has been chosen time and time again to be keynote speaker at some of the top conventions and consistently receives top ratings from their attendees. He shares his remarkable journey of inspiration with audiences in a humorous, no-nonsense style, to demolish limiting beliefs and realize one's full potential.

"You delivered a message that just plain exceeded our expectations. I appreciate that you actually took the time to learn our language, arrived early, paid attention to what the other keynote speakers said and wove it into your speech, picking up on the key themes. This makes you a rare breed."

Rafael Alvarez,
– CEO of Atax

"Thanks again for your awesome contributions to getting our women's leadership program off the ground. We could not have done it, in our wildly ridiculous time frame, without your high energy, passion and zeal."

– Susan Weitz,
CEO of the Women's Leadership Consortium

"Edward Muñoz's presentation was extremely content-rich and very interactive. Everyone was involved from start to finish. Tremendous value!"

– Juan Guillen,
CEO, Latin Trends Publishing & Media Group

For More Info – Visit **www.EdwardMunoz.com**

Or call our office: 877-440-5299